PIPE FITTINGS

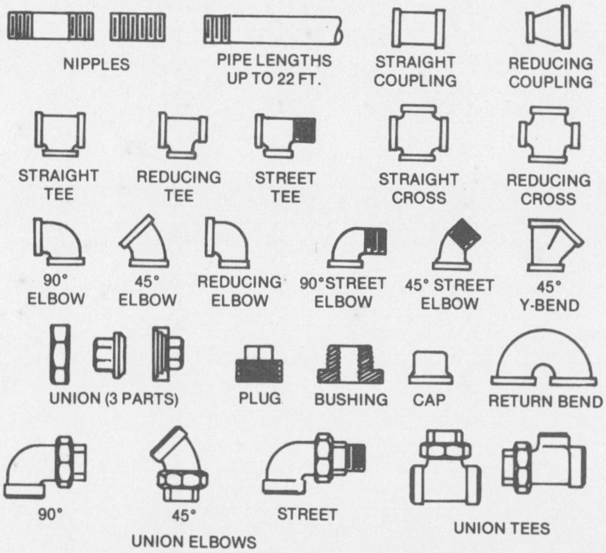

Here are the common steel pipe fittings. Nipples are simply short lengths of pipe threaded on both ends. Reducing fittings join two different sizes of pipe.

Compression fittings of the flared-tube type are the easiest for the novice to handle when working with copper tubing.

STANDARD STEEL PIPE (All Dimensions in Inches)					
Nominal Size	Outside Diameter	Inside Diameter	Nominal Size	Outside Diameter	Inside Diameter
1/8	0.405	0.269	1	1.315	1.049
1/4	0.540	0.364	1 1/4	1.660	1.380
3/8	0.675	0.493	1 1/2	1.900	1.610
1/2	0.840	0.622	2	2.375	2.067
3/4	1.050	0.824	2 1/2	2.875	2.469

SQUARE MEASURE

144 sq in = 1 sq ft
9 sq ft = 1 sq yd
272.25 sq ft = 1 sq rod
160 sq rods = 1 acre

VOLUME MEASURE

1728 cu in = 1 cu ft
27 cu ft = 1 cu yd

MEASURES OF CAPACITY

1 cup = 8 fl oz
2 cups = 1 pint
2 pints = 1 quart
4 quarts = 1 gallon
2 gallons = 1 peck
4 pecks = 1 bushel

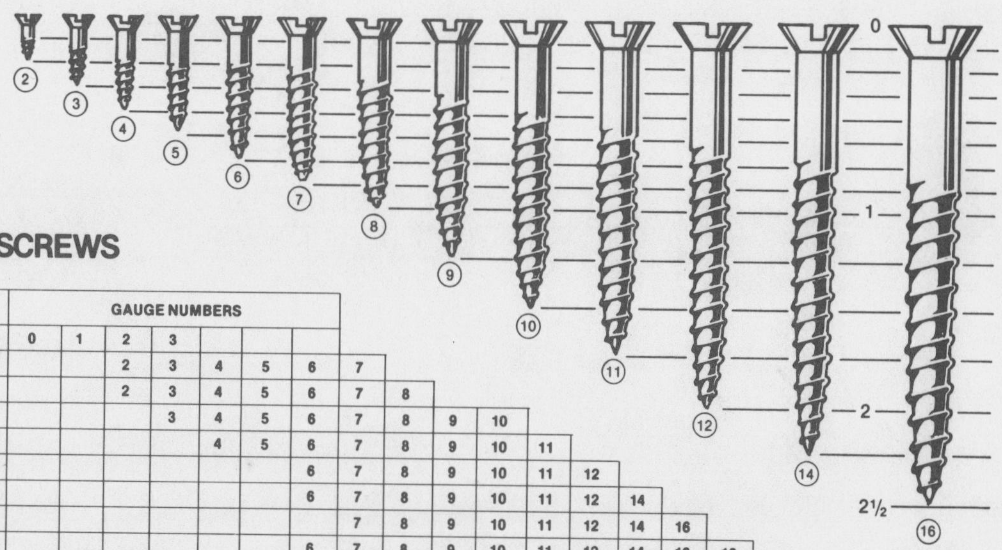

WOOD SCREWS

LENGTH	GAUGE NUMBERS																
1/4 INCH	0	1	2	3													
3/8 INCH			2	3	4	5	6	7									
1/2 INCH			2	3	4	5	6	7	8								
5/8 INCH				3	4	5	6	7	8	9	10						
3/4 INCH					4	5	6	7	8	9	10	11					
7/8 INCH							6	7	8	9	10	11	12				
1 INCH							6	7	8	9	10	11	12	14			
1 1/4 INCH								7	8	9	10	11	12	14	16		
1 1/2 INCH							6	7	8	9	10	11	12	14	16	18	
1 3/4 INCH									8	9	10	11	12	14	16	18	20
2 INCH									8	9	10	11	12	14	16	18	20
2 1/4 INCH										9	10	11	12	14	16	18	20
2 1/2 INCH													12	14	16	18	20
2 3/4 INCH														14	16	18	20
3 INCH															16	18	20
3 1/2 INCH																18	20	24
4 INCH																18	20	24

WHEN YOU BUY SCREWS, SPECIFY (1) LENGTH, (2) GAUGE NUMBER, (3) TYPE OF HEAD—FLAT, ROUND, OR OVAL, (4) MATERIAL—STEEL, BRASS, BRONZE, ETC., (5) FINISH—BRIGHT, STEEL BLUED, CADMIUM, NICKEL, OR CHROMIUM PLATED.

INEXPENSIVE and readily available at your local lumberyard, standard moldings let you "sculpture" your walls. For especially attractive designs, see page 1904.

In this volume . . .

WOULD YOU BELIEVE (without looking twice) that the same basic piece of furniture is the focus of all four rooms shown on these pages? Actually, it's a modular frame that you can adapt to many different uses. We show it as a service bar (above); a desk (above right); a personal grooming center (right); and a compact sewing center (far right). In the article on page 1890 you'll also see it as a handsome room divider. We'll bet you'll find other uses for the modular frame, too. And it's easy to build!

FOR A DRAMATIC CHANGE, simply add wood moldings to your walls. Use wallpaper or fabric inside the molding to create a new mood. For ideas, see page 1904.

THREE MOBILE cooking centers are detailed in an article on page 1865. Roll one of these carts onto a deck and you have an efficient, attractive outdoor kitchen.

Popular Mechanics

do-it-yourself encyclopedia

in 20 volumes

a complete how-to guide for the homeowner, the hobbyist—
and anyone who enjoys working with mind and hands!

All about:

home maintenance
home-improvement projects
wall paneling
burglary and fire protection
furniture projects
finishing and refinishing furniture
outdoor living
home remodeling
solutions to home problems
challenging woodworking projects
hobbies and handicrafts
model making
weekend projects
workshop shortcuts and techniques
hand-tool skills
power-tool know-how
shop-made tools
car repairs
car maintenance
appliance repair
boating
hunting
fishing
camping
photography projects
radio, TV and electronics know-how
clever hints and tips
projects just for fun

volume 12

ISBN 0-87851-077-X
Library of Congress Catalog Number 77 84920

MANUFACTURED IN THE UNITED STATES OF AMERICA

contents

VOLUME 12

MAP READING
How to know the lay of the land 1764
MARKSMANSHIP
Zeroing-in for hunting 1768
Double-duty target box 1771
MARQUETRY
Marquetry: a difficult art made easier 1772
MASONRY, PAINTING
How to paint masonry so it stays painted 1778
MASTS
Rugged masts from thinwall conduit 1782
MEASUREMENTS
Guide to the right measurement 1784
METAL CASTING
Make your own metal castings 1786
METAL-LATHE ACCESSORIES
Make a boring-bar set for your lathe 1790
Make a king-size toolpost 1792
Make a lathe indexing attachment 1795
Setscrew chucks you can make 1796
A swing toolholder for your lathe 1799
METAL-LATHE TECHNIQUES
Turning rings on a lathe 1800
Filing on a lathe 1804
Put a fine finish on lathe projects 1808
Turn plastic on your lathe 1814
METALWORKING
A shop forge you can build 1819
Build an energy-saving fireplace cover 1820
METRIC SYSTEM
Learning to live with the metric system 1822
MICROMETERS
How to 'enlarge' your micrometer 1828
MINIATURE HOUSES
Two enchanting dollhouses 1830
MINIBIKES
Modernize your old minibike 1836
MIRRORS
Two mirrors: authentic Lincoln reproductions 1840
MISFIRING, AUTO
Tracking down engine misfire 1846
MITER BOARDS
Two miter boards 1850
MITER JOINTS
Make angle blocks for miter cuts 1854
MIXERS, AUDIO
Mix your way to better sound 1856
MIXERS, FOOD
How to troubleshoot a food mixer 1858
MOBILE FURNITURE
Mobile entertaining, indoors and out 1865
MODELMAKING
Build models like a pro 1883
Three scratch-built control-line fighters 1886
MODULAR FURNITURE
Easy-build modular furniture 1890
MOLDING CUTTERS
Storage for molding cutters 1900
MOLDINGS
Moldings—the finishing touch 1901
How to work magic with moldings 1904
MONTAGES, PHOTO
Make a photo montage 1910
MOTOR OIL
How to diagnose oil consumption 1912
MOTORCYCLES
A trail-bike carrier for your car 1915
The secrets of safe cycling 1916

How to know the lay of the land

Big-scale U.S. Geological Survey maps show every hill, pond, brook and maybe even your own house. They add fun and excitement to camping, hiking and exploring trips—and at an insignificant cost. Here's how you can get one for any area

By NORMAN CARLISLE

FINDING THE RIGHT map for a particular area is easy. You first get a USGS index map for the state you live in or plan to visit. It is marked off into small sections, as shown above. The sections represent available maps and are identified by names. When you locate the area you want, you order the corresponding map section from the U.S. Geological Survey.

SEE ALSO

Backpacking . . . Binoculars . . . Boat camping . . . Camping . . . Hunting . . . Outdoor photography . . . Recreational vehicles . . . Trailers, tent

THE FARMER shook his head hopelessly. "It's way back there in the woods and no trails to it," he said. "You'll never find it."

The native Vermonter who gave me this firm opinion about a marsh I wanted to get to turned out to be wrong. I, a first-time visitor to this wilderness region of forest-clad ridges and dashing streams, was able to go right to it.

I can't attribute my success to any feat of superior woodsmanship. It was just that I had a map and he didn't—not an ordinary map, but one of the unique topographical maps put out by the U.S. Geological Survey.

These remarkable maps, bargain-priced at a dollar or two each, give you a picture of the landscape you can't get any other way. On the scale they're drawn, they show not only roads and natural features of the land, but also man-made additions such as footbridges, mine shafts, gravel pits, fence lines, even individual houses. If you're an outdoor man of any kind—fisherman, hunter, hiker, birdwatcher, rockhound, amateur prospector or nature photographer—a USGS map will get you around strange territory with sure-footed confidence. You *know* the lay of the land even before you get there.

As a motorist, you'll find that USGS maps can add a new dimension to family vacation fun. They're the perfect tool for the shun-piker, the guy who wants to get away from the smooth boredom of the turnpike once in a while and see some parts of the country that can only be seen

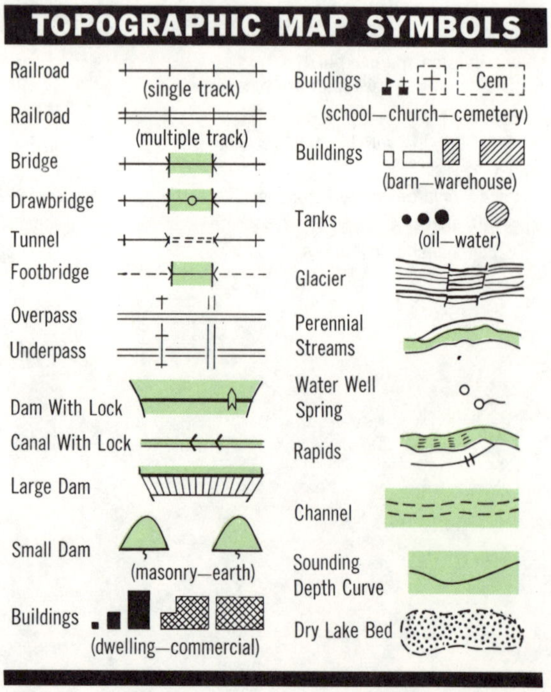

Lake Peekskill
376
400
500
291
Lake Peekskill

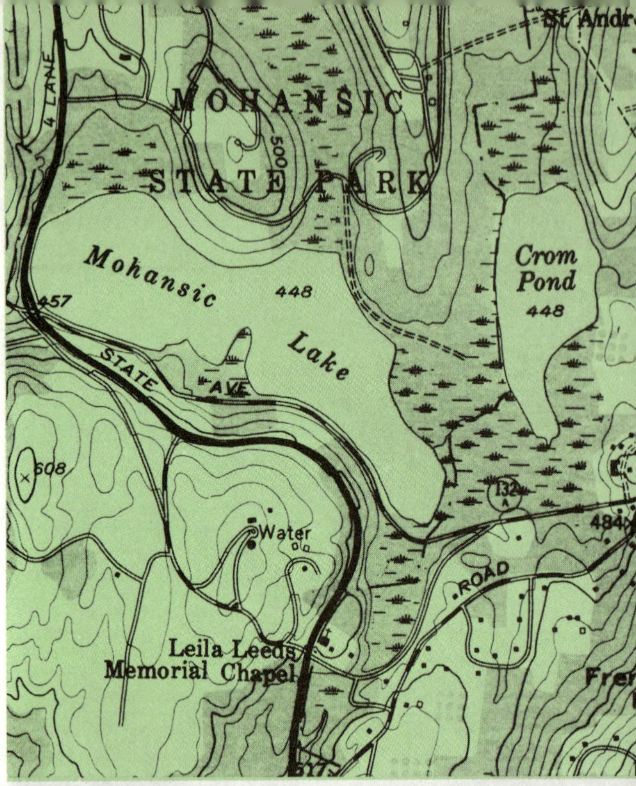

on back roads. If you're heading for a national park or monument, a USGS map will pinpoint hundreds of features most tourists miss.

Closer to home, in territory you *think* you know, you're in for a surprise when you unroll a USGS map. If you live in the country or in a small town, it may even have your house on it. You're likely to see on it a lot of stuff you didn't know was there—a jeep trail too unimportant to be marked on an ordinary road map, a pond you've missed because you can't see it from the road.

What gives USGS maps their unique usefulness is their scale. It's much larger than those of other maps. A typical USGS scale is 1 to 24,000. This means that one inch on the map equals 24,000 inches on actual land. That's 2000 feet or less than half a mile. By contrast, one inch on a road map equals anywhere from 5 to 10 miles or more. Other USGS scales used are 1 to 62,500, where an inch equals about one mile, and 1 to 125,000 where an inch is two miles.

topographical symbols

Scales like these enable the USGS to cram in a tremendous amount of detail. The use of carefully designed colored symbols lets you easily identify objects as small as a water tank or an earth dam across a creek. A few of these symbols are shown in an accompanying table.

You'll also find a lot of squiggly brown lines wandering over the map. These are contour lines and they tell at a glance how the land lies. If you're accustomed to maps that show all land as being equally flat, these contours will come as a great joy. Each one is an imaginary line connecting points of similar altitude above sea level. Depending on the map, the lines represent heights from 10 to 80 feet apart. The closer the lines are together, the steeper the slope. A lot of lines bunched together indicate a cliff. Exact elevations are printed in brown at various points along the lines.

For easier reading, the map makers print index contours. Every fourth or fifth line is a darker shade of brown. It's easier to run your finger along this darker line, and the distance between such index lines will give you a clear picture of the rate of climb. You'll feel like a pro when you can look at a map and tell that you're going to climb exactly 320 feet in a given stretch of trail.

In mountain country where you're picking your own trail, you can find the easiest route by following the contour lines. The shallowest grade will be where the lines are farthest apart.

For some areas, the Survey has prepared shaded relief maps. These will give you an even better idea of terrain than the regular maps, as the shading accentuates the physical features. Most of the National Park and Monument maps are available in this form, as are those of many states.

It's a good idea to know just how old your map is so you can make allowances for possible changes that may have occurred since the map was made. Some USGS maps go back several years. I remember a time when I was exploring a section of Vermont with my sons, using a 1950 map. We came over a rise and looked down where the map said a farmhouse should be. But no house was in sight. Was the map wrong?

We decided to continue on. As we broke out of the trees into a clearing, there was the answer —an empty excavation, some charred timbers and a stone doorstep overgrown with brush. A

CALLED QUADRANGLES, USGS maps commonly come in two scales, as shown in the diagram at the right. Large scale covers 7½ minutes of latitude and longitude. Smaller scale includes four times as much area or 15 minutes of latitude and longitude. The maps above, containing sections of the Hudson River in southern New York, show how the two scales differ. The full map at the left represents 15 minutes of area. The one at the right is a 7½-minute section taken from its lower left-hand corner. In some cases, such a portion is referred to as the southwest section of the larger quadrangle. Additional maps cover the northwest, northeast and southeast sections. Note how much detail the 7½-minute quadrangle shows—important when you're exploring an unknown region. The 15-minute maps help in a general study of larger areas.

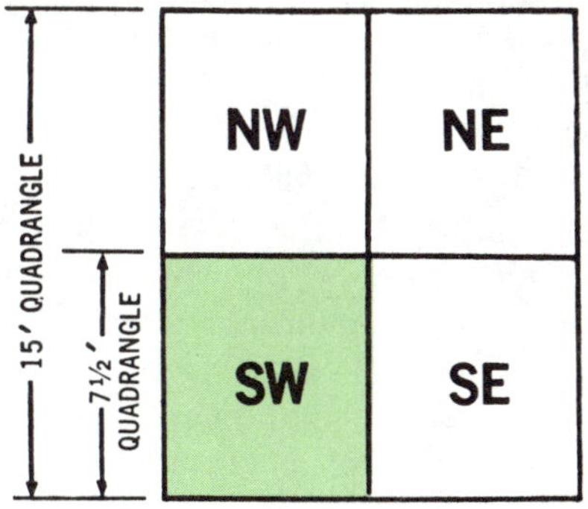

little bit of history had been written since the map was made.

The year in which a map was first made or revised is shown in the lower right-hand corner under the map name. If you buy your maps by mail from the Survey, you'll get the latest ones.

Ordering maps by mail is simple, but service is likely to be best from the office most concerned with the area that interests you. For states east of the Mississippi plus Minnesota, write to Eastern Region Branch of Distribution, U.S. Geological Survey, 1200 S. Eads St., Washington, D.C. 22202. For states west of the Mississippi, including all of Louisiana, write to the Central Region Branch of Distribution, USGS, Box 25286, Federal Center, Denver, CO 80225.

Request an "index map" of the state concerning you; it's free. Its numbered sections tell the section map to order. Large-scale maps, 1:24,000 to 1:125,000, cost $1.25; smaller-scale state and regional maps and shaded relief maps are $2. On a 1:24,000 map, the width of this column of type represents just over a mile. You can see that there's room for lots of detail at so large a scale.

But plan well ahead; the Survey can take two to six weeks to answer. If you're rushed, most big map stores and some bookstores and hobby shops handle USGS maps—but they charge higher prices, as you'd expect.

Even if you never use a USGS map in the field, you'll find them among the handsomest wall decorations you can hang.

A wilderness map of some of the remoter parts of Alaska is just the thing for a sportsman's den. Even if you never go there, the maps are so detailed that it's easy to conjure up a very realistic daydream.

A map hung in a child's room showing a place visited on a family vacation brings back many memories. Because of the detail involved, your children can show their friends exactly where their cabin was and the spot on the lake where they caught their first fish.

Zeroing-in for hunting

By TOM FAULKNER

NO MARKSMAN, no matter how skillful, can hit anything consistently unless his gun shoots where he's aiming. The guarantee for a bull's-eye every time is top-grade equipment that is properly zeroed-in. This means gun sights that are adjusted correctly so you hit the target at which you're aiming. We all do miss at times, but the miss should be *your* fault—not the gun's.

The purpose of sights on rifles and handguns is well known to most shooters, but many do not realize it is possible and important to zero-in shotguns as well.

most rifles have open sights

Almost all rifles come with simple factory-installed sights, known commonly as "open sights." The adjustable rear sight consists of a piece of metal with a V or U-shaped notch cut in the middle of the upper edge. The front sight usually is a fixed blade or bead that is lined up in the rear sight notch. The process of placing the front sight on the target and simultaneously lining it up with the rear sight is called the "sight picture." Obtaining the correct sight picture and repeating it without variation for every shot is the key element of accurate shooting.

Two other types of sights are also used on rifles. One is the rear aperture or "peep" sight with a circular disc and a small hole in the middle. The shooter looks though the hole and places the top of the front sight blade or post in the middle of the circle. The third type is the telescopic sight which magnifies the target and utilizes adjustable cross hairs, a single post, or a combination of both.

Theoretically, a perfectly sighted-in rifle, fired with a completely steady hold and a perfect sight picture, should put every bullet in exactly the same place. Actually, this doesn't quite happen, although it's possible to come very close. The limitations on perfect accuracy are the result of four variables. These include the limitations of your own eyesight in correctly lining up the sights on the target; the fineness of sight adjustments; the steadiness of your hold; and the inherent accuracy (or lack of it) of the rifle itself and the ammunition. All four limitations can be overcome somewhat. Peep and telescopic sights reduce eyesight limitations and permit finer adjustments. A steady rest helps. Highly sophisticated target rifles and custom ammunition are more accurate than standard rifles. But for normal hunting or plinking, any sporter rifle and standard ammunition made by reputable manufacturers have all the accuracy you will need.

you'll need a steady rest

Regardless of the type of rifle or sights you use, a steady rest is a must for zeroing-in. This should go under the fore-end of the rifle. Com-

SEE ALSO
Gun cabinets . . . Gun racks . . . Hunting . . . Map reading . . . Muzzleloading . . . Shooting . . . Shotguns

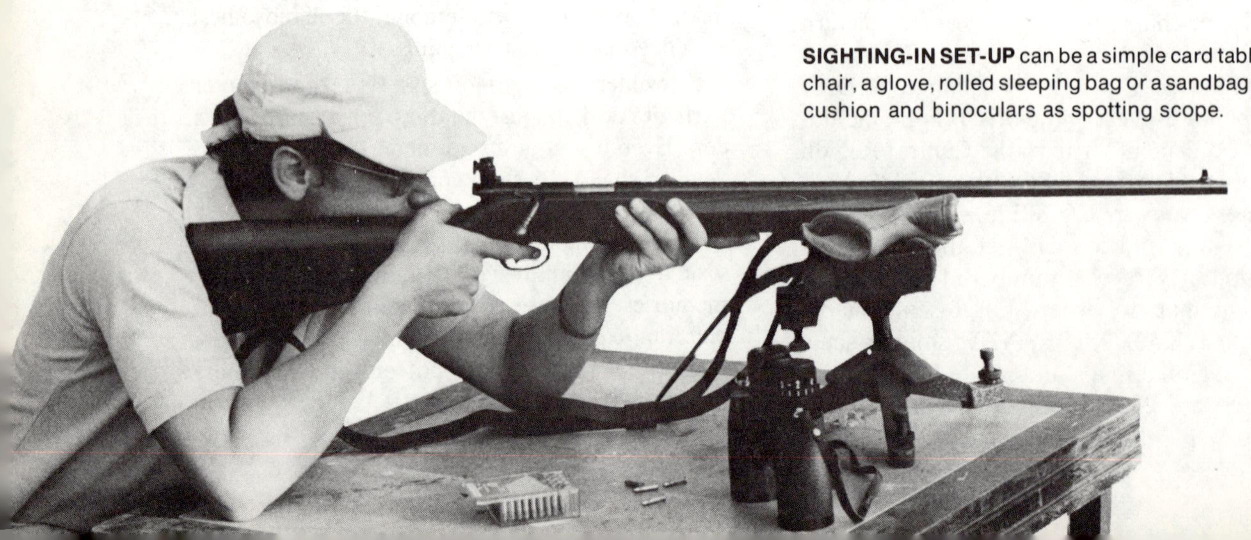

SIGHTING-IN SET-UP can be a simple card table, folding chair, a glove, rolled sleeping bag or a sandbag for barrel cushion and binoculars as spotting scope.

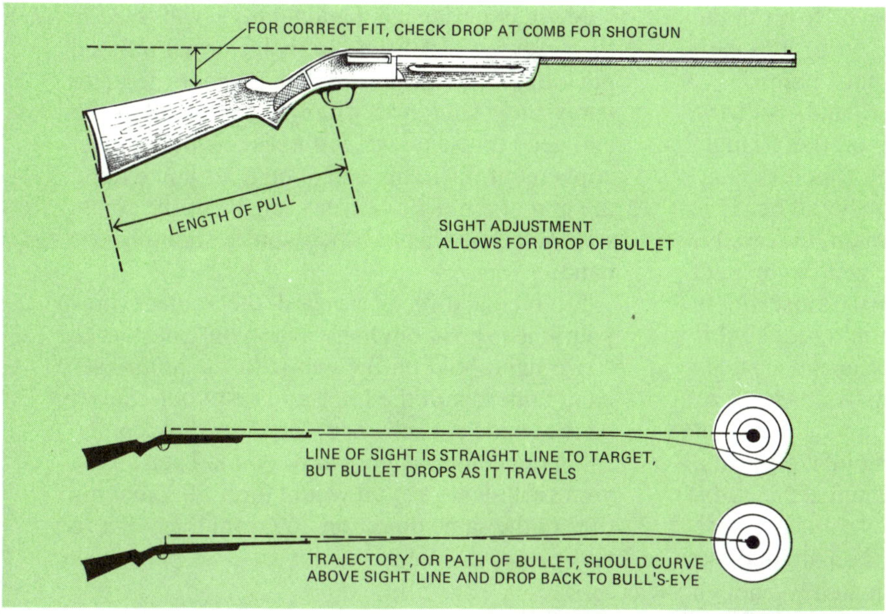

SHOTGUN IS POINTED rather than sighted. Proper fit helps determine accuracy and measurements shown at left can be adjusted or altered by a gunsmith.

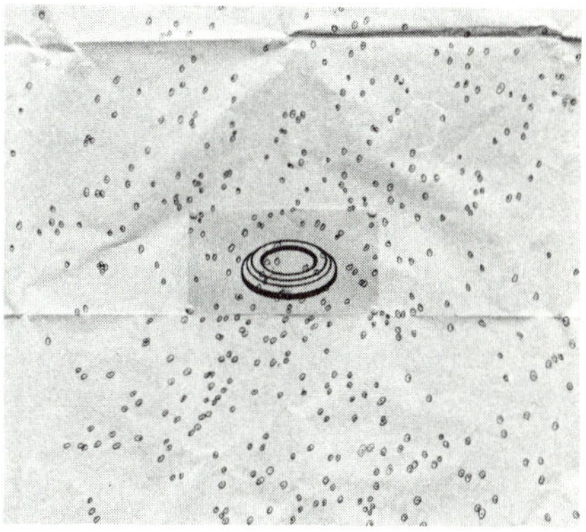

GROUPING FOR SHOTGUN (above) shows the pattern clustered properly around a clay pigeon picture. Rifle two-shot groups (far left) are moved toward the center by moving rear sight in the same direction. Experienced handgunner can fire five-shot groups offhand for zeroing-in.

mercial rests can be purchased and are often available at club or public rifle ranges, but it's just as easy to improvise a rest out of an old pillow, a rolled up sleeping bag or several sand bags. The rest you choose should have flexibility to simulate the normal "give" of your hand when shooting without a rest. If you use a hard rest, place a sponge or thick glove between it and the rifle. Otherwise, the muzzle jump at firing will bounce the rifle upward off the hard surface and give you a shot that is high, and when you correct for it, the rifle will shoot low when the rest is no longer used.

The steadiest positions are prone, (down on your stomach) or sitting at a bench or table. If there is a rifle range nearby, use it by all means. It usually offers fixed target holders, measured distances and shooting tables and positions. Otherwise, find a safe open area with a good backstop and pace off the desired range. Shoot from a prone position or use a folding chair and card table.

For .22-cal. plinking rifles, sight-in at 25 or 50 yards. Most hunting rifles in .22 cal. or the larger centerfire calibers are best zeroed-in at 100 yards.

sighting-in your rifle

Here's the procedure for sighting-in. Set up your target and fire two shots as carefully as possible. Squeeze slowly and avoid jerking the trigger. If the two shots are on the paper and within a few inches of each other, mark the point midway between them and adjust the sights to move this point toward the bull's-eye. You always move the rear sight in the direction you want the bullet to go. If the group is low and to the left, for example, move that rear sight higher and to the right. If your first two shots don't even hit the paper, move your rest closer to the target until they do. Work the group in toward the bull's-eye, then return to your 50 or 100-yard position and make your final adjustments.

Final groups should be three shots and the zero should be in the middle of the triangle formed by the three holes. Many shooters wonder how small these final groups should be. This depends on you and your equipment. Generally, at 100 yards using open sights, you can expect three to four inches between the two most widely separated shots. Peep sights should reduce this to two to three inches, and telescopic sights could narrow it down to two inches or less. At 100 yards, top marksmen can cover five-shot groups with a nickel. For zeroing-in at 50 yards, divide the above figures by two; and at 25 yards, by four.

If you can't achieve groups as small as those mentioned, you may not have a steady enough rest, you may be jerking the trigger, your sights may be loose (check all mounting screws) or, sadly, you may just have a rifle of poor accuracy.

Shooters who sight-in rifles or switch sights frequently should consider purchasing a collimator. This device is hung on the end of the rifle barrel and permits preliminary sight adjustments before firing that should get your initial shots on the paper. They cost about $15 to $25. And if you become a frequent rifle range shooter, a spotting or target scope lets you see where your bullets are striking without your leaving the shooting position.

Bullets, of course, are subject to the law of gravity and start dropping the instant they leave the rifle muzzle. Your line of sight will be a straight line to the target, but the bullet must follow a curve above the line of sight. As a result, a rifle sighted "dead on" at 100 yards will shoot a bit high at 50 yards and low at 150 and beyond because of bullet drop. Major ammunition manufacturers like Federal, Remington and Winchester include trajectory charts in their ammo catalogs so you can determine where a bullet will strike at other than zeroing-in range and enable you to zero-in your rifle for, say, 200 yards while shooting at a 100-yard target.

handguns

In general, handguns are less accurate than rifles and are shot at much shorter ranges. Proficiency is more difficult, and a beginner should try to get expert instruction. Some handguns without adjustable sights are acceptable for short-range plinking, but rear sight adjustment is needed for serious marksmanship.

Most experienced handgunners will zero-in their sights by shooting in their normal offhand position. Less practiced handgunners tend to spray their shots too widely for a useful group and need to use a rest. Sitting is one of the most convenient positions and should let you extend the gun at almost full arm's length so the sights will look the same as when you're shooting offhand.

Sit facing directly toward the target, draw your knees up about halfway to your chest, take a two-hand hold on the gun with the nontrigger hand underneath the butt, and rest your elbows on the inside of each knee. Fire five-shot groups, using the center as your zero point. Then adjust your rear sights as you would for a rifle, moving then in the same direction you want the bullet to move.

shotguns

Your shotgun doesn't have sights in the normal sense and is pointed rather than aimed, but it must hit where you look. Rather than adjusting sights, you need proper fit.

Pace off a distance compatible with your shotgun's choke—40 yards for full choke, 30 for modified and about 22 yards for improved cylinder. Then put up a large sheet of paper with a dark mark in the middle. Mount your shotgun as you normally would afield and fire at the mark. The resulting pattern should spread evenly around it in a rough circle. Several shots and sheets of paper should give you an average.

If your patterns are too high, your stock may be too straight for you or too long. If the patterns are too low, your stock may have too much drop, (the measurement from the middle of the top of your stock to a flat surface against which the top of the barrel and receiver are held). Generally, standard field stock dimensions will fit most shooters with sleeve lengths between 31 and 33 inches.

A gunsmith can shorten your stock if necessary, or lengthen it by adding a recoil pad and butt spacers. He can also alter the amount of drop if this is a problem. When a shotgun shoots consistently to the left or right, it may mean the shooter is not mounting it so that he is looking straight down the barrel. Occasionally, this can also result from a barrel that has been bent or damaged. A gunsmith can check this out for you.

A properly fitted shotgun is the same as a correctly zeroed-in rifle or handgun. Always take time to make sure the gun you use is zeroed-in.

DESIGNED TO CATCH both plastic practice rounds and lead bullets and pellets, this easily constructed target box uses a hinged inner deflector.

INNER-HINGED and steel-shielded door lifts to snap into cabinet latch. Then it acts to deflect bullets into sand layer in the bottom.

LOWERED DOOR acts as floor of box when reusable plastic bullets are used. The bullets strike a towel backstop, then fall undamaged to the bottom of box.

Double-duty target box

By MARSHALL LINCOLN

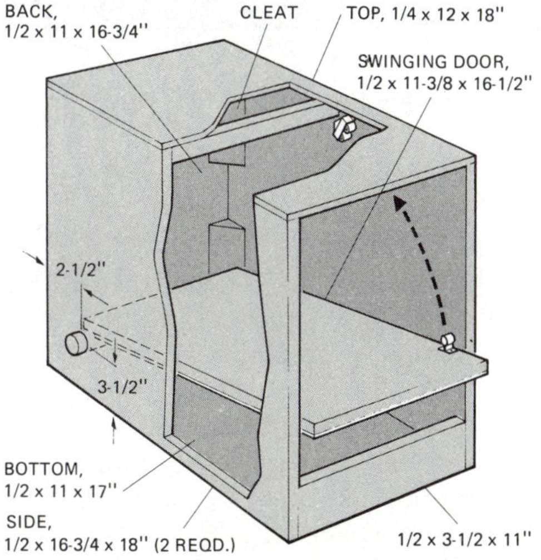

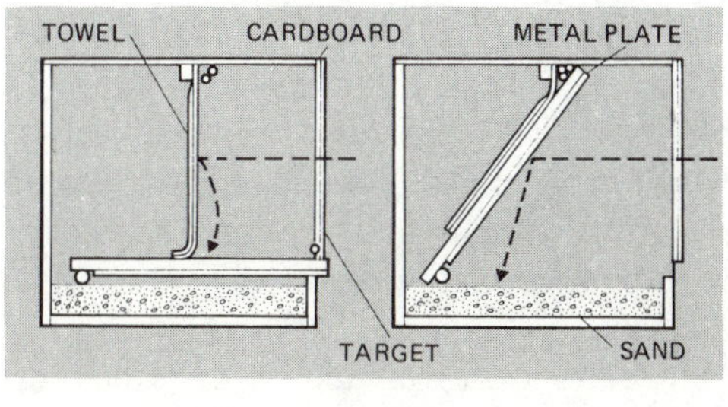

A SWINGING DOOR is the unique feature of this simple target box. With metal boiler plate or sheet-metal door in 45° up position, pellets and lead bullets are deflected down into a sand cushion in the bottom of the box. With the door tilted down to floor the box, a folded bath towel hangs midway back to stop plastic pellet practice rounds so that they are undamaged and can be collected and reused after the indoor or outdoor shooting.

The simple ½-inch-plywood box can be built in any size. As shown, it easily mounts standard pistol targets on a piece of corrugated cardboard stapled over the front of the box. The swinging door hinges on a dowel and is held up by a cabinet latch. Mount a carrying handle on the top of the target box.

SEE ALSO

Gun cabinets . . . Gun racks . . . Hunting . . . Muzzleloading . . . Shooting . . . Shotguns

Marquetry: a difficult art made easier

By RAYMOND CAPOTOSTO

Marquetry is the art of making pictures using inlaid wood veneers. Now this art form is available to do-it-yourselfers in kits with patterns and all necessary wood

SEE ALSO

Frames, picture . . . Inlays, cloth tape . . . Jewelry boxes . . . Laminating wood . . . Veneering . . . Woods

MARQUETRY, the craft of making pictures with inlaid wood veneers, used to be an art form practiced only by craftsmen with unusual skills. But that's been changed.

Now, regardless of the level of your skills, you can try this fascinating hobby and be assured of success even on your first attempt. A revolutionary new technique of sequential, or progressive, cutting simplifies the work.

The old method used veneers 1/28-in. thick which were necessarily cut with a fret saw so that the required accuracy made it a rather difficult task. The new method utilizes veneers of only 1/40-in. thickness which are easily cut with a sharp utility knife in conjunction with the "window technique." The result is finer work with less effort.

Marquetry kits are available in a wide range of

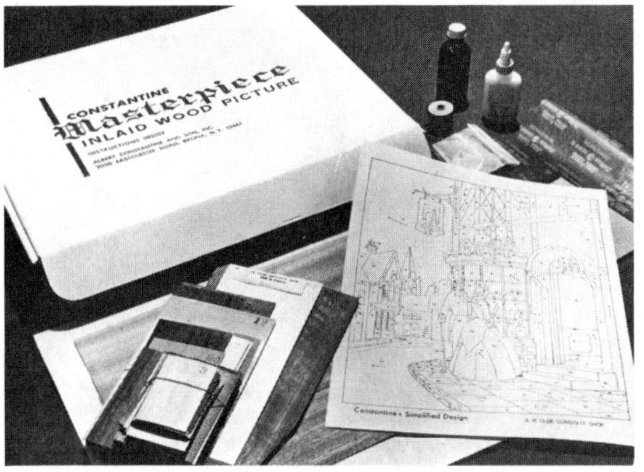

1. THE MARQUETRY KIT contains all materials to "paint" a picture in wood. Many designs are available.

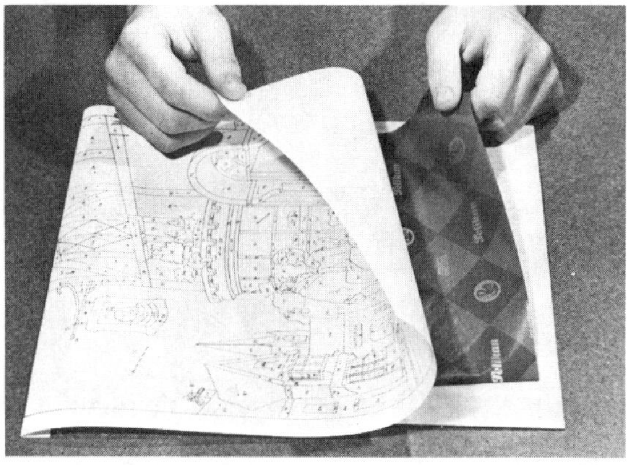

2. TAPE THE PATTERN to one edge of the waste veneer for the duration of the cutting.

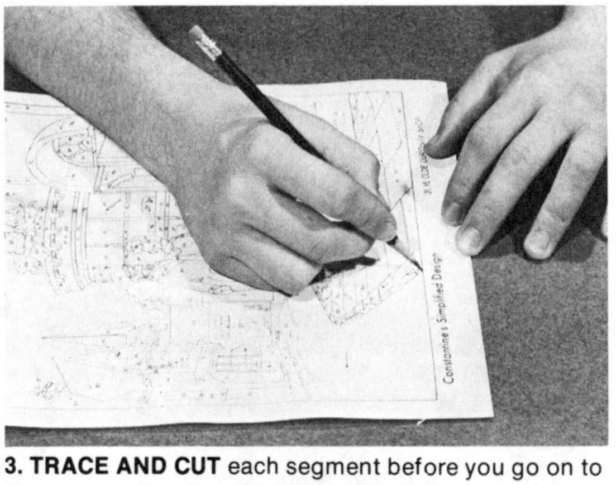

3. TRACE AND CUT each segment before you go on to the next segment as the work progresses.

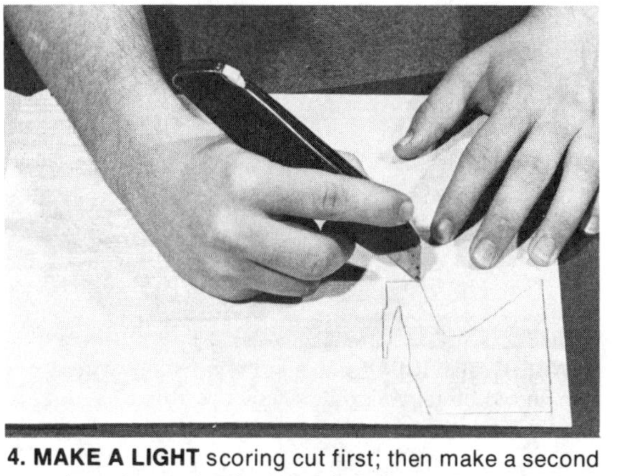

4. MAKE A LIGHT scoring cut first; then make a second pass to cut completely through the veneer.

5. INSERT VENEER under the "window." Number and select each wood specie according to the key.

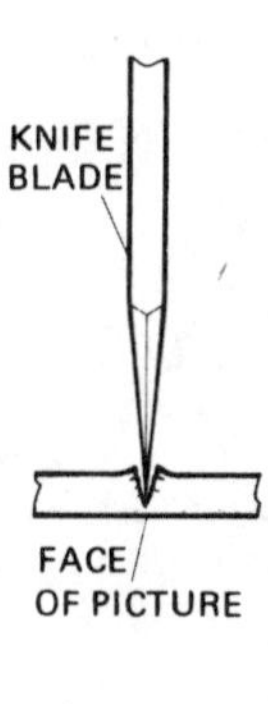

6. THE WINDOW TECHNIQUE provides a template. Make a light score and then remove the veneer for severing.

7. HERE IS THE INITIAL cutout segment. When it's carefully scored and cut, it matches the opening.

8. INSERT THE INLAY piece in the opening, where it remains to be joined gradually by the others.

9. TAPE THE INLAY in place, then use carbon paper and the pattern again to trace an adjoining segment.

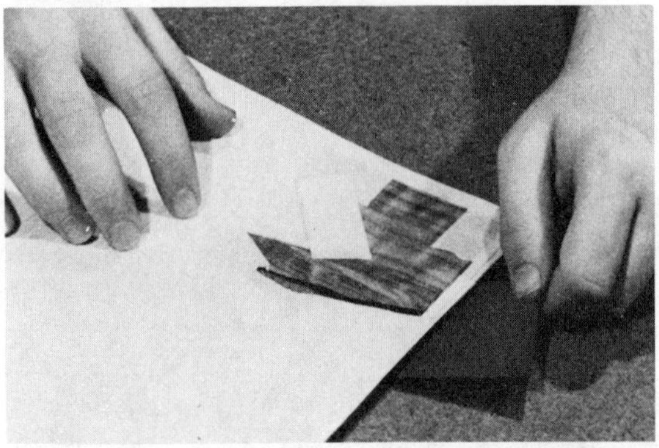

10. INSERT DARK colored veneer under the second opening cut in the waste; then score and sever it.

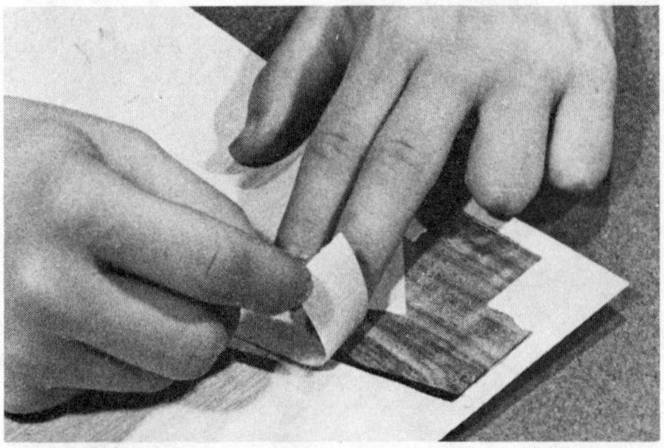

11. TAPE THE DARK narrow band, the second inlay, in place. This procedure is repeated for all segments.

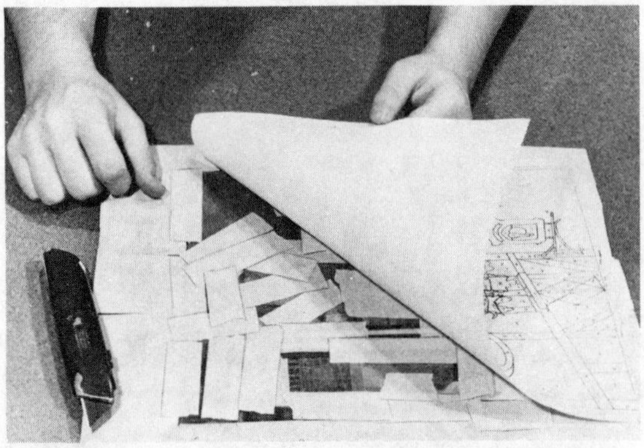

12. PROGRESS VIEW of the half-completed picture showing the fake side. Tape is on the back.

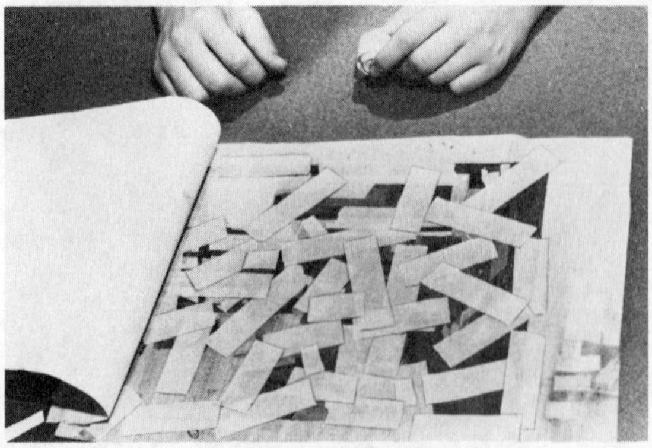

13. THE COMPLETED INLAY ready for the final steps. Remove all tabs of tape prior to gluing.

interesting scenes and subject matter. Unlike many hobby-craft kits that contain prefabricated parts requiring only assembly, these kits contain the necessary colorful veneers, a full-size working pattern and accessory items—but none of the veneers are precut. The finished product reflects your efforts and creativity. There are, however, precut kits available for those who prefer the easy way.

The window method is derived from the simple process of cutting a hole, or window, in a piece of "waste" veneer supplied with the kit. This is actually a piece of good veneer which serves as a template for cutting the inlay required to fill the window. As the picture progresses, the waste veneer is gradually discarded and replaced by the picture segments.

The full-size pattern from which you work is printed in reverse so that you do all cutting from the back. The reason for this is that when a knife blade cuts into veneer it forms a V-shape as it forces the fibers apart (see diagram page 1773). This means that the face side of the veneer will produce a tight-fitting joint because it is cut with just the tip of the blade.

You begin by taping the working pattern along one edge of the waste veneer so that it can be flipped back and forth as required. A sheet of carbon paper is placed between the pattern and the waste. Use a hard, sharp pencil and trace the first segment to be cut. Lift the pattern, remove the carbon and with light pressure on the knife, cut around the line you have traced to make a score cut. Make another pass with the knife to sever the fibers cleanly.

veneers are number-coded

The varied veneers supplied in the kit are numbered, as are the various segments of the picture in the pattern. The veneers have been selected and numbered with care in order to produce the necessary colors and contrasts which make up the total picture. The recommended grain direction for each component is also indicated in the pattern.

Now, with the opening in the waste as a starting point, select the proper veneer and place it under the opening. Use the edge of the opening as a template to guide the blade around the contours to make a light score cut. Remove the scored veneer and proceed to cut it through. Finally, insert the segment into the window and secure it with tape. Flip the pattern back into place over the waste, insert the carbon again and trace an adjoining segment of the picture. Cut

14. REMOVE THE TRACING PATTERN now and turn the work right-side up for front taping.

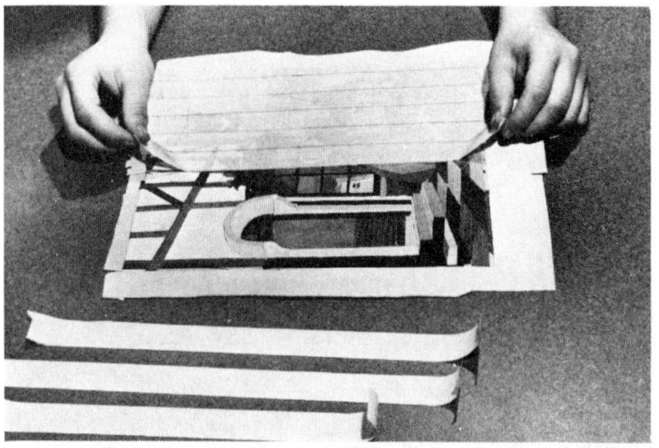

15. COVER THE COMPLETE FACE of the picture with long strips in order to hold the inlays in position.

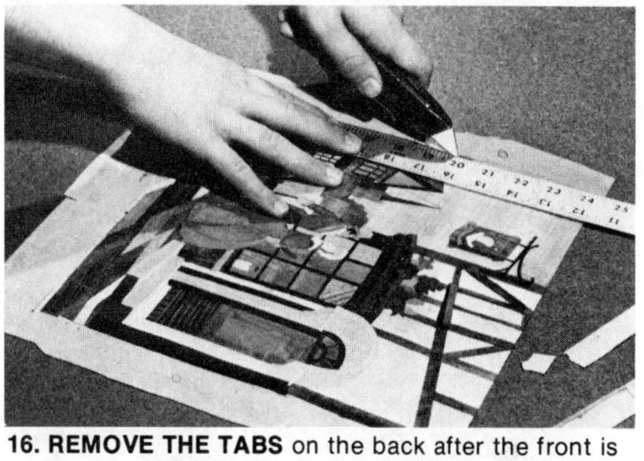

16. REMOVE THE TABS on the back after the front is covered with tape; then trim the borders.

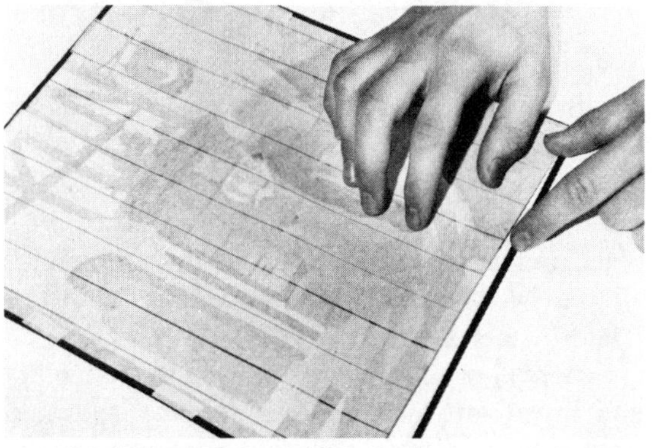

17. ADD BORDER STRIPS of contrasting wood to the four sides and miter the corners for a neat fit.

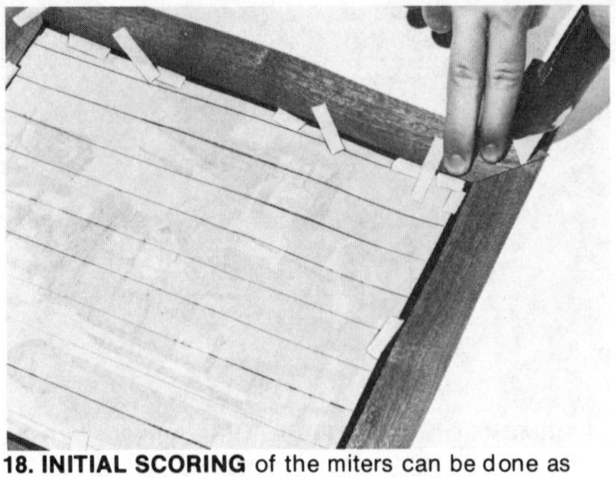

18. INITIAL SCORING of the miters can be done as shown, but make the final cut from the outer edge.

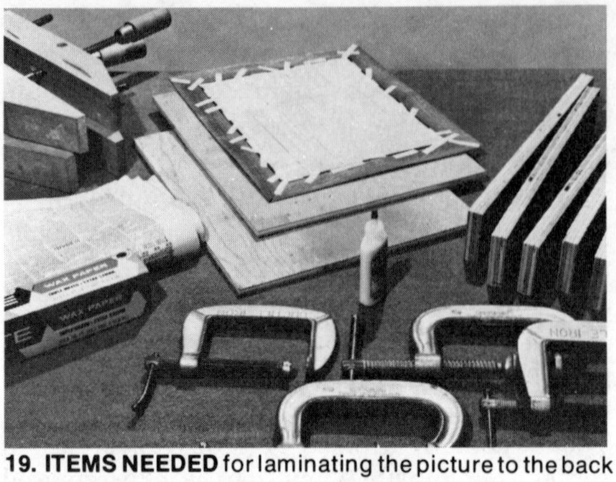

19. ITEMS NEEDED for laminating the picture to the back panel. Use as many clamps as can be applied.

20. BRUSH WHITE GLUE on both surfaces. Here the back veneer is already in place on the back panel.

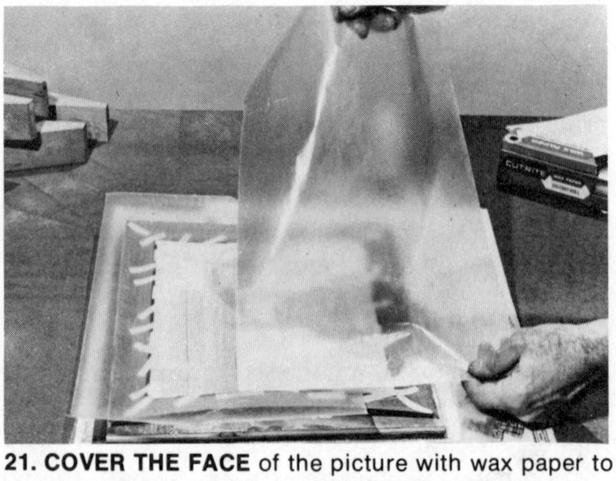

21. COVER THE FACE of the picture with wax paper to prevent excess glue from sticking to the paper.

22. NEWSPAPER PADDING over the glued-up sandwich takes up irregularities in the surface.

out the window and an inlay veneer, tape it into place and continue to repeat the procedure until all the waste veneer has been filled with the inlaid veneer segments.

When all of the inlay segments have been cut and taped into place, the assembly is turned right-side up. Long strips of tape are now used to cover the entire surface of the picture. Border strips of veneer are cut to fit with mitered corners and these, too, are taped into place.

All the original bits of tape are now carefully removed from the backside preparatory to gluing the veneer to a background panel which can be either hardboard or plywood. In order to prevent warping of the panel, a backing veneer is supplied. This is glued to the back of the panel to counteract any warping tendencies. Apply white glue to all surfaces to be joined, insert a sheet of kitchen waxed paper against the veneers, back and front, then place a layer of newspaper between the wax paper and two pieces of ¾-in. plywood. Use as many clamps as you can to apply pressure.

When dry, the surface tapes can be removed by dampening them with water. A thorough sanding, followed with several coats of clear wood finish will complete your picture.

Marquetry kits are available from Albert Constantine and Son, Inc., 2050 Eastchester Road, Bronx, NY 10461.

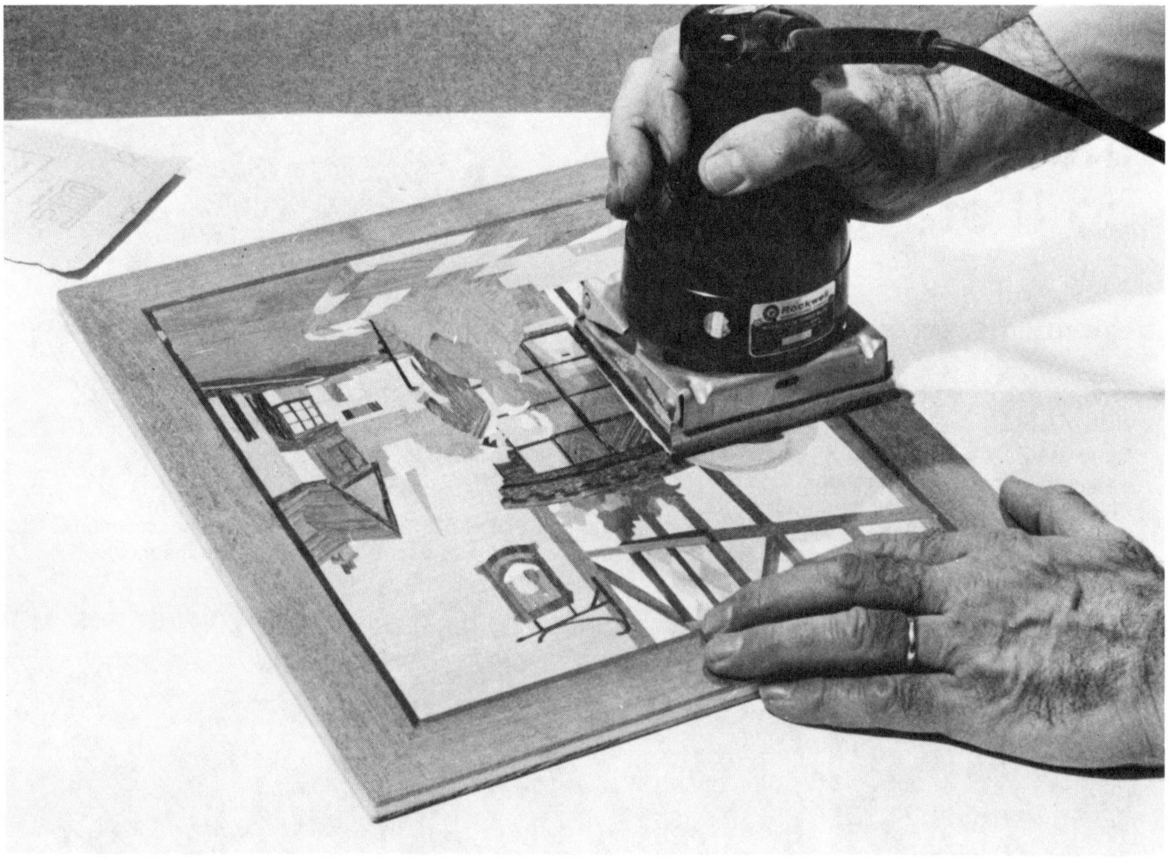

23. A POWER FINISHING SANDER and fine abrasive paper can be used to clean the surface if you work carefully.

24. BRING OUT THE BEAUTY of different colored wood veneers by applying two coats of a clear finish.

How to paint masonry so it stays painted

By RICHARD E. DEMPLEWOLFF

SEE ALSO
**Concrete . . . Concrete blocks . . .
House painting . . . Paint rollers . . .
Painting, exterior . . . Painting, interior . . .
Retaining walls . . . Scaffolding . . . Steps**

POOR ADHESION. Paint scuffs under furniture. This is due to a hard surface beneath the paint.

SOME SYMPTOMS OF TROUBLE

FLAKING. Chunks lift off; caused by water, frost or wrong paint.

ALLIGATORING. Lines are usually due to hard paint on soft undercoat.

FINE BLISTERING, FLAKING. Bare spots may be due to moisture.

BLISTERING AND PEELING. Paint crumbles due to alkali on concrete.

HOW TO TEST FOR MOISTUR

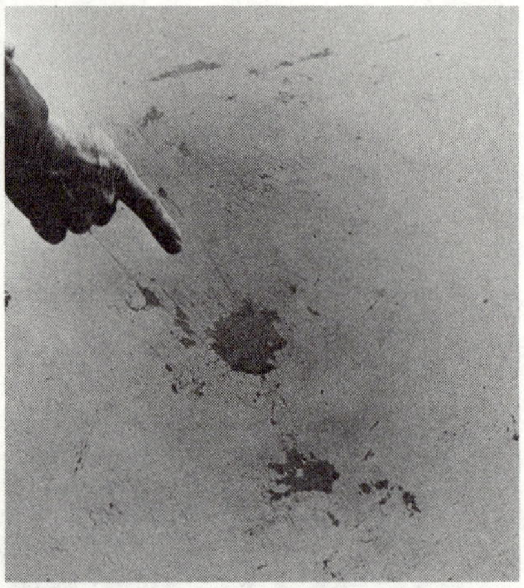

PICK A BARE spot where blistering has occurred and mark off patch.

COVER exposed concrete with etching acid, then rinse thoroughly.

MANY HOMEOWNERS who have painted a concrete patio deck later have been plagued by any of several diseases to which some painted concrete and masonry surfaces fall heir. What causes the blistering, flaking, alligatoring or poor adhesion on some concrete surfaces? And can you do anything about it?

The symptoms may be due to one or more of the factors we'll cover here. You can do something about it in most cases.

Ninety percent of all failures in painted masonry surfaces, says Robert Toothill, lab chief at United Gilsonite Laboratories in Scranton, PA, are due to what's known as *effluorescence.* "Most concrete, mortar and cement," he explains, "contains alkali. Any moisture present dissolves the alkali, and this solution eventually wicks to the surface where the moisture evaporates. The salts are left behind on the surface. This process causes the white material you often see on bricks." Those salts, trapped beneath paint, destroy its adhesion.

Moisture may come from uncured concrete, it may wick up from wet soil beneath the concrete, or it may have been absorbed through the surface before painting, or through improperly applied paint.

Here is a list of familiar trouble symptoms, their causes, and what can be done about them.

1. Blistering and peeling. Cause: Either effluorescence, surface moisture or "dusting" (concrete

WICKING

COVER AREA with commercial paint remover and wait while it acts.

THOROUGHLY STRIP all paint from patch with a scraper.

USE ELECTRIC sander with coarse grit to score troweled surface.

IF RUBBER MAT placed over concrete overnight is wet, you're in trouble.

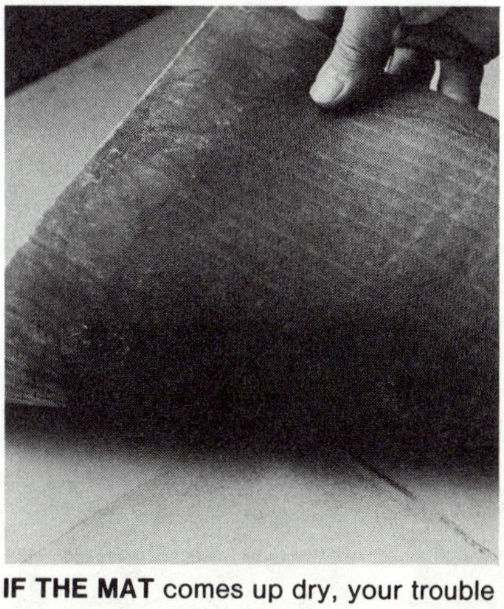

IF THE MAT comes up dry, your trouble may be a hard-troweled finish or dusting.

IN CASES of blistering and poor adhesion, you must sand and totally refinish.

surface powders, due to rapid curing). In efflorescence beneath oil-base paints the alkali salts may soften the paint to a soapy consistency; rub it and it emulsifies. Paint chemists call this *saponification.*

Cure: Strip off paint with a good chemical stripper that will also remove the sealer (if any) beneath it—or rent a commercial floor sander with extra-coarse-grit abrasive to remove all paint and sealant, and score the concrete surface as you go to insure better adhesion for the new coating. Prepare the surface with a deep penetrating sealer, according to manufacturer's instructions. Let this dry before applying a good latex or other paint specified for concrete by the same maker. Apply no more than two coats. (Note: If a concrete deck is on soil that regularly traps water, trouble may recur in a short time. Paintmakers recommend getting rid of the moisture source, or stripping the surface and leaving it bare).

2. Bubble blisters. Cause: Hot weather. The paint dries faster than the solvent can evaporate, so it expands under the paint and lifts dome-shaped blisters which are known to the trade as "solvent blisters."

Cure: Strip blistered areas as described in No. 1, and repaint in cooler weather at a time when the sun does not strike the surface directly.

3. Flaking. Cause: Surface moisture followed by frost; too many coats of paint (no more than two coats are recommended for a bare masonry surface), or poor paint structure (brittle or shrinking undersurface).

Cure: Same as for No. 1.

4. Alligatoring. Cause: A rare phenomenon on concrete, due to either too much zinc oxide in-paint, or a top surface paint that's harder than the base coat—such as an enamel applied over a flat finish, or applied over wax, grease or oil spills.

Cure: Remove as much old finish as possible in the damaged area and refinish as indicated in No. 1.

5. Poor adhesion (paint scuffs easily, strips when furniture is dragged over it). Cause: Concrete may be too dense or hand-troweled to a high finish; it may be of a poor mix, with too much sand, making a "punky" surface. Dusting also may be the cause.

Cure: Same procedure as No. 1. If the problem is too high a finish, use extra-coarse sanding discs to remove old paint and to score the surface. With punky or floury concrete surfaces, ask your paint dealer to prescribe a good concrete protector-sealer before applying any paint.

6. Chalky (powdering) **paint surface.** Cause: The sun is breaking down the paint.

Cure: Wire-brush and vacuum all chalky areas, wash with detergent. Apply a concrete protector or a low-solids varnish, to recombine the chalk, before applying fresh concrete paint.

How can you determine if moisture and efflorescence are, indeed, the cause of a concrete paint problem? Paint and masonry experts suggest the following standard procedure for concrete patios, which are the primary victims of these troubles:

1. Pick a spot where the paint has deteriorated.

2. Strip a section with either a good paint remover or by sanding it with extra-coarse grit on an electric hand sander.

3. If surface is hard-troweled (a dense, polished finish) use etching acid to deepen and extend scoring produced by the sanding.

4. Rinse the area of all acid and allow it to dry thoroughly.

5. Lay a rubber mat on top of the bare concrete and leaves it there overnight.

6. If, when you lift the mat in the morning, it is wet underneath, moisture is wicking up through the concrete. If the mat is dry underneath, moisture and/or effluorescence is not your trouble.

7. Whether it is or isn't wet your best bet is to use a commercial floor sander as described before.

If moisture is found, it is very important that a deep-penetrating concrete protector-sealer be applied (in the driest weather possible) before painting. This will block upward flow of water through pores in the concrete. For best results, experts recommend that the paint be applied with a brush or airless spray—*not* with an air spray or roller.

Needless to say, brick, block and other masonry structural materials (especially in basement walls) also are subject to effluorescence and other problems damaging to paint. While most natural fieldstone is free of paint problems, the mortar holding the stones together may not be.

Most of the good paint makers have specially prepared paint formulations with built-in resistance to alkalinity as well as waterproofing sealers made especially for waterproofing porous masonry walls. Usually these are substantially different chemically than paints and sealers recommended for concrete decks. It is important to describe to your paint dealer the details of your particular problem, and ask him to recommend materials you need to prepare the surface and refinish it so that it will stay put.

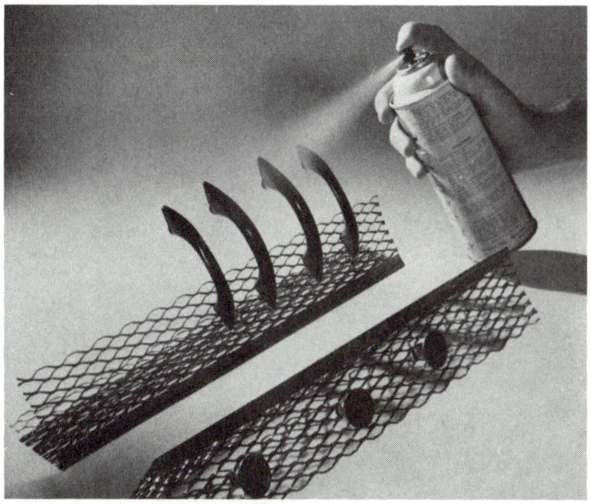

CORNER BEADING scraps left over from a plastering job make ready-made holders for small parts such as knobs and pulls. Whether you lay the scraps on their side or stand them upright, they provide handy racks for the parts while you spray-paint and dry them.—*Gene Rapp.*

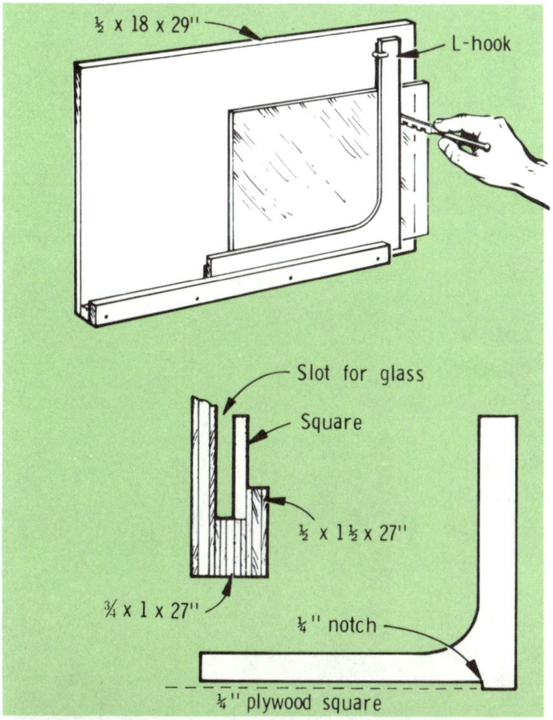

CUTTING GLASS squarely is no problem when you have this handy cutting board mounted on your shop wall. Its built-in square helps hold the glass and assures a right-angle cut every time.

To make it you start out with a flat panel of plywood and add a trough along the bottom edge. This is formed with two strips, one wider than the other.

The square, which provides a straight-edge for the glass cutter, is cut squarely from ¼-inch plywood to slide freely in the trough, and is notched along the bottom. The notch helps hold the square in place at the bottom, while an L-hook serves to clamp it at the top. A steel carpenter's square will save you the trouble of making a square and then having to worry whether it is square.

The glass is all you need to hold when drawing the cutter along the guide. With the glass held vertically, you'll find it easier to make a clean score than when it's cut on a flat surface.—*G.E. Hendrickson.*

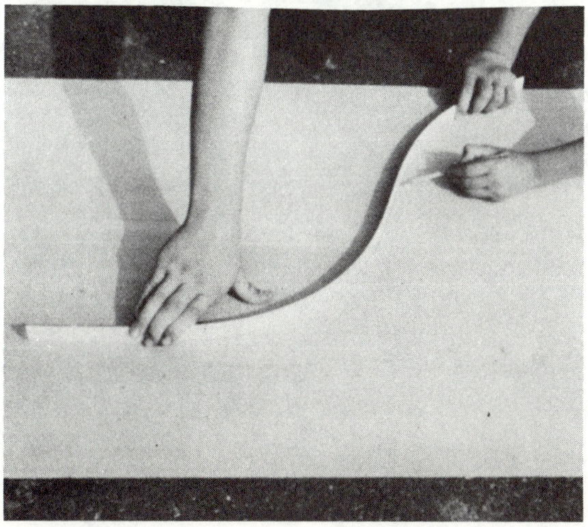

A SCRAP of decorative laminate will help you draw a large irregular curve. Ripped into a long strip about ½ inch wide, the laminate is an improvement over wood strips for drawing curves. It's flexible enough to assume the shape of almost any curve and the plastic is as strong as is needed. One drawback is that it takes three hands to use it, but with the assistance the job is quick and easy. If there's no one available to help, you can place weights alongside the strip to hold a curved position.—*Rosario Capotosto.*

BLOCK SPACERS are cut from 2x4 stock. Spacers are laid out, corner holes for conduit drilled before spacers are cut to shape.

Rugged masts from thinwall conduit

By R. S. HEDIN

WHETHER USED to support a TV antenna or a 10-room martin birdhouse, a high-rise mast can weigh and cost like the dickens. But you can assemble a sturdy lightweight one for a few dollars from standard lengths of thinwall conduit.

You have a choice of bracing the three-legged masts with a series of thinwall spacers (A) flattened at the ends, or with wood blocks placed every 12 in. The wood blocks (B) are attached with 1½-in. No. 10 screws; the thinwall sections are brazed. A three-hole wood fixture keeps conduit legs uniformly spaced while being brazed.

If the mast is to support a birdhouse, it's anchored to long bolts imbedded in a concrete footing, and metal angles are used at the top to attach the birdhouse. If used to mount a TV antenna on the roof, the legs of the mast are bolted to three angle-iron feet. In the case of a TV mast, the upper ends of the three legs can be "gathered" around an additional single length of conduit and cross-bolted together. In some cases, you may need to brace the mast with guy wires.

SEE ALSO
Antennas, TV . . . Birdhouses . . .
Citizens band radio . . . Hi-fi centers . . .
Interference, TV . . . Television antennas

CONDUIT LEGS and wooden spacers are joined with screws. To avoid stains from rust, be sure to use galvanized screws.

HIGH-RISE MAST is slipped over the anchor bolts and then cross-pinned with three ¼-in. bolts. Use washers under legs, if needed, to level legs.

ANCHOR BOLTS, two ⅝-in. and one ½-in., are set in concrete to project 3 to 5 in. The smaller bolt makes up for misalignment.

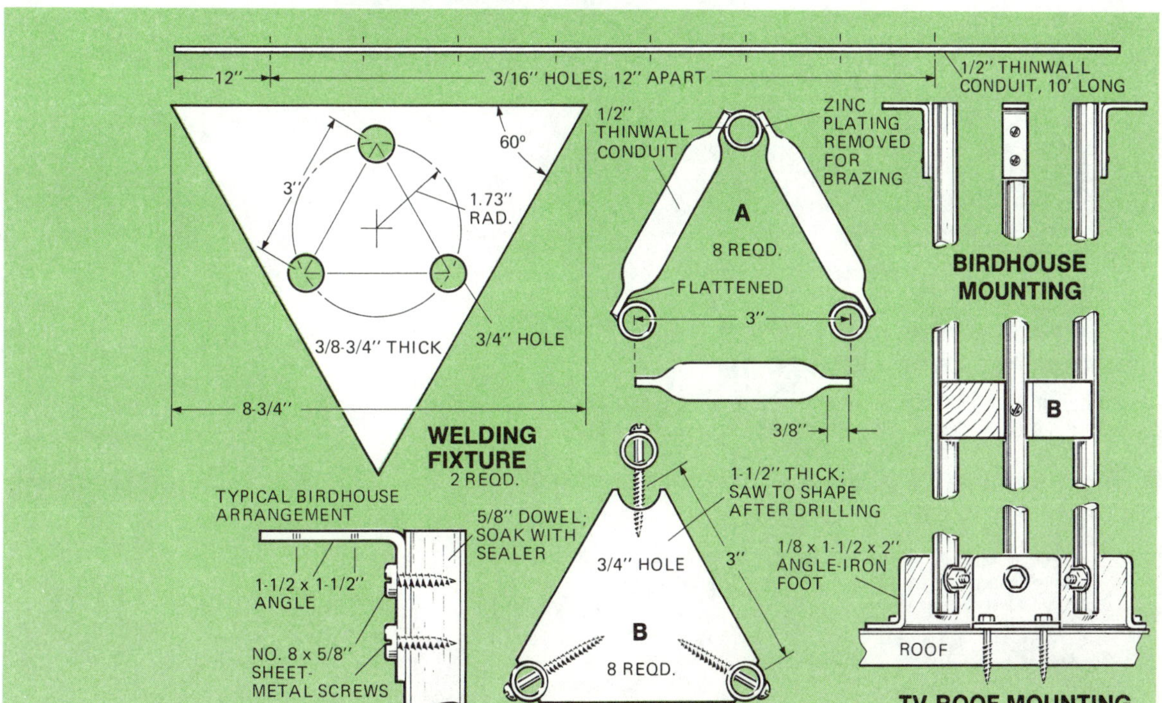

Guide to the right measurement

WHETHER YOU WANT to remodel your kitchen or add a room to your house, this guide can help you in the planning stage. It provides some basic measurements of common structures, equipment and material and recommended minimum dimensions. Widths are given as the narrower horizontal dimension or as the distance from left to right from the front of an item. Heights are given from the floor or from the bottom of suspended items. Depths are from front to rear. Some measurements are not given since they vary widely.

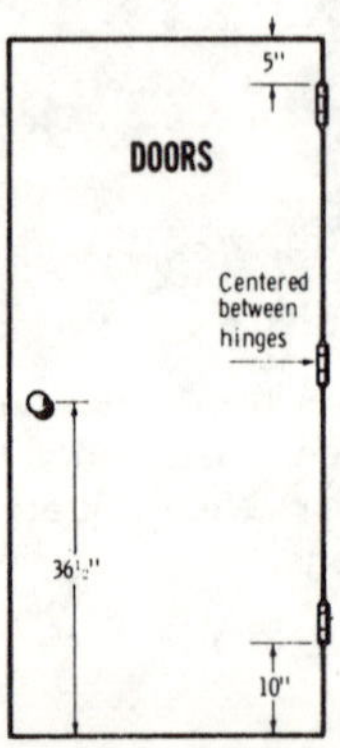

FRAMING
Width and height of rough opening are 3½" larger than the door. Head and side casings are ½" x 1¾"; exterior door sill is 1⅝" x 7⅜"; a stock jamb with a ½" rabbet is 1$\frac{5}{16}$" or 1⅝" x 5¼"

ENTRANCE DOOR
Standardly 2'6", 2'8", 2'10" and 3' wide, and 6'8" and 7' high; thickness is 1¾"

INTERIOR DOOR
Most commonly 2'4" and 2'6" wide; 6'6", 6'8" and 7' high; thickness is 1⅜" or 1¾"

DOORBELL BUTTON
Commonly 45" above top of doorsill

DOORKNOB
Commonly 36½" from floor

STAIRS Recommended stairway width 2'10"-3'

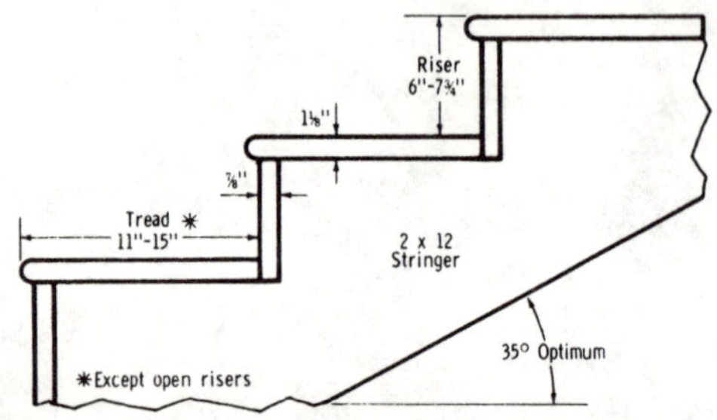

Outside stoop should be 4'6" deep to allow for storm door swing. Minimum step tread is 12" with ¼" pitch. Brick steps should be header fronted

WINDOWS
Placement height is based on aligning with room door top. Measure distance from ceiling to door molding. Window sizes are widely variable. Common wood double-hung sizes: 2', 2'4", 2'8" and 3' wide; 3'2", 3'10" and 4'6" high

RAILINGS
STAIRCASE—Height 2'10"-3'
PORCH AND DECK—Height 3'

HOUSE WIRING
MAJOR EQUIPMENT WATTAGE RATINGS

Air conditioner	850-1200, 3100	Motor, ¼ hp.	530
Attic fan	500-1500	Oil burner	300-550
Clothes dryer	to 4500	Range	7000-14,000
Dishwasher	530-1000	Refrigerator	200-670
Disposer	380-530	Television	200-400
Furnace blower	380-670	Toaster	600-1350
Heater	1000-1650	Washer, automatic	350-900
Home freezer	300-670	Water heater	750-3000

ROOMS—MINIMUM SIZE RECOMMENDATIONS

	WIDTH	LENGTH	HEIGHT THICKNESS	DEPTH
KITCHEN, for 4 persons, depends on layout and equipment	7'	10'		
BATHROOM	5'	7'		
DINING ROOM with 36" chair room	10'	10'		
BEDROOM, including 8' of clothing drawer space per person:				
Single bed	8'	12'	or 10'x10'	
Double bed	12'	13'	or 10'x15'	
Twin beds	12'	15'6"	or 10'x17'6"	
GARAGE without laundry or shop:				
One car with 8' or 9' door	12'	22'		
Two-car with 2-8' or 16' door	19'	22'		
Storage above car hood			4'	5'
Workbench on side, add to width	3'6"		36"	
Floor should pitch toward door ⅛" per foot				

FURNISHINGS & APPLIANCE RECOMMENDATIONS

KITCHEN	WIDTH	LENGTH	HEIGHT THICKNESS	DEPTH	CLEARANCE
Base Cabinet (undersink and corners not included in frontage; height includes counter top)	6'-10'		36"	22"-25"	
Common individual widths: 12", 15", 18", 21", 24", 27", 30", 36", 42", 48"					
Wall cabinet—for 4 persons	6'-10'			12" 13" 14"	
—for service for 12	10'-14'				
Common individual widths: 15", 18", 21", 24", 27" 30", 33", 36", and 44"-60" (triple units)					
Common heights: 15", 18", 21", 24", 30", 31". Top shelf maximum height from floor is 6'					
Cabinet placed above range					30"
above sink					22"
above counter					15"-18"
Counter space needed (not including corners; may be reduced by multiple use)					

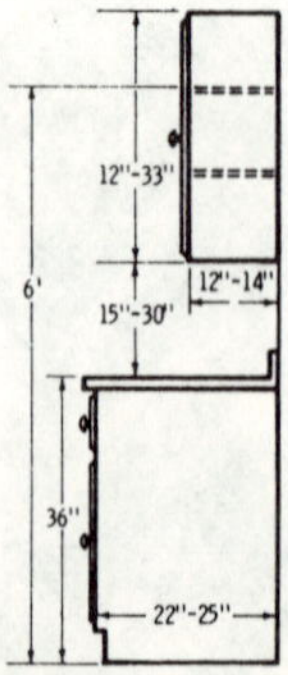

	WIDTH	LENGTH	HEIGHT THICKNESS	DEPTH	CLEARANCE
next to: Refrigerator	15″-18″				
Sink, each side	18″				
Food preparation, mixing	36″				
Range	15″				
Oven	15″				
Wall oven—Open door should be 3″-5″ below wife's elbow. Average height from floor to bottom of oven is 27″-32″					
Common kitchen appliance sizes:					
Refrigerator	36″		59″		
1-bowl sink	24″				
2-bowl sink	36″				
Range	30″		36″		
Built-in range	30″				
Built-in oven	24″				
Dishwasher	24″		34½″-36″		
DINING AREA					
Dining table, allow 2′ per person	30″-42″		30″		36″ 20″ knee
8 persons fit at a 5′ round, a 4′ square or a 3′x8′ rectangle					
Dining counter			36″		
Barstool (footrest 6″-8″ from floor)			24″-25″		12″ knee
Wainscoting			30″		
BATHROOM					
Sinks			31″-36′		
Tubs, square & square corner	3′10″, 4′1½″				
Tubs, rectangular	2′6″-2′9″	4′-5′6″			
Free-standing shower cabinet, square and corner	2′6″-3′6″	6′3″-7′			
Toilets	17¾″-29¼″			26″-31⅜″	18″ front
Shower head			74″		
Curtain rod for tub			78″		
Towel bar			36″-42″		
Medicine cabinet from floor			48″-54″		
Tiling (4¼″x4¼″)—room walls, plus trim			10 tiles		
—tub area from floor, plus trim			16 tiles		
BEDROOM					
Double bed (inside frame measure)	54″	75″, 78″			
Twin bed (inside frame measure)	39″	75″, 78″			
Clothes closet (depth is minimum)			7′-7′6″	22″	
Closet rod			5′3″		
Chest of drawers	36″ up		28″-34″	18″-21″	
WORK AREAS					
Laundry area space in front of washer and dryer	66″			36″	
Space for hand ironing	72″			52″	
Bookshelves and cases (adjustable shelves have pin holes 1″ o.c.)			6′6″ to top shelf	8″-9″	

MATERIALS

BOARD & LUMBER SIZES

Nominal & actual dimensions: 1x2=¾″x1⅝″, 1x3=¾″x2⅝″, 1x4=¾″x3⅝″, 1x5=¾″x4⅝″, 1x6=¾″x5½″, 1x8=¾″x7½″, 1x10=¾″x9½″, 1x12=¾″x11½″; 2x4=1⅝″x3⅝″, 2x6=1⅝″x5⅝″, 2x8=1⅝″x7½″, 2x10=1⅝″x9½″, 2x12=1⅝″x11½″

SHEET MATERIALS

Interior plywood—Most common sizes: 4′x8′, 4′x10′ and 4′x12′; also available, widths 30″-48″, lengths 5′-12′, thicknesses 3/16″ and ¼″-¾″ by eighths

Exterior plywood—Same dimensions as interior except in thicknesses: 3/16″ and ¼″-1⅛″ by eighths

Gypsum wallboard—Width 4′, lengths 4′ and 8′, thicknesses ¼″-⅝″ by eighths

Asbestos cement wallboard—Width 4′, lengths 4′ and 8′, thicknesses ⅛″ and 3/16″

Fiber wallboard—Standard width 4′, lengths 4′-12′, thicknesses ⅜″-¾″ by eighths. Also 4′x14′ & 16′, 8′x14′ & 16′ and 8′x18′

Hardboard, standard & tempered—Widths 2′, 4′ and 5′; lengths 2′-16′; thicknesses ⅛″-5/16″ by sixteenths

Plastic laminate—Widths 24″, 30″, 36″, 48″; lengths 60″, 72″, 84″, 96″, 120″, not all combinations; thickness 1/16″

MASONRY

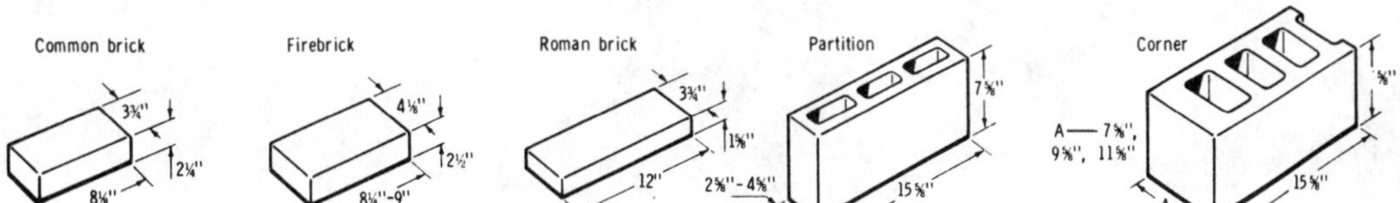

Common concrete blocks

Concrete—General-purpose mix is 1:2¼:3. To make 1 cu. yd., use 6¼ sacks of cement, 14 cu. ft. of sand, 20 cu. ft. of gravel and 6 gal. of water per bag of cement

INSULATION—Commonly available are rolls and loose insulation. Rolls are 16″ o.c. x 36′; loose comes in 4-cu.-ft. bags; also 16″ and 24″ o.c. 4′ batts and 8′ blankets (o.c.=on center)

GUTTERS—4″ and 5″ wide, 10′ long; add connectors, corners and leader adapters to measure length; minimum slope is 1/16″ per foot

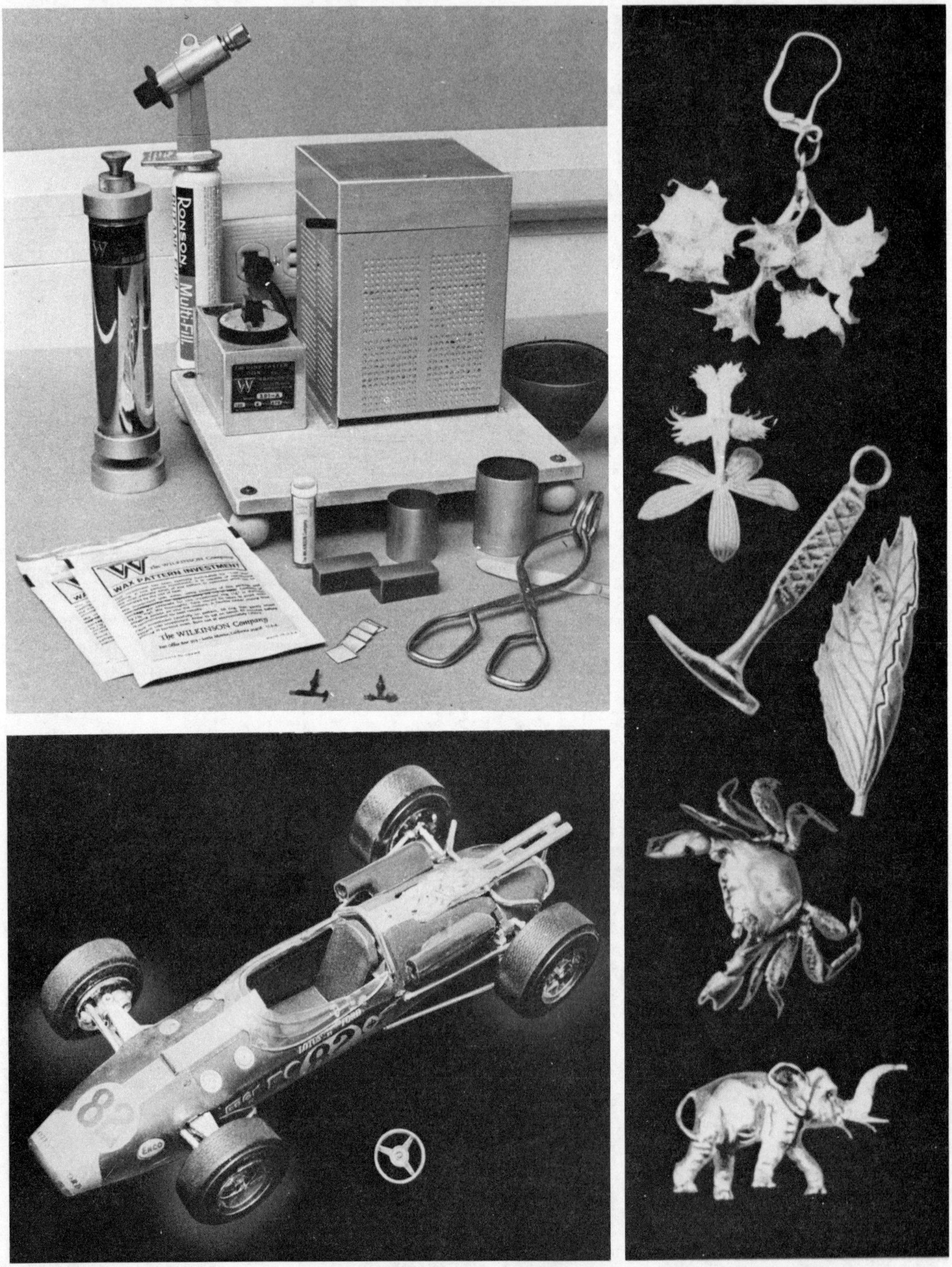

EQUIPMENT YOU NEED for metal casting is shown at upper left. Main items are (l. to r.) a hand air pump, propane torch and electric burnout oven. Other supplies are powdered mold mix (in packets), metal tubes to hold the mold, blocks of carving wax, tongs, small metal ingots, wax sprues and a mixing dish, preferably a flexible rubber or plastic. Tiny steering wheel for the model racing car at lower left and charms and trinkets at right are examples of the many intricate shapes you can cast by lost-wax method.

Make your own metal castings

By C. W. WESTRICK

Like to make special parts for models? A shiny piece of jewelry? The ancient art of "lost wax" casting combined with modern equipment make it easy to turn out just about any metal shape

THERE'S A BIG thrill in seeing a design you have created yourself turn almost magically into gleaming metal. But maybe you figure this requires special know-how and a lot of fancy equipment.

Not today. Hobby shops and lapidary supply houses stock everything you need to cast small model parts or pieces of jewelry in glittering gold, silver and other metals. The process, known as investment or "lost wax" casting, is the same as that used centuries ago by early Egyptians. You carve the shape you want in soft wax, embed the wax in a plaster-like material that hardens around it, then bake it in an oven. Under high heat, the wax vaporizes—is literally "lost"—leaving an empty mold. Molten metal forced into the mold then produces an exact copy of the original wax pattern.

You can make your own wax patterns using a special carving wax, or you can buy patterns ready to use. The latter come in a wide variety of ornaments, charms and small pieces of jewelry. You can also copy actual specimens, such as leaves and insects—anything that will vaporize at 1200° F., leaving little ash.

The equipment you'll need includes a small electric oven for burning out the wax, a propane hand torch for melting the metal, an air pump for forcing the molten metal into the mold, and a supply of metal tubes, called rings or flasks, in which the molds are formed. The rings come in a variety of diameters depending on the size of the pattern you want to copy. The mold material, called the "investment," is a white powder that's mixed with water to form a creamy paste.

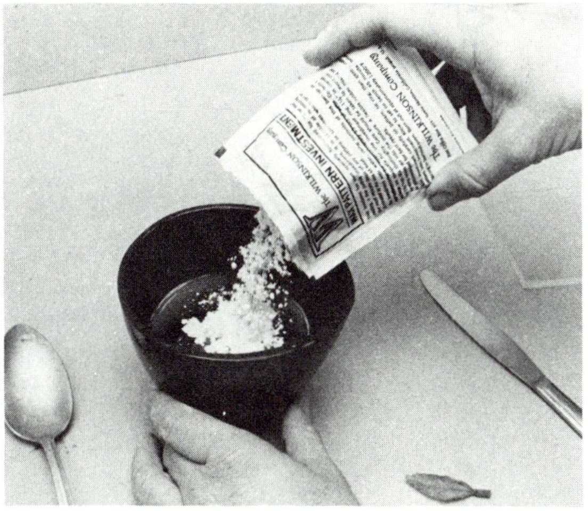

POWDERED MOLD material is poured into a small dish and then mixed with water to a creamy paste. Stir it gently to avoid whipping up air bubbles in the mix.

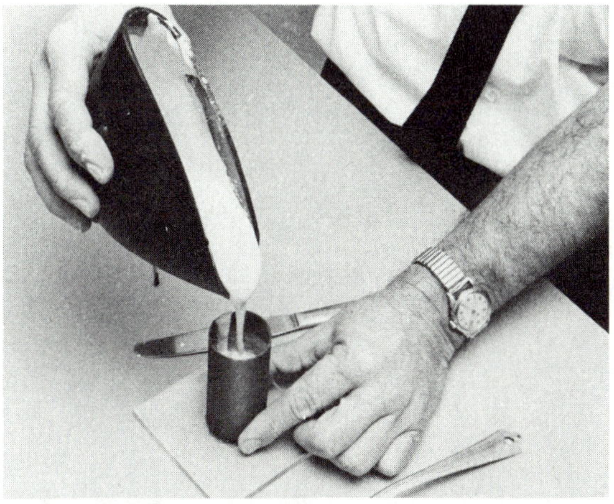

A METAL TUBE, called a ring or flask, serves as a container for the soupy mold mix. Fill it flush to the top. You can use a flexible dish to make pouring easy.

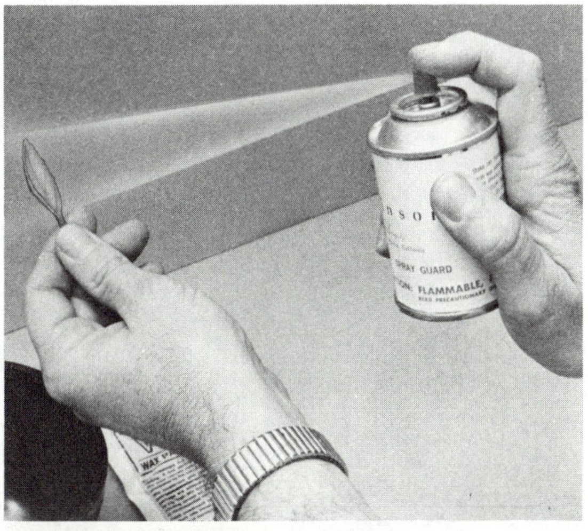

SPRAY THE PATTERN—in this case a small leaf—with a wetting agent before embedding it. This lets the mold mix flow smoothly over the entire surface.

SEE ALSO
Internal carving . . . Jewelry . . . Lapidary . . . Modelmaking . . . Shops, modelmaking . . . Torches

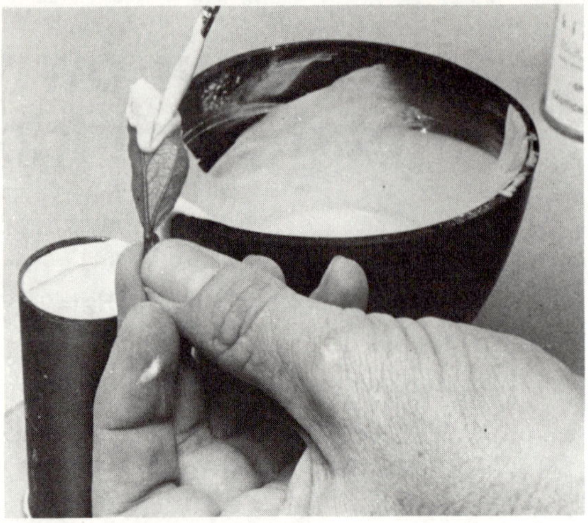

ON INTRICATE OBJECTS, it's best to coat the surface with the mold mix first, using a brush. This insures that the mix will get into all the crevices.

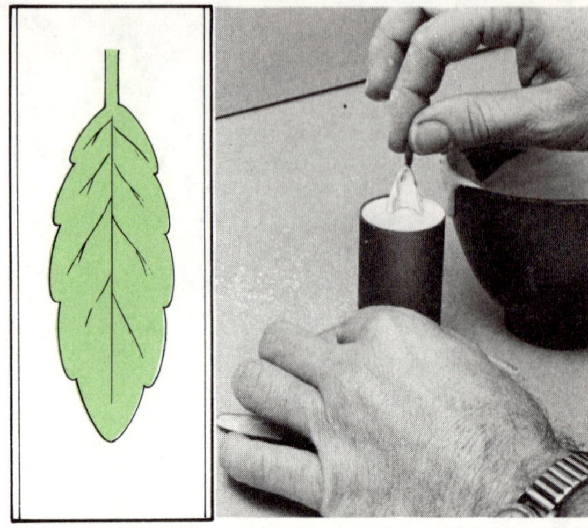

THE PRECOATED pattern is now dipped into the ring containing mold mix. Be sure it is submerged and fully surrounded by the mix with no air pockets.

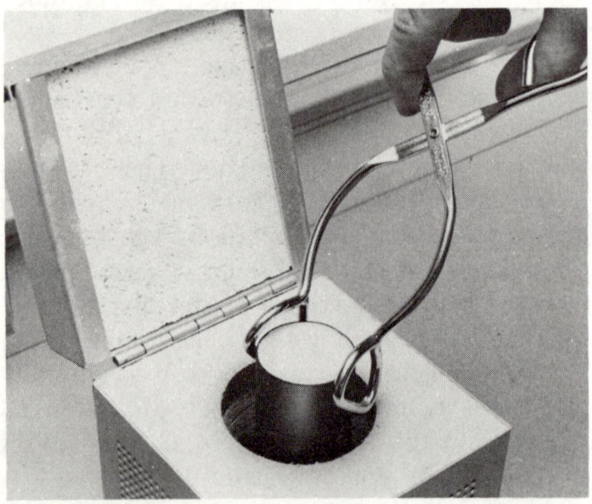

PLACE THE MOLD in the oven crater-side down. Burnout takes from 30 to 60 minutes for wax patterns. Less combustible materials may need several hours.

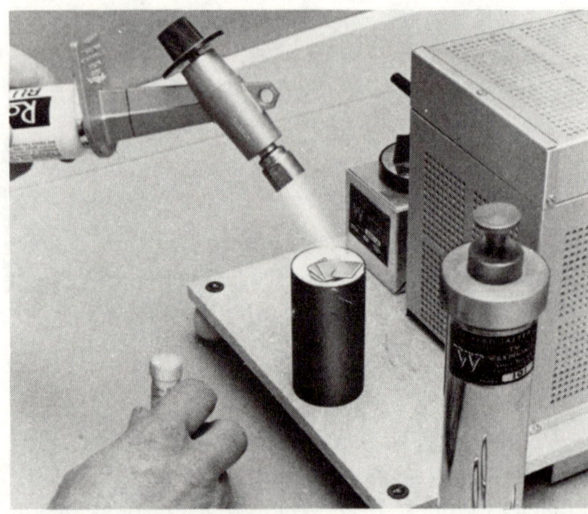

FILL THE MOLD'S crater with several small metal ingots after the burnout. Play the torch flame over them until a ball of molten metal is formed.

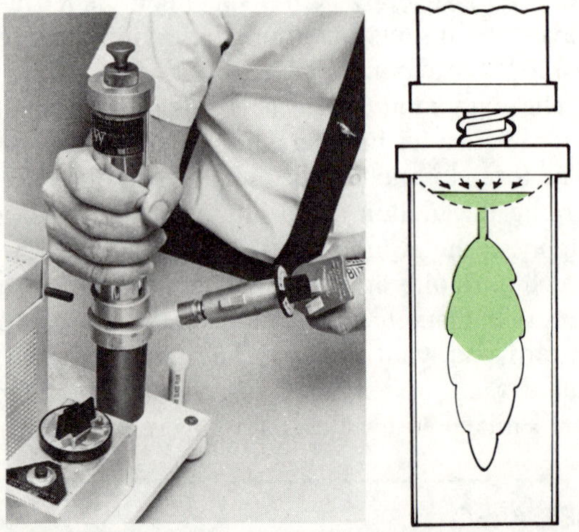

PRESS THE PUMP down over the mold ring without removing the torch. The pump's pressure forces the molten metal down in the mold, as the sketch shows.

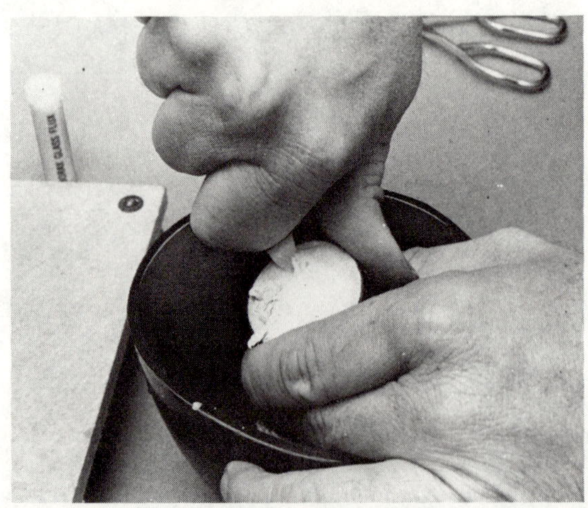

SOAKING THE MOLD in water loosens it and allows it to be peeled away from the casting. The remaining bits can easily be taken off with a toothbrush.

LET THE MOLD harden for 45 minutes or so, then scoop out a shallow crater on top to hold the metal. Be sure that this exposes the sprue on the pattern.

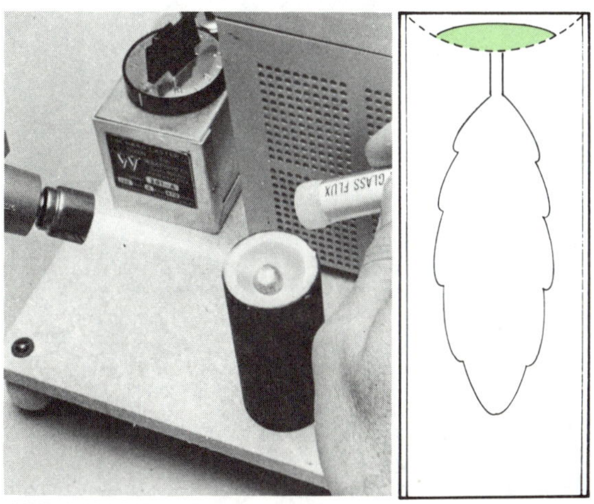

ADD A DASH of flux to the molten metal. This reduces oxides that produce a crust. The sketch shows how the metal forms a puddle above the empty mold.

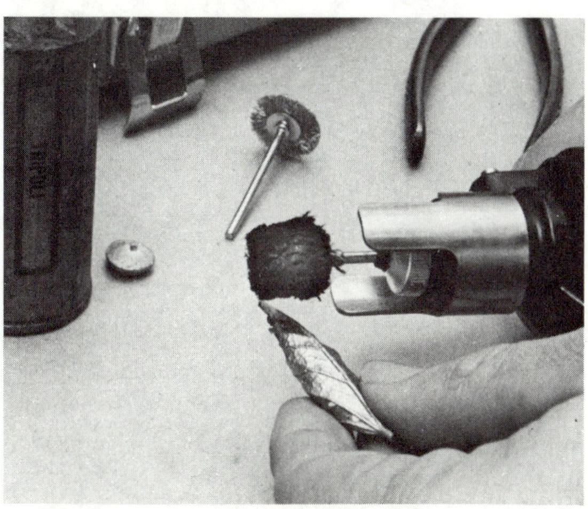

FINISHED CASTING can be polished to a sparkle with a small buffing wheel like the one shown. Use tripoli or jeweler's rouge for best results.

Altogether, everything you need for investment casting can be had for around $100.

In some areas, it may be possible to rent the burnout oven and casting pump.

One large supplier of casting equipment and materials is the Wilkinson Co., P.O. Box 303, Santa Monica, CA.

It's important to use clean metal as dirt particles can result in an imperfectly formed casting. It's also important not to trap air bubbles around the wax pattern when embedding it in the mold. Tiny bubbles leave pockmarks in the mold.

The accompanying photos show the procedure for making a typical casting. Before the pattern is embedded in the investment material, it's necessary to add a small stem, called a "sprue," so it sticks up through the mold to the top. When the sprue, usually made of wax, melts away, it leaves a tiny hole in the mold. This enables you to get molten metal down into the mold cavity from the outside.

"casting" the metal

Note that the molten metal will not just flow down the sprue hole by itself—surface tension prevents it. You must actually force the metal into the mold under pressure, and this is what's known as "casting." The usual casting device is a small hand-operated air pump. Pressure is first built up in the pump by giving the plunger about 15 strokes. Then the pump is placed over the investment ring and pressed down. This releases the air, driving the molten metal into the mold.

Hold the pump over the mold 30 seconds until the metal has become completely solidified or "frozen." To remove your casting from the mold, place the mold in a bowl of water. Allow it to stay there until the water has completely soaked into the material. This should cause the mold to break away easily from the casting. Breaking renders the mold unusable a second time.

It's quite likely that the casting will appear discolored. This discoloration is a surface oxide and is easily removed by pickling the casting in an acid solution—two parts muriatic acid to one part water is usual.

After pickling, remove the sprue stem from the casting with a pair of wire-cutting pliers. Then grind or file off the remaining stub. The best method of polishing your casting is with some type of rotating polisher. The most common compounds used for final finishing are tripoli and jeweler's rouge, applied with a soft buffing wheel.

Make a boring-bar set for your lathe

By. R.S. HEDIN

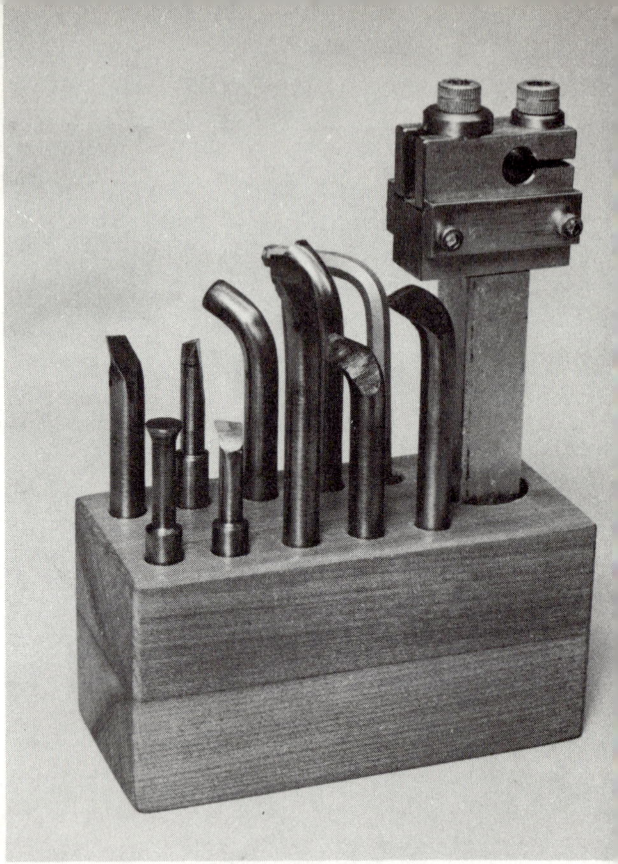

FINISHED SET nestles in hardwood stand with spare boring-bar blanks and Allen wrench.

■ EVERY OWNER of a metal-turning lathe should have a boring-bar set to increase his machining capability. This set has features that make it especially useful: It will bore a large range of hole diameters, and the holder is made so that bars can be rotated to set the rake angle, while a separate adjustment sets the tool to the spindle center.

The holder is made from ½-in.-square stock. The shank is of two pieces, welded or screwed together. Depending on the lathe used, it may be necessary to adjust the location of part B on part A so bits can be adjusted for center; the prototype was made for a 10-in.-swing Maximat lathe. Part C has a reamed hole to fit the boring bars'

UPPER SCREW on toolholder clamps the boring bar. The lower screw clamps vertical adjustment to set the cutting edge on center.

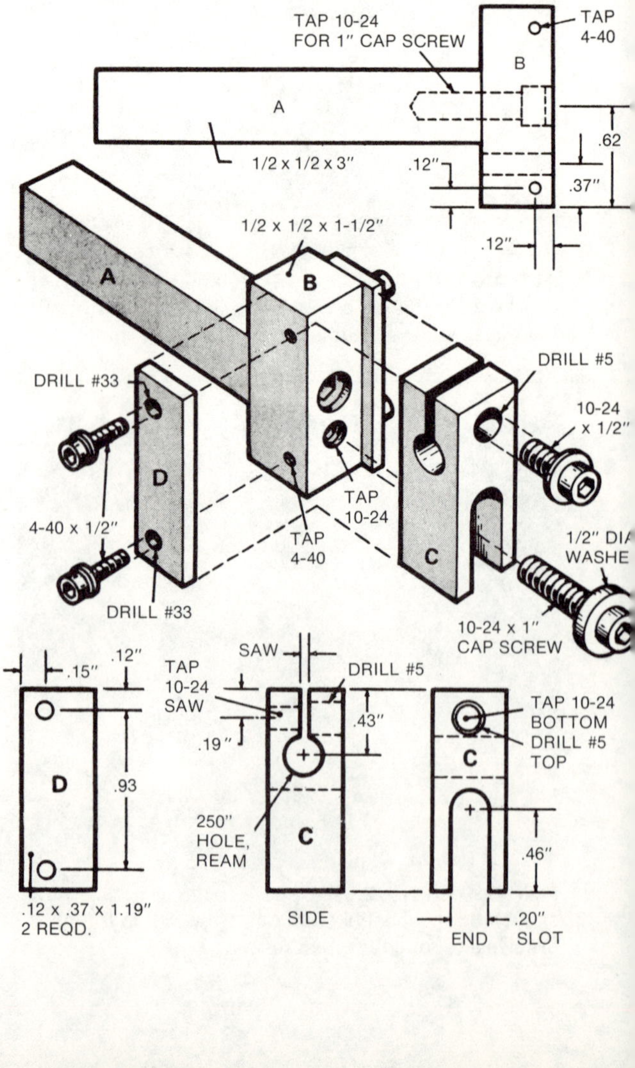

SEE ALSO

Angles, drilling . . . Drill press techniques . . . Metal-lathe techniques . . . Shop techniques

shanks; saw the clamping slot after reaming the hole. The washer for the capscrew that holds part C to part B was made thick so it would not be deformed in use.

The boring bars are made from .250-in.-dia. water-hardening drill rod. Two styles are shown; forged and turned. Bars for boring large holes are heated and bent to form an offset. To bend the offset on a boring-bar blank, heat the end until it is bright red, then insert it into a hole drilled into a scrap steel plate, and bend the blank over; two torches may be necessary to get enough heat. The offset is then ground or filed to shape the cutting edge.

Small-hole bars are made by turning the shank down and leaving a knob on the end, then grinding or filing to form the cutting edge. These bars can be used to bore holes as small as .20-in. dia.

Harden the cutting end of each blank by heating it to a bright-red color and quenching it in water to which a little table salt has been added to prevent soft spots. Remove surface discoloration with abrasive cloth, and draw the hardened end by heating the bar with a low flame until the end is a light straw color, then quench again in water. Apply heat about ¾ in. from the end and watch the color crawl to the cutting edge. Overheating (to a dark straw or blue color) will make the edge too soft.

After hardening and drawing the end, grind the cutting edge and hone it with an oilstone. Because this is carbon steel and not alloy steel, the bars will not take high heat—so use low speeds and feeds when machining with them.

BLANKS AND their finished boring bars: Above, left: turned blank and bit made from it. Above, right: forged blank and bit; bit at right is threading tool.

TOOLHOLDER HAS a 3-inch shank that allows it to be clamped firmly into the toolpost.

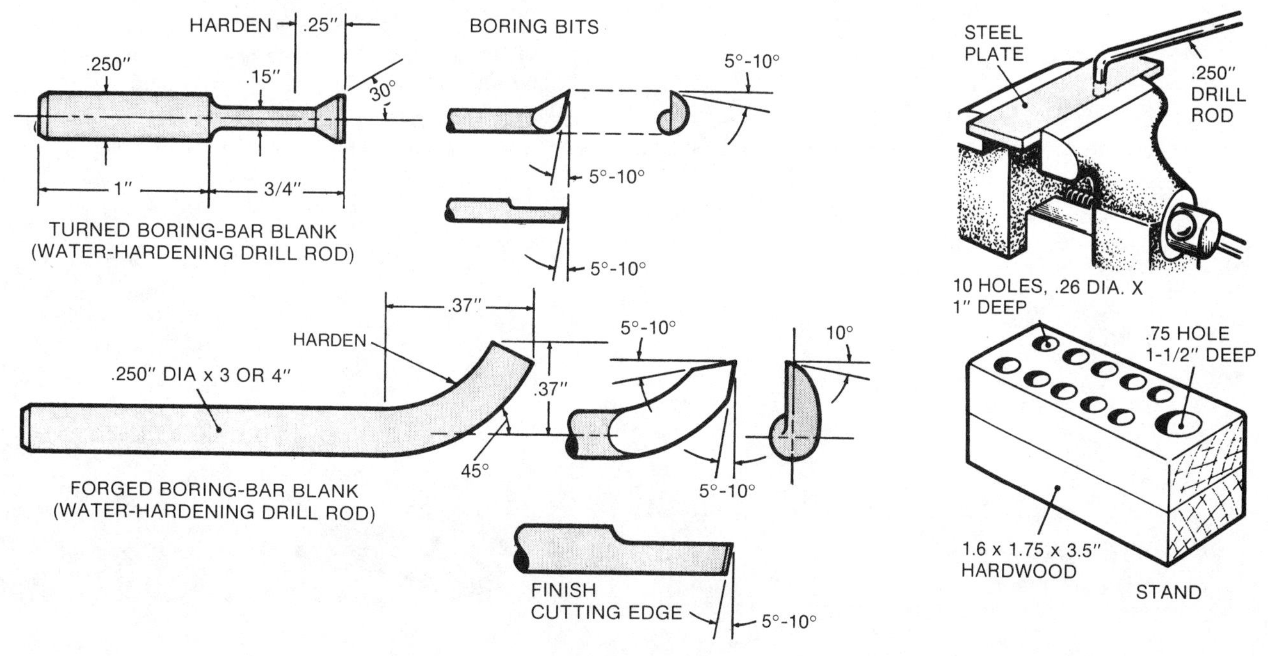

Make a king-size toolpost

High-speed steel or carbide bits are better for some jobs on a small lathe. The problem is finding a toolpost to accommodate them. The solution is to make your own.

■ HEFTY, HIGH-SPEED steel or carbide bits are more rigid and in other ways superior to the toolholder-bit combination widely used on small lathes—but a conventional toolpost has too narrow a slot to accommodate them. Even if the slot were wide enough, some sort of block or shim system would have to be improvised to position cutting edges at the proper height.

SEE ALSO
Metal-lathe techniques . . . Tools, hand

THE OVERSIZE POST starts as a 1⅛-in. rod. The bottom hole is drilled and tapped for a mounting stud.

THE TOP HOLE should be drilled and tapped for a ⅜-16 clamping bolt, preferably with a square head.

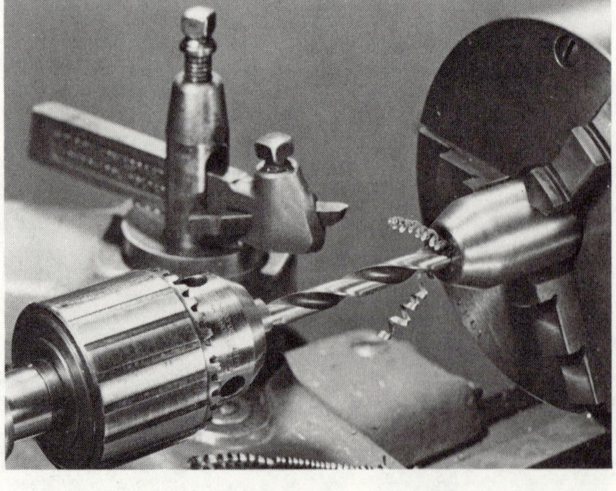

EASY-TO-SHAPE PARTS go together as shown in the exploded view below. Two setscrews may be needed.

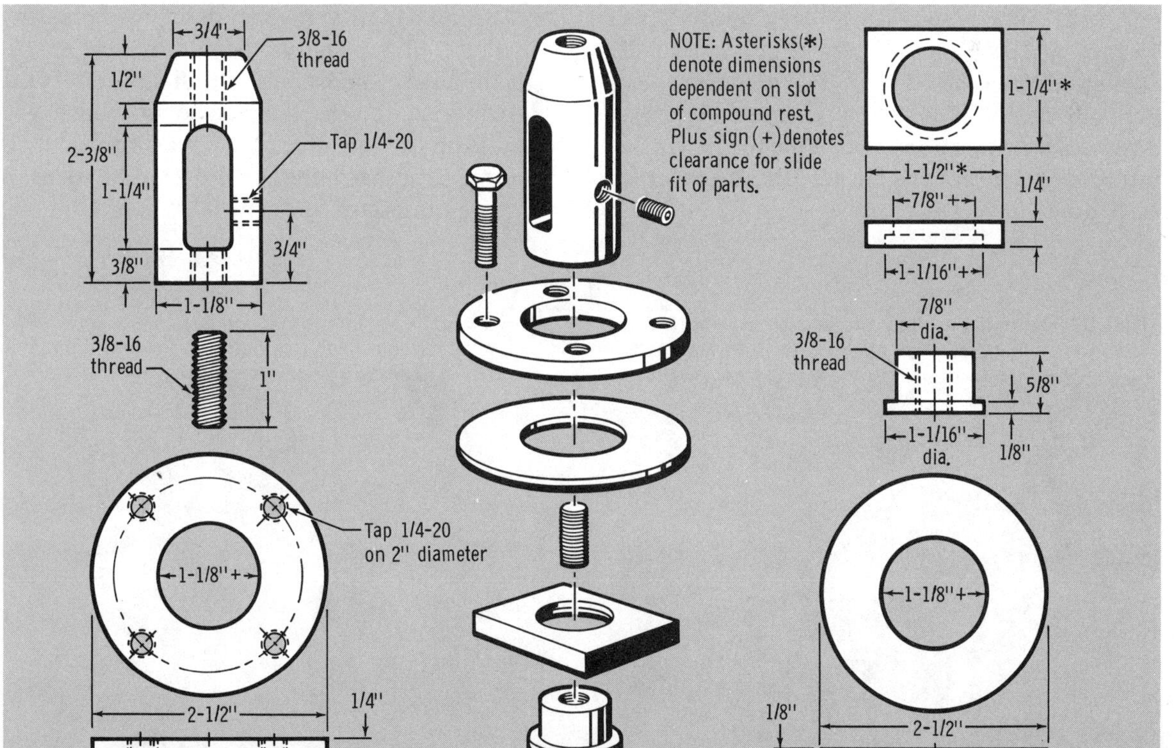

TO CUT a slot in the post, first drill two ½-in. holes about ¾ in. apart (measured center to center).

MILLING is the best way to remove the rest of the material. Alternately, excess could be sawn and filed.

Not so with the toolpost shown, however, since it was specifically designed to accommodate bits up to ½-in. wide. It has an easily set height-adjustment feature consisting of a steel ring supported by a quartet of bolts. It also provides firm support for boring bars or large bits ground as boring tools. All parts can be made of ordinary or tool steel, although for maximum durability, parts subjected to wear should be hardened.

Because of the wide tool slot, the diameter of the post is greater than that of the conventional post—yet the button and the block forming the base of the post assembly must be kept small enough to enter the toolpost T-slot on the compound rest. Therefore, the post assembly must be made in two sections so that the block can be installed (these sections are held together by the ⅜-16 stud).

The ¼-20 setscrew in the side of the holder will prevent possible side shifting of the bit, especially when it does not completely fill the wide slot. You could install two or more screws, if required, which would be most effective when the bit is making heavy side cuts.

The tool bit rests on a ring assembly consisting of a thick upper ring through which four ¼-20 bolts extend to rest on the thinner ring. By adjusting the 1-in.-long bolts to control the height of the upper ring, it's possible to set the bit at the proper cutting height.

The top bolt used to exert downward pressure on the tool bit should be a standard ⅜-16, square-head toolpost bolt. The dimensions in the drawing are for the holder shown, which will handle up to ½-in.-thick bits on a 9-in. lathe. Of course, for other lathes or different bit sizes, it may be necessary to vary dimensions.

THE BUTTON on the bottom of the post assembly is machined to fit T-slot, then fitted on ⅜-16-thread stud.

THE BUTTON should be a loose fit in the shouldered block. Check the clearance before removing the block.

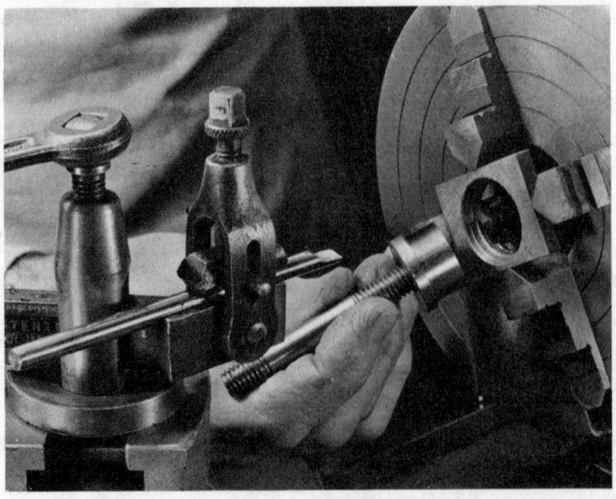

Make a lathe indexing attachment

By CHARLES J. KSANDA

■ THIS SIMPLE lathe indexing attachment is perfect for precision circular dividing and angular indexing. You can make it yourself.

The attachment consists of a U-shaped bracket which holds a single-thread worm, or tangent screw, graduated dial disc and an index that permits accurate settings. The unit is permanently mounted on the headstock of the lathe with a single bolt. One turn of the tangent screw turns the spindle 15° (since the spur gear on the spindle has 24 teeth).

The attachment is fitted with two dial discs: One is divided into 60 parts, the second into 90. Between the two, you can graduate a circle to within ¼ to 1/6 of one degree. With appropriate setting of the dial, the circle can be divided into any even or odd number of parts.

The drawing (side view) shows the tangent screw engaged in the spindle spur gear. Directly below, the latter is shown when not in use. To engrave the lines, use a cutting tool mounted on the compound slide and determine the length by using the micrometer scale on the cross-feed screw.

SEE ALSO
Metal-lathe techniques . . . Tools, hand

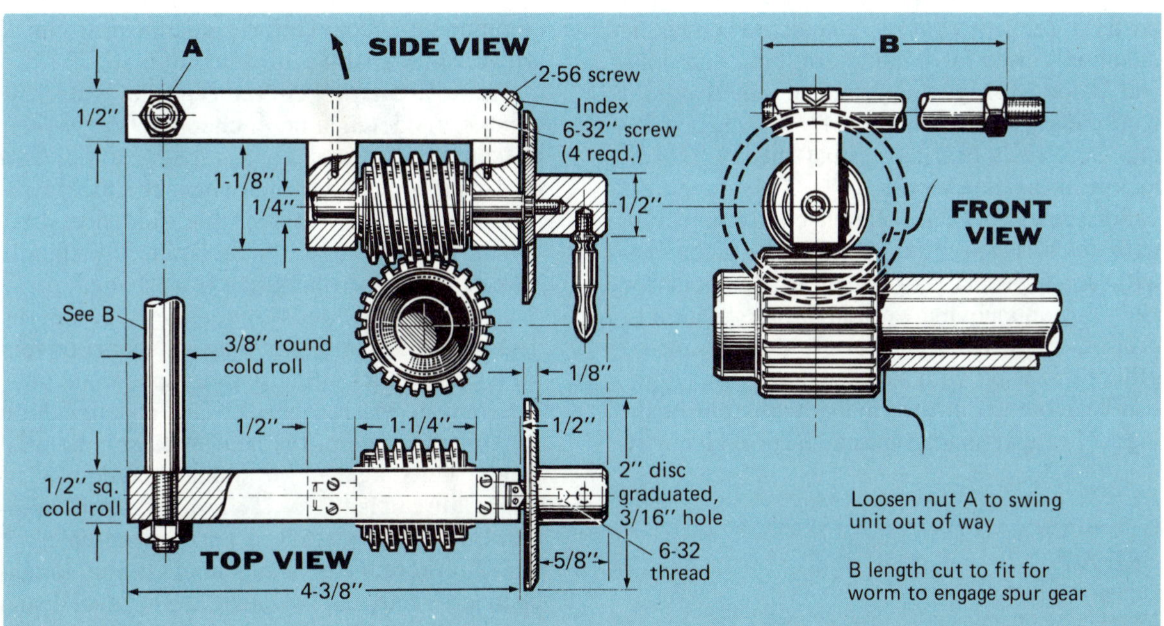

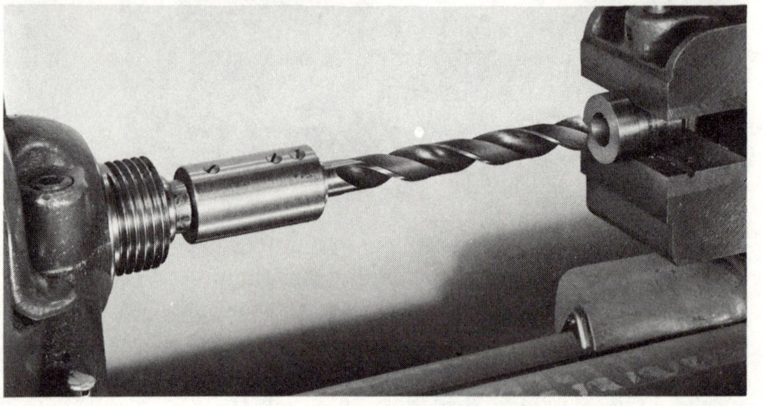

MOUNTED in screw-on setscrew (top photo), a Woodruff-keyway cutter is used to slot a ring. Work is held in carriage-mounted milling attachment. Taper-shank setscrew chuck (bottom photo) is better suited for drilling and operations in which pressure is lengthwise.

Setscrew chucks you can make

By WALTER E. BURTON

■ A SIMPLE SETSCREW chuck for the headstock spindle of a lathe can be as useful as a costly three-jaw chuck. A setscrew chuck is commonly used for holding drill bits, end mills and Woodruff-keyway cutters. It can also hold workpieces, such as shafting, for turning or drilling. Setscrews bearing against the tool shank lock it in the chuck bore.

Setscrew chucks are often used in connection with a carriage-mounted milling attachment, with an angle plate or other arrangement for clamping and moving work in proper relation to drill bit, reamer, milling cutter, slitting saw, or other tool. Tools with shanks smaller than ½ in. can be mounted in the chucks with split bushings. The taper-shank type can be provided with two or more interchangeable heads having different hole diameters. A setscrew chuck can accommodate a conventional geared drill chuck with a ¼-in. shank projecting an inch or two.

There are two general types of setscrew chucks. As detailed here, chuck A screws over the spindle nose, and is preferable with minimum overhang is desirable and where the tool might be subjected to considerable side pressure. Chuck B has a taper shank fitting the spindle bore and a somewhat greater overhang.

Carefully made and fitted, either type can run as true as the average multijaw chuck or conventional drill chuck fitted with a taper shank.

• **Screw-on setscrew chuck.** This is screwed on the threaded end of the headstock spindle until firmly seated against the spindle shoulder. Cutting its thread is tricky. To fit a 9-in. lathe spindle, the thread is 1½-8 in a 1-in.-deep hole.

A 2-in. round steel blank about 2½ in. long is clamped in a three-jaw chuck, the end faced, and a ½-in. axial hole drilled 1 in. deep. With larger

SEE ALSO
Drill press techniques . . .
Metal-lathe techniques . . . Tools, hand . . .
Twist drills

drills and a boring bar the hole is enlarged as required by the spindle-nose thread—here to about 1.345 in. dia., slightly larger than the standard 1.3376-in. for this thread. The bore diameter is further enlarged to a generous 1½ in. at both ends. Length of the inner, 1½-in.-diameter bore is determined by the clearance required by the threading tool—about 3/16 in. To determine various dimensions of the threaded bore, the spindle nose and back plate of a chuck that fit the nose were used as guides.

The internal thread is cut next. Care must be taken not to jam the end of the threading tool against the bore bottom. For each cut (average depth about 0.0025 in.), the lathe is stopped a bit short of the end, and the cut finished by pulling the headstock belt by hand. A 60° point threading bit is used.

Careful measurements can produce a precise fit of threads, but a gauge threaded like the spindle nose is handy for testing the internal threads. For another test remove the lathe chuck without loosening its jaws, turn it and the setscrew-chuck blank end for end, and try to screw the blank onto the spindle.

When the threading fits the spindle nose snugly, remove the workpiece from the chuck and drill a radial wrench hole (for a ¼-in. rod) as shown. This hole enables the chuck body to be loosened readily.

The chuck blank is installed on the spindle, and the outer end machined to the form shown. Then a hole is drilled through its center, starting with a small bit, to a diameter of about 7/16 in. Because it is possible for a drill bit to produce a hole slightly out of line, a boring bar is used to bring the hole to final diameter of ½ in. This diameter depends on the tool-shank diameter and clearance necessary for easy installation or removal of the tool, and might be around 0.501 or 0.502 in. (Many cutting tools have precise ½-in. shanks.) Another way to achieve an accurate, true-running hole is by internal grinding. If such a chuck is hardened, final grinding would be done afterward.

After the outside surface has been smoothed with file and abrasive cloth, remove the chuck body from the spindle and drill and tap the two ¼-20 setscrew holes. Make an internal back-up disc (part Y) to help the setscrews handle end

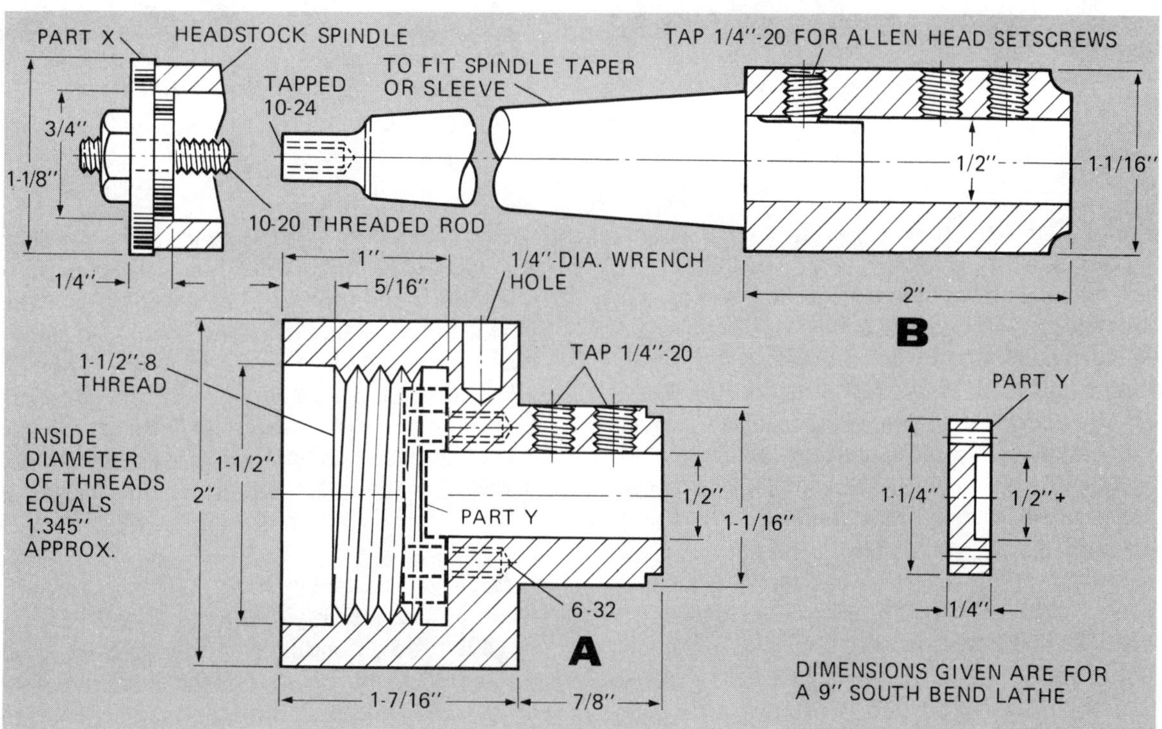

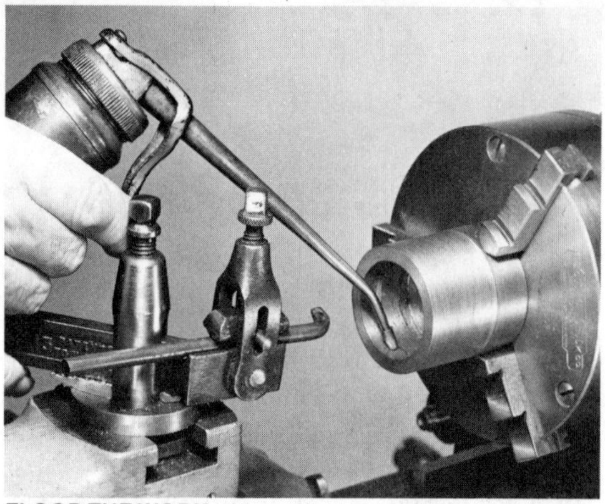

FLOOD THE WORK with a sulfurized cutting oil when you bore the spindle-nose recess in the chuck body.

AFTER RECESS is bored, 1½-in. x 8 threads are cut into the chuck body to fit the 9-in. lathe spindle.

REGULAR TWIST DRILL is used to bore a slightly undersized axial hole in the body of the screw-on chuck.

BORING BAR is used to finish-bore the axial hole. The hole in the side is for a chuck-removing wrench.

thrust such as that which is produced when a large-diameter drill is driven by the chuck.

The steel disc covers the hole and has an outside diameter that fits inside the headstock-spindle hole without jamming. Two 6-32 bolts with heads filed for clearance anchor it in place. (Four would be stronger.) Disc can be removed when chucking long shanks or rods.

• **Taper-shank setscrew chuck.** This is sometimes used on drill-press spindles. The shank shown is from a broken No. 2 Morse taper twist drill. The drill is annealed and the flute section sawed off. Then the shank is installed in the lathe spindle, and punch-marked for later alignment with spindle sleeve and spindle itself.

The projecting portion is machined to ½-in. diameter and a setscrew-flat filed on it.

The chuck body is made from 1⅛-in. steel rod. It is chucked, and an axial hole about 7/16 in. in diameter bored through. The outer ¾ in. of this hole is bored so that the taper-shank end, previously machined to ½ in., will fit snugly. Then the piece is unchucked, and a hole for the setscrew that clamps it to the shank is drilled and taped for a ¼-20 thread. The two parts are assembled and installed in the lathe spindle for final boring of the ½-in. tool-shank hole, and finishing the surface.

Because the taper shank might come loose when in use, a safety feature is added—a long, threaded rod extending from the tapered shank through a cap machined to fit the outer end of the headstock spindle. A nut tightened against this cap, part X, locks the shank in place.

A swing toolholder for your lathe

By MARTIN CLEEVE

■ ONE OF THE MOST bothersome tasks in lathe work is adjusting the tool bit to the correct height. With this universal swing-away-type toolholder, I not only can check the progress of thread cutting by simply swinging the tool upward, but I can return it to exactly the same position without retracting the cross slide.

I made the holder to fit my 7-in. lathe and milled the jaw to accept ⅜-in.-square-shank bits. To make frictional adjustments so the holder swings without play or binding, you simply tighten the ¼-in. capscrews in the pivot pin. Use a single bolt to attach the holder to the cross slide. Placing a fiber washer between the holder and cross slide improves friction and eliminates the need for excessive tightening.

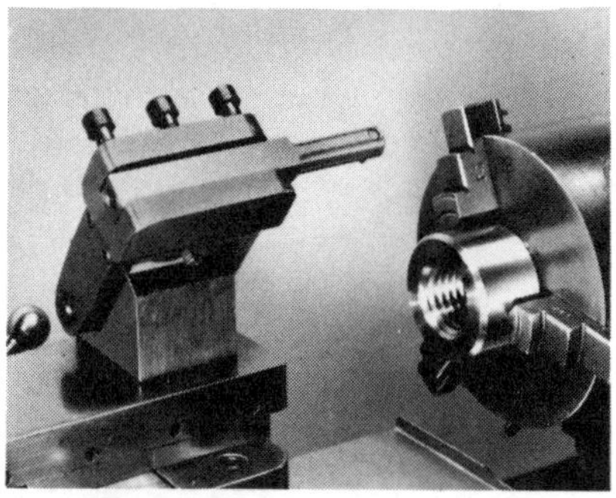

PIVOTED to block bolted to cross slide, cutting tool is swung upward and clear to check progress.

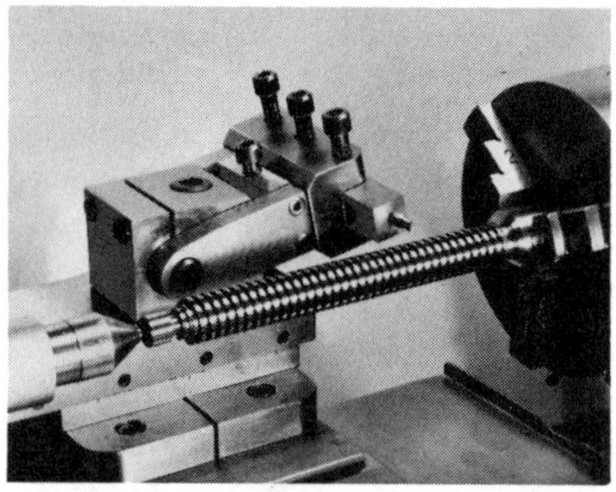

FOR ORDINARY turning or thread cutting, holder is swung around so toolholding jaw is at right angle.

FOR INTERNAL boring or thread cutting, toolholding jaw is positioned so it is parallel to lathe.

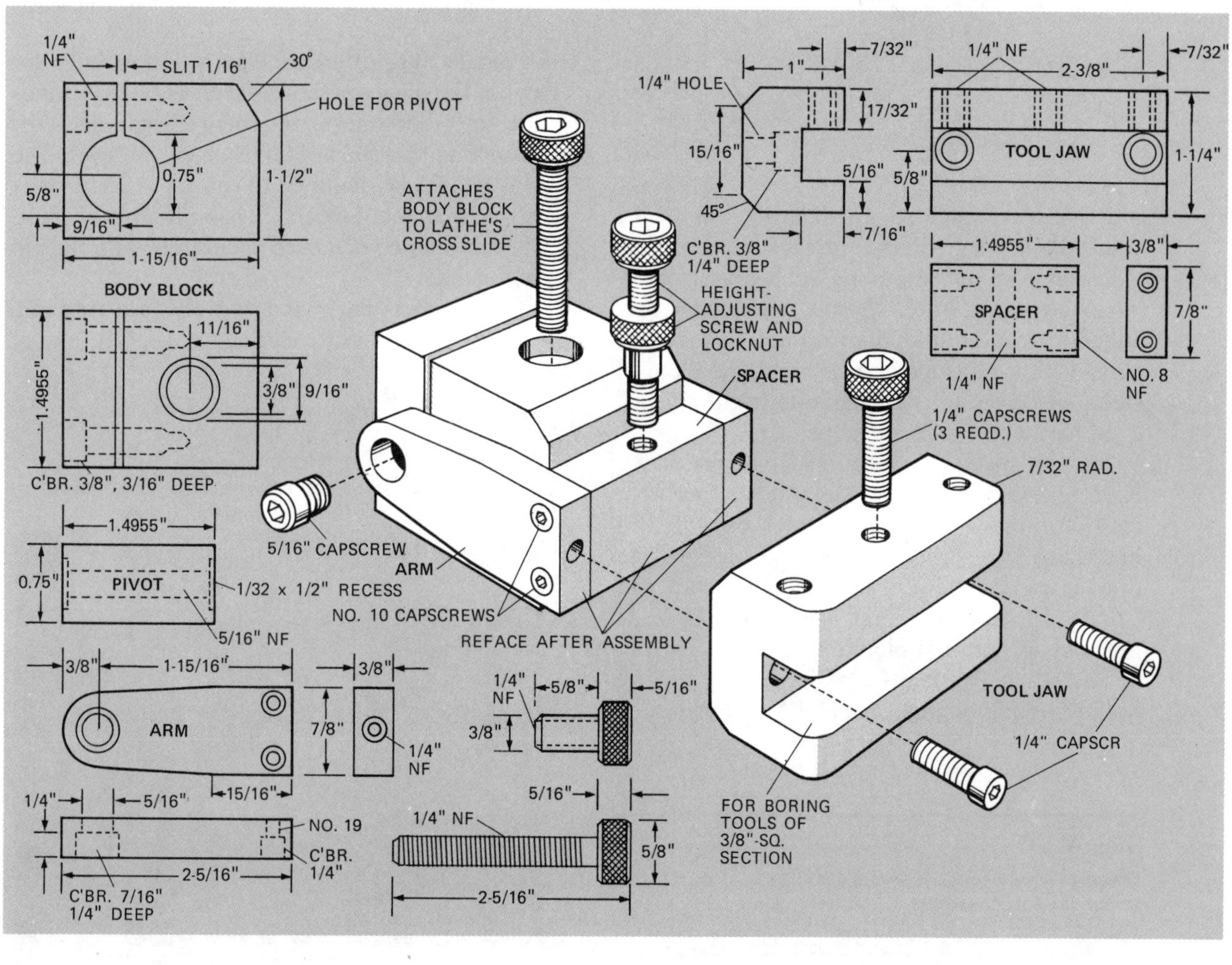

Turning rings on a lathe

By WALTER E. BURTON

■ RINGMAKING IS an exciting but often overlooked talent of the metal-working lathe. You can turn out sizes and shapes you could never buy—big, little, square, rectangular, triangular, oval, round, half-round, hexagonal, octagonal—you name it. You can make them of steel, cast iron, brass, aluminum, rigid plastic, even hardwood such as maple.

Turned rings are, of course, jointless. They have a handsome, elegant look that makes them ideal for pieces of jewelry and ornamental hardware. They can be used as decorative drawer and cabinet pulls, ladies' brooches and stands for models. Large rings can serve as bracelets or unusual picture frames.

The stock you use for making rings can be hollow tubing or pipe or solid bar material in round, hexagonal or other shapes. If you start with bar stock, you first bore out the center. Plain rings can be made simply by slicing sections off your stock like cutting a loaf of bread. If the width of the slice is the same as the wall thickness of your stock, you have a ring of square cross section. By making cuts at various angles, you end up with a ring of triangular, diamond, hexagonal or octagonal section.

As a matter of safety, it is not a good idea to let the stock project excessively beyond the chuck. The shorter the projection, the better. Chuck jaws can grip a tubular piece on either the outside or inside. Sometimes the outer end of a solid bar can be steadied on a tailstock center if you don't bore away the material at the bar's center until later.

support and secure workpiece

When rings are to be cut from long stock, the piece should be supported near its outer end by a steady rest, as shown in some of the photos. The end toward the headstock should be gripped firmly by the chuck or lashed securely to the faceplate to prevent endwise crawl from occurring.

Single rings often are clamped in a chuck for minor finishing operations such as filing or sanding for smoothness, rounding sharp edges, or removing the "flash" left by a cut-off tool. The ring should be clamped to run true. Sometimes an independent-jaw chuck is preferable because the ring can be centered accurately with the aid of a gauge.

Remember that when you clamp a ring in a chuck, jaw pressure springs it slightly out of

SEE ALSO
Drawers . . . Jewelry . . . Metal casting . . . Metal-lathe accessories . . . Modelmaking . . . Tubing, metal

PLASTIC RING, turned from a section of plastic plumbing pipe, gets a polishing below before final cut is made to separate it from the remaining stock.

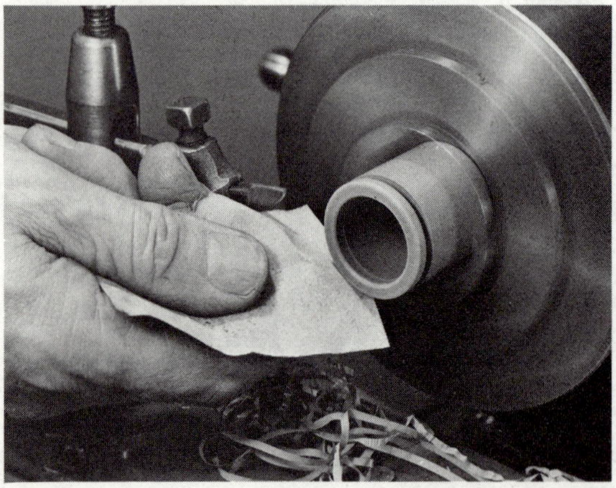

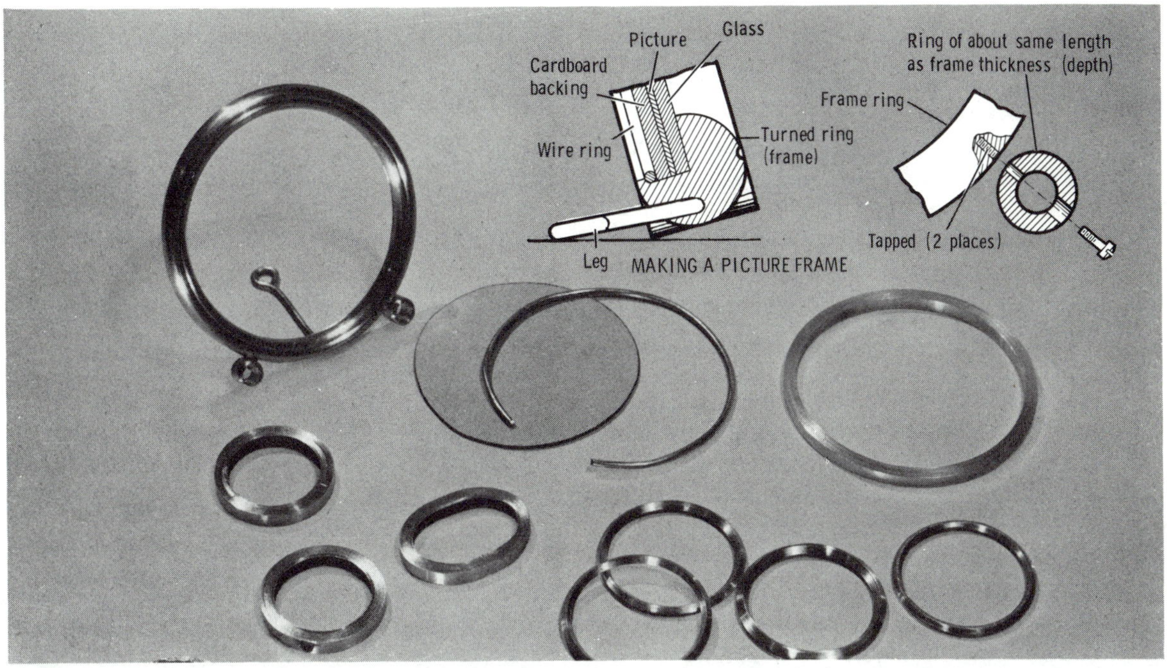

SOME OF THE MANY rings you can make are shown above. The oval ring to the left of center was made by squeezing a round ring with pliers to flatten it slightly. At the top of the photo is an example of how a large ring can become a decorative picture frame. A recess is machined at the back to hold the picture and the legs are added as shown in the sketch. Big rings of this type could also make interesting and novel ladies' bracelets.

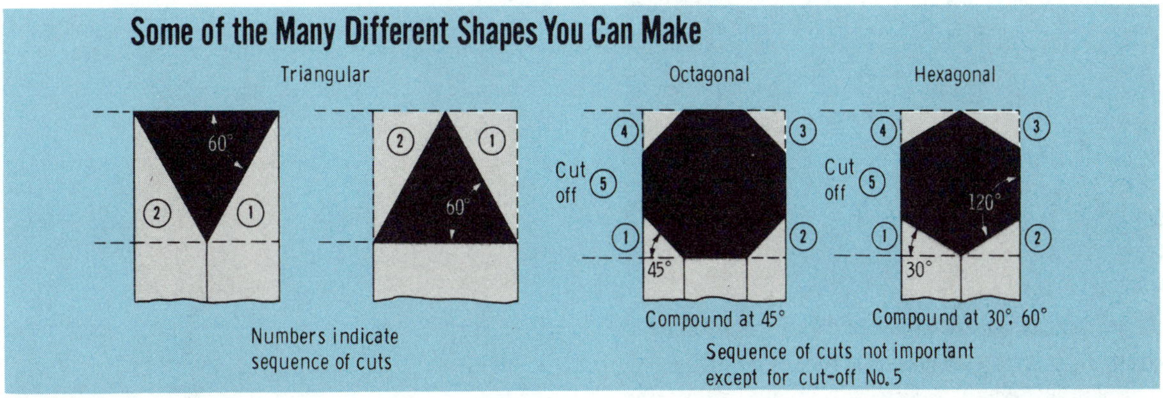

RINGS DROP OFF one after another and slide neatly onto this automatic catcher. The simple device consists of a bent wire held in the tailstock chuck.

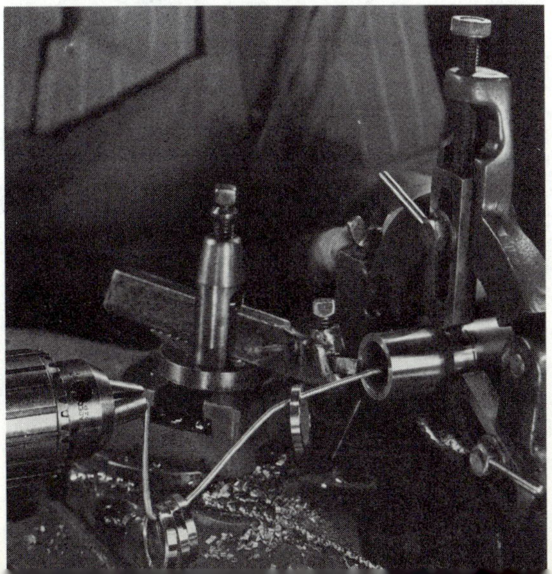

FREEHAND TURNING enables you to shape round, oval and other curved-section rings. The tool is handheld. A bar clamped in the toolpost serves as a toolrest.

round. Tubular stock is similarly distorted near the chuck. A ring machined from a blank distorted in this way, will not be perfectly circular when jaw pressure is released. In most cases, this is probably not important, but it could affect ring fit in close-tolerancε vork, such as in making optical-instrument pa ts.

Metal, plastic and wood rings can be shaped freehand on a metal lathe in much the same manner as parts are formed on a wood-turning lathe, the tool being handheld and supported by a fixed rest.

Carbide-tipped turning chisels are available for use on metal parts, or you can grind suitable ones from tool steel or high-speed-steel lathe bits. Various common wood-turning chisel shapes are useful in working metal rings. The skewer shape is particularly handy. Such tools can be manipulated to cut, rather than scrape, metal neatly from the work, with the formation of fine, thin chips. The hand-turning technique is

HOMEMADE BITS speed the work on special jobs, such as turning out round or oval-section rings in quantity. The one below, for round-section rings, was made from an old file. Two holes of ring diameter were drilled, the material between them removed, relief angles filled, and the tool was rehardened. The bit is held in a regular boring-bar holder as shown above.

Turning a Diamond-Shaped Ring

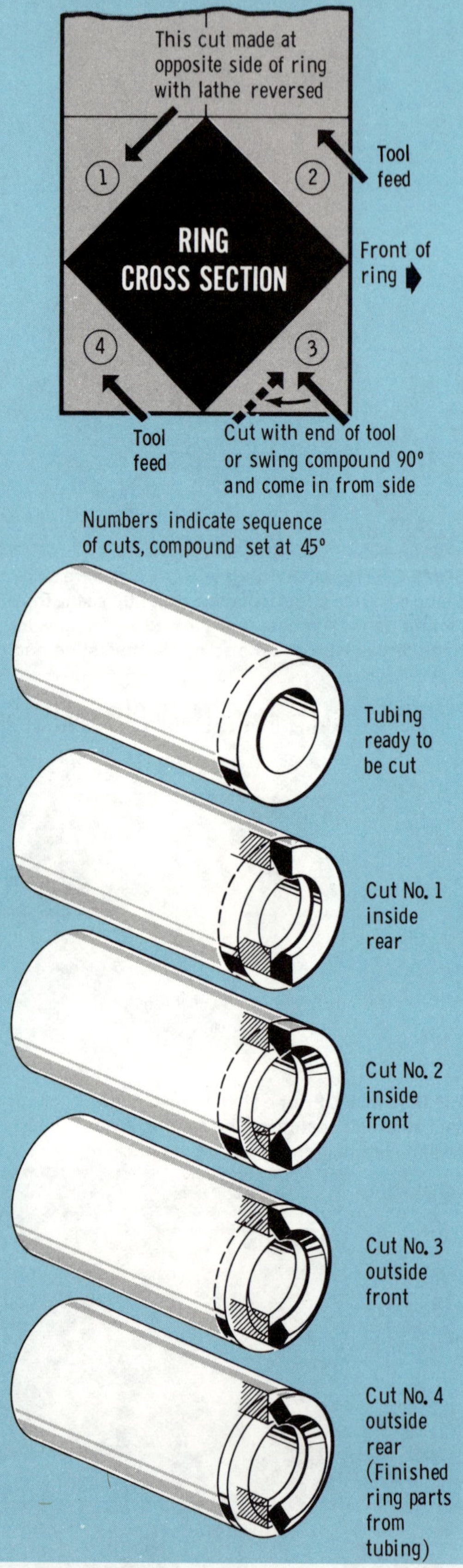

INSIDE CUT on diamond-shaped ring is made at far side of stock with lathe reversed. All other cuts are made at stock's near side.

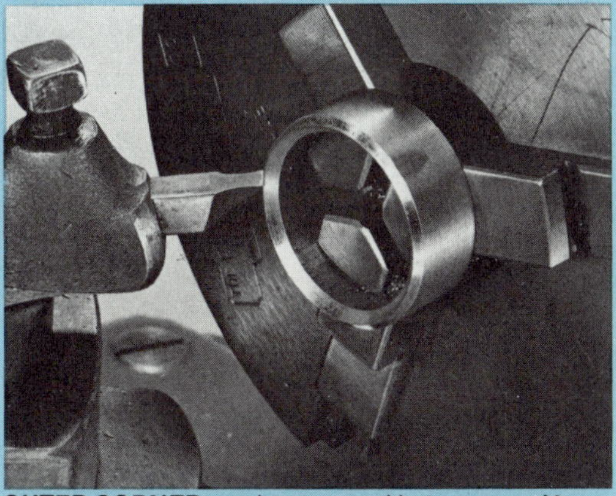

OUTER CORNER can be removed in two ways. You can feed toward headstock, as here, using square end of bit, or swing compound 90° and feed from opposite.

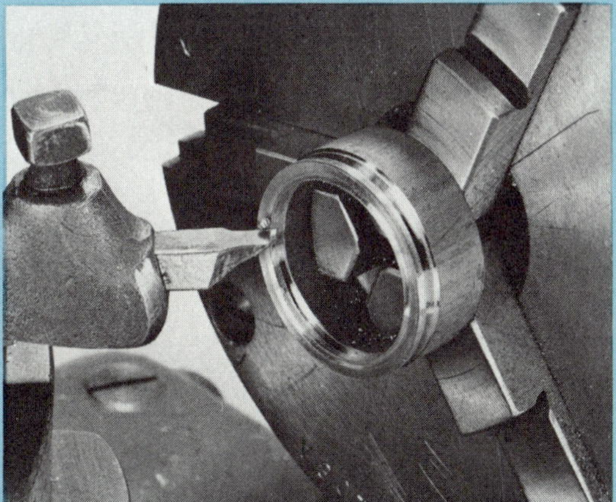

INNER lip of stock is machined by feeding tool with compound-slide screw. Final cut has been started here, will be deepened later to part ring.

useful in shaping rings having round, oval, or similar cross section and in making decorative grooves and ridges.

Rings having diamond-shaped, triangular, hexagonal and octagonal sections can be formed by feeding the tool with the compound rest set at the proper angle. Here is a helpful way to work out the machining sequence: Draw a scaled plan of the desired ring cross section, showing it as if you were looking down on top with the side facing you representing the side toward which the tool will feed. With this, you can easily determine the angles, dimensions of various faces, and distances the tool must travel in making different cuts. These values are then used to control the movement of the tool bit by means of the micrometer collars on the carriage screws, particularly that controlling the compound slide.

numbers indicate cutting sequence

The drawings show the cross-sectional layout of rings of various sections. The numbered segments indicate waste material to be machined away. In some cases, the numbers represent a suggested cutting sequence, selected to make it easier to establish starting points for measuring tool movement.

You can make nonmetal rings from such materials as rigid PVC (polyvinyl chloride) pipe available in many stores. Such plastic material is machined much as if it were metal. It is easy to cut and requires only moderate tool pressure. Chuck-jaw pressure should be controlled according to the strength and bendability of the material.

A ring can be machined to serve as a frame for a round picture, plaque or other object. In the back of the frame, machine a recess to receive the picture, a glass or plastic cover if one is used and a piece of backing material, such as heavy cardboard. The simplest holding arrangement consists of an open ring of wire sprung into a shallow groove around the inside of the recess. Feet for the frame to stand on can be made from smaller rings attached to the main ring with screws, rivets or solder.

finishing the rings

You can finish turned rings in the same way as other items of the same materials. Files and abrasive paper or cloth are suitable for smoothing most materials. Rings can be given various distinctive textures by knurling them while they are in the lathe, or by some other suitable treatment such as peening, engraving or stamping.

Filing on a lathe

■ A FILE IS MORE than just a useful lathe tool. True, it will produce a fine finish—smoother, in fact, than that made by the turning tool. But it can also reduce a diameter by the merest fraction of an inch or millimeter—or it can rapidly cut down a shaft for a drive fit in a pulley or a running fit in a bearing.

In seconds, it can whack off the center tip left by a cutoff tool as shown in the above photo. It can make and smooth round, vee, or other odd-shaped grooves and fillets on turned work. A file can also serve as a miniature taper attachment for such operations as converting rod sections into taper pins, and it can quickly produce a neat point on punches and scribers. A pair of files can be manipulated to smooth and size simultaneously a small-diameter rod that's too limber for regular machining.

SEE ALSO
Metal-lathe accessories . . . Sharpening, tool . . . Tools, hand

In fact, almost any type of file could be used in some form or other for lathe work. A common, single-cut, mill file can do a good job of smoothing turned work such as a shaft. Conventional three-square or triangular files are handy for touch-up work on small shoulders and grooves.

AS YOUR LATHE FILING needs increase, you'll find your selection of lathe files growing to this size.

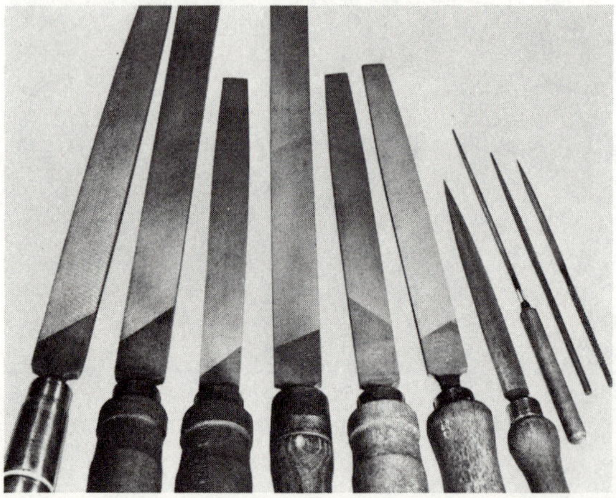

For very fine finishes, or delicate shaping and sizing, Swiss-pattern files are often used. Even a conventional ignition file is handy where a thicker one would not do the job.

Thus, the lathe owner will indeed find it worthwhile to obtain one or more "lathe files." These are similar to conventional mill files, but their tooth angle is steeper, so that they cut with a more pronounced shearing action. This results in less clogging, smoother cutting, less chatter, more freedom from drag and faster cutting action—but they tend to crawl sidewise a bit more readily than a conventional file. On a sample mill file, the tooth angle (measured with respect to file length) was approximately 65°; tooth angles on similar lathe files are 45°.

Perhaps you can handle most of your routine lathe filing with as few as two files: a 10 or 12-in. lathe file for rapid, rough work, and an 8-in. lathe file for finishing. For greater all-around filing flexibility, however, you may want to supplement these with other files.

As a start, the Nicholson File Co. suggests: a 12 or 14-in.-long-angle lathe file for operations where a considerable amount of stock is to be removed rapidly (as when sizing a shaft for a drive fit in a pulley); a smooth-cut mill file for producing a smooth finish (as on a shaft where it is to run in a bearing) and a Swiss-pattern, hand or pillar file in No. 4 or No. 6 cut, for a very fine, smooth finish.

For a fine, *polished* finish, consider making an "abrasive file"—it's simply a strip of fine-grit or well-worn aluminum-oxide or silicon-carbide sheet abrasive. Tack or glue it to a flat wooden stick, or to a stick shaped for polishing contours.

Procedures for filing work in a lathe are not very complicated. The workpiece can be mount-

SINCE FRICTION will heat the work and cause it to expand lengthwise, centers must be well lubricated.

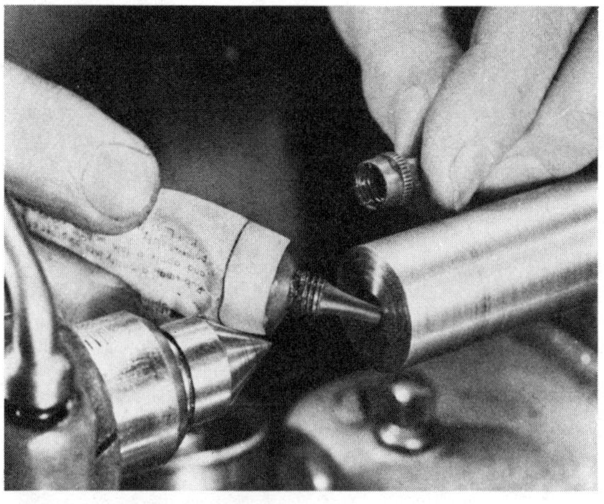

LATHE CENTERS should not be tight, but should have enough play to allow a slight workpiece movement.

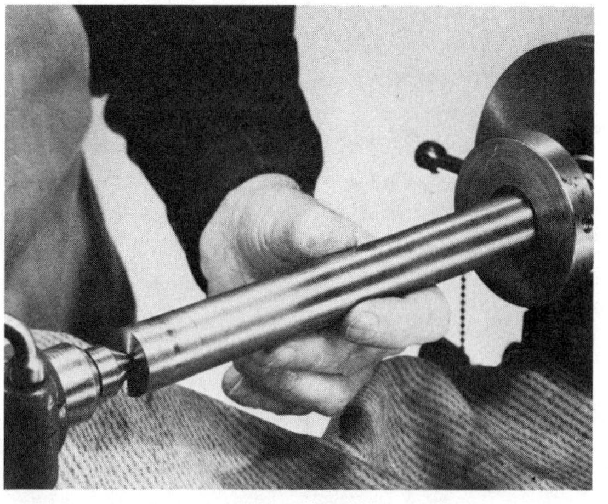

A COARSE, FAST-CUTTING FILE can be used in the first stage of filing, keeping it at a right angle to the work.

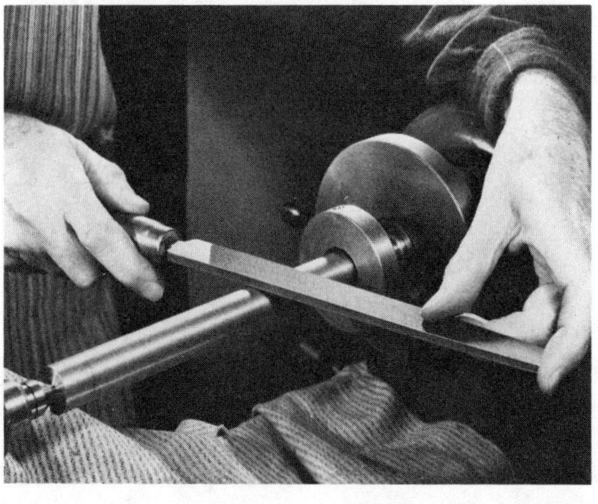

FOR A FINELY POLISHED surface, an abrasive file can be made of a stick and strip of abrasive cloth.

ed in a chuck or collet, or between centers. If between centers, remember that filing friction can cause the workpiece to heat-expand lengthwise and bind on the centers. To prevent this, put a little oil on the headstock center, and liberally lubricate the tailstock center. Then adjust center clearance so the workpiece can move freely.

Stop the lathe occasionally during prolonged filing and check for possible binding. If any squealing develops where the workpiece revolves on the tailstock center, stop the lathe immediately, loosen and relubricate.

For finish filing, run the lathe at a high speed—especially for any small-diameter work. But for simply filing off a sharp edge or tip, normal turning speed will do.

With smooth, even and medium-pressure strokes, keep the file moving across the revolving work. Normally you should hold the file square with the work axis, or nearly so. You may find, however, that a smoother overall finish results if you move the file in a slightly diagonal path.

If the file begins to lose its bite, or if it tends to skip or cause streaks on the work, clean the teeth with a file card or small wire-bristle, suede-shoe brush.

Although file technicians suggest that the surface be oil-free, you may find that a sulphurized cutting oil or similar fluid can be helpful. When filing a rusty shaft, a dash of cutting oil will minimize nose-irritating dust and also reduce the depositing of filings on the lathe bed and carriage. A sulphurized cutting oil I used on various occasions seemed not to decrease the files' efficiency, and perhaps it tended to reduce tooth wear. But because the oil does hold filings in the

SMALL SWISS-PATTERN FILES are handy for shaping and smoothing small parts. In the photo below a dimpling punch is being used for this purpose.

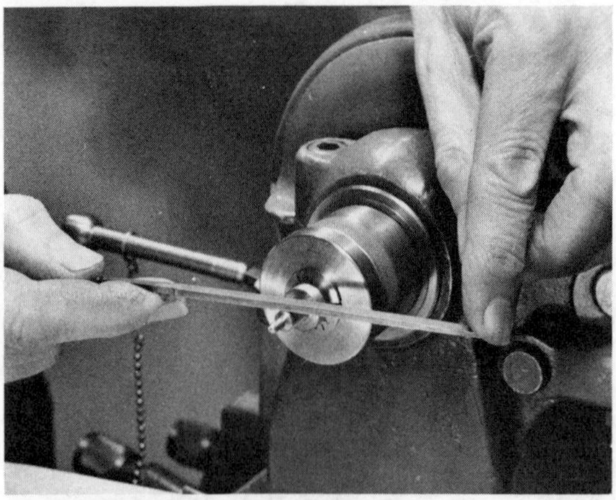

DISC-SHAPED SECTIONS where a precise radius is not required can be both shaped and finished with files. As shown here, the file is hand-held.

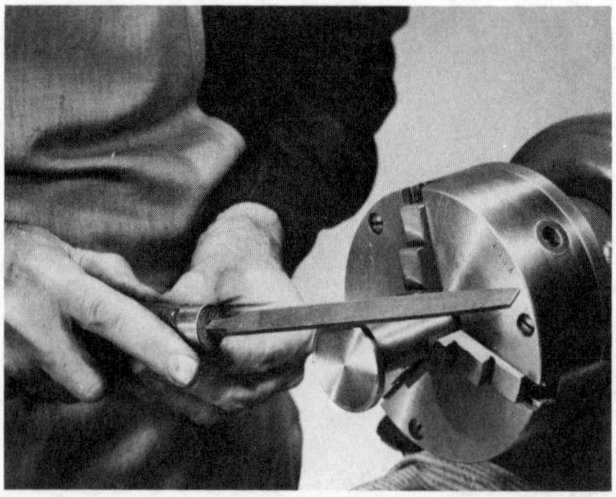

GROOVED SECTIONS can be made or smoothed by using an appropriately shaped Swiss-pattern file. If you do much fine work, you'll want to purchase a set.

AN EASY-TO-MAKE GUIDE helps control the depth of degree of filing. This kind of guide is especially handy for producing bullet or dome shapes.

teeth, the accumulations had to be wiped off after just several strokes of the file.

Regular lathe files have "safe" edges—that is, the edges are smooth, without teeth. The file thus can be used close to a chuck or other part without tending to bite into it. If you use conventional files lacking such safe edges, be careful that the edge doesn't touch any moving surface. One practice is to grind toothed edges smooth before attempting to do lathe filing.

When filing work that is revolving in a lathe, use sensible safety precautions. Hold the file firmly, and be careful that it does not catch on the workpiece to be tossed your way, or become entangled with a chuck.

It's always a good idea not to stand directly in line with the file handle. When you reach over the lathe to grasp the outer end of the file, be careful not to be grabbed by the chuck or dog. On your forearms, wear tight-fitting sleeves or, better yet, none at all.

taking care of files

The life of a lathe file can be greatly reduced by improper care or carelessness. Never throw a file into a drawer or toolbox—also avoid stacking them on top of one another. Instead, always keep them separate by hanging them in a rack placed out of the way so they won't be knocked off accidentally and damaged.

Before storing the file, however, make certain that all chips have been brushed out of the file ridges. If oil or grease is left on the file, it can be removed by wiping with a soft clean cloth, then rubbing chalk into the file teeth. A soft iron "pick" should also be kept on hand for removing troublesome filings that may become imbedded in the teeth.

FILING ATTACHMENTS and accessories include a filing guide and two-file assembly for thin limber rods.

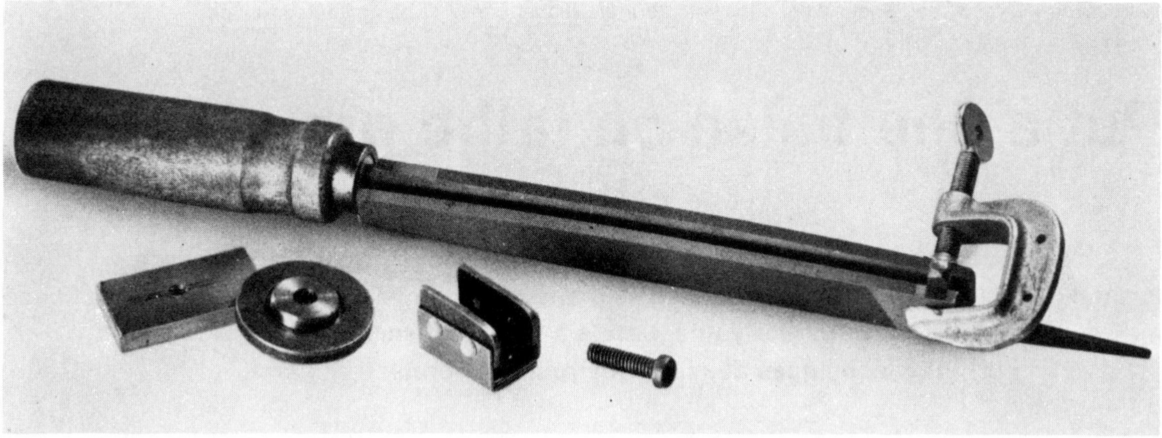

A DOUBLE-FILE ASSEMBLY should be used at high speed. The cutting pressure is set by squeezing the open end to produce the desired diameter.

A SIMPLE BALL-TURNING GAUGE can be formed from a suitable washer, then used to check the ball diameter. Continue until you get a snug fit.

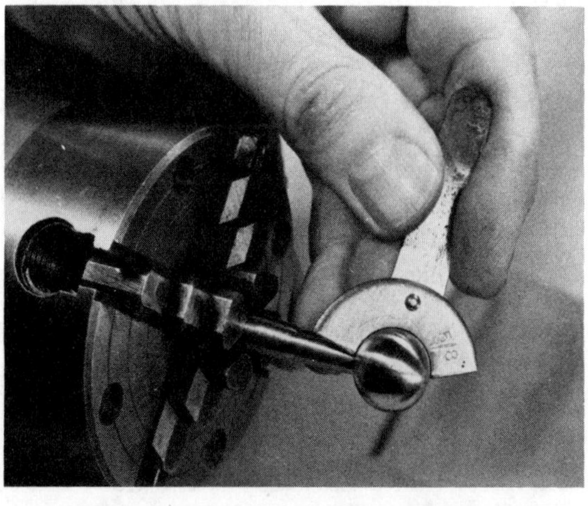

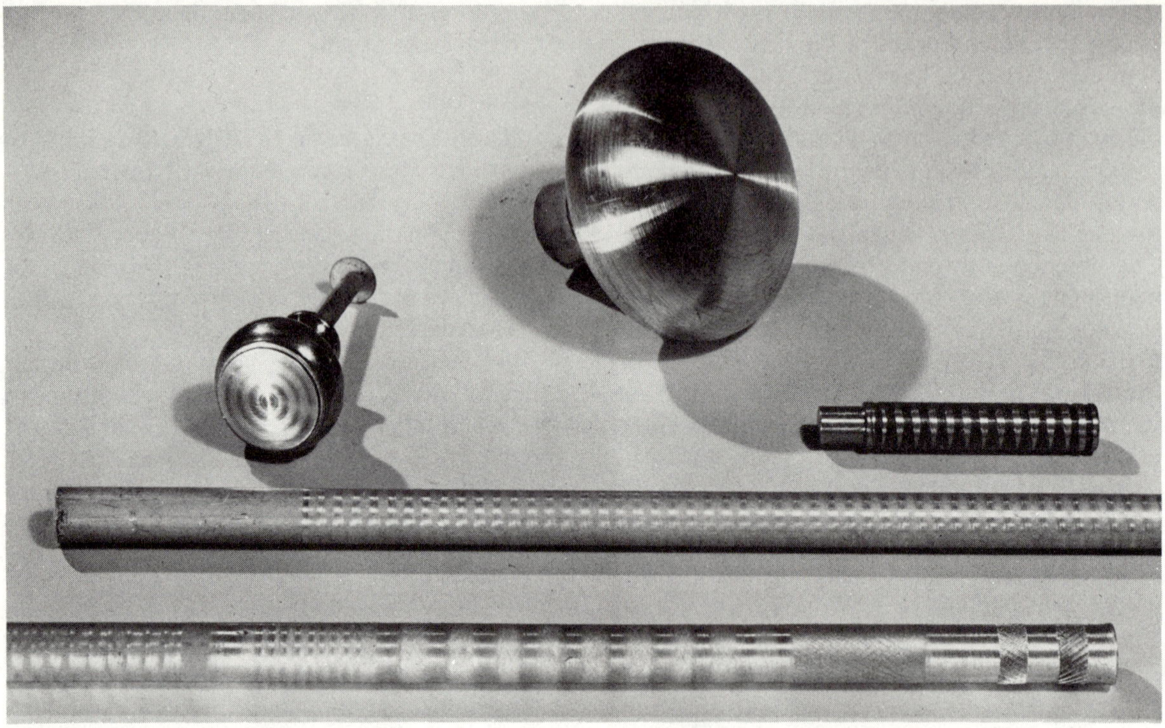

TYPICAL LATHE-PRODUCED FINISHES. Aluminum tubes were polished with abrasive rubber; their decorative bands were made with a knurler. Knobs were done with abrasive-rubber pencil or bit and abrasive cloth.

Put a fine finish on lathe projects

A craftsman's skill and patience are often judged by the appearance of his finished job. There are many ways of finishing a metal-lathe project. The secret is to choose the one that's right for yours. Here's a survey of some of the techniques available for your next project

■ A COMPLETED SHOP PROJECT is generally rated by the appearance of its finish—the treatment applied to the surface to bring out its beauty and, perhaps, enhance its functional value. This can be particularly true when doing home shop lathe work on a model, a special tool or an instrument part.

There are so many ways of finishing turned metal that it's just about impossible to present them all in one article. But this abundance can be

SEE ALSO
Abrasives . . . Metal-lathe accessories . . . Sharpening, tool . . . Tools, hand

A SHARP TURNING TOOL used with a light touch produces smoothness. The lathe bit should have a rounded tip.

stimulating—it provides a lot of room for experimenting; you can enjoy the adventure of working out and trying other stunts on your own.

As a general rule, the type of finish to apply depends on the use to which the turned article is to be put. Roughly, some procedures can be grouped, as follows:

• *Turned finish.* For many purposes, as in making a punch for rough work, the finish left by the turning tool is good enough. A rounded tip is likely to produce a smoother finish-cut than a sharp, pointed tip. For the final, finishing pass, set the tool for a shallow cut and feed it very slowly along the work. Sulphurized oil or other lubricant may help. You'll find that the nature of the metal, as well as tool shape and sharpness, has a lot to do with the appearance of the turned surface.

Finish can be improved by using an oilstone (such as an Arkansas stone) to hone the cutting edge keen and smooth. *Tip*: If, when you attempt a very light cut, chatter develops and mars the turned surface, a switch to a lower spindle speed (even through back gears) may be a cure.

• *Filed finish.* When a turned surface isn't quite smooth enough, a bit of filing may be all that is needed. Although conventional files can be used on a lathe, steeper-toothed lathe files designed specifically for smoothing rotating work are better. Flat lathe files usually have untoothed edges. The work and file should be free of oil and other material, and the teeth kept clean by frequent brushing with a stiff wire brush. Bits of metal accumulating on and between file teeth can produce some unsightly grooves in the area being smoothed. Some mechanics rub a file with chalk to discourage chip pile-up. (When using a lathe file, take care to prevent fingers, sleeves and other parts of clothing from being snagged by the chuck, dog, or workpiece and always grip the file as if you are left-handed.)

• *Abrasive paper and cloth.* Coated abrasive materials include cloth and paper treated with aluminum oxide, silicon carbide, emery, crocus, or other abrasives such as grains or powders in various degrees of fineness. Grit size indicates the number of holes per inch in a sieve through which the grit will pass and may be expressed by that number, a fraction such as 4/0 or by an adjective such as "fine." You can use loose abrasive grit; there will be more on this later.

You often see emery cloth or paper recommended for polishing steel and other materials. (Emery, a natural variety of corundum, contains aluminum oxide and other minerals.) Probably

A FLAT FILE with its teeth cut at a sharper angle than a conventional file removes marks left by a turning tool.

ABRASIVE CLOTH mounted on a stick can be used for smoothing. Like a file, the abrasive should be kept moving.

A RIGID plastic-foam block, rubbed over a cake of buffing compound, provides an adequate sheen, too.

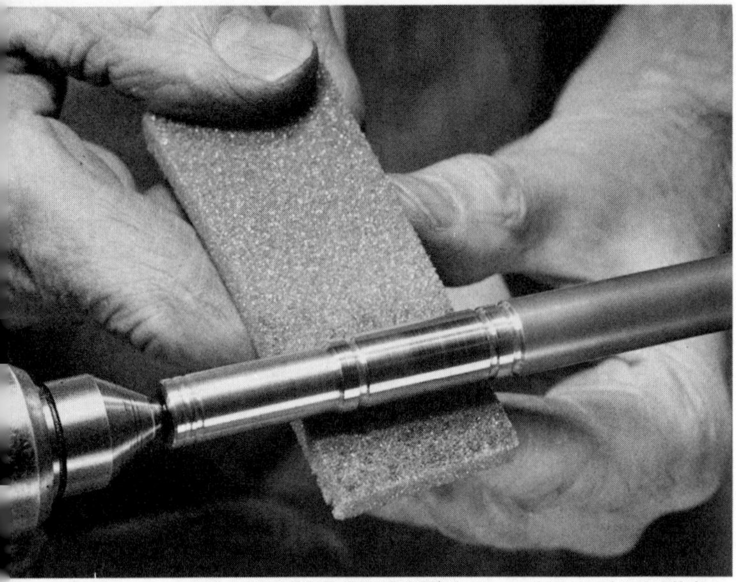

AN ABRASIVE-CHARGED foam pad is used to polish a brass rod after you smooth it with an abrasive cloth.

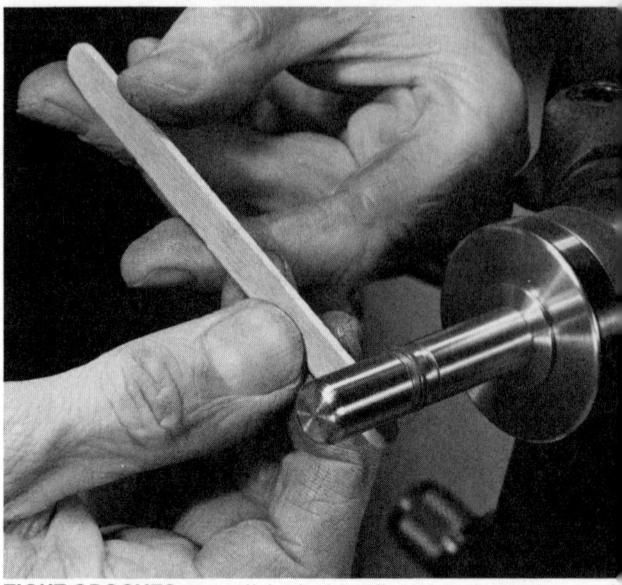

TIGHT GROOVES are polished with a flat stick charged with abrasive grit mixed with a light oil.

IMPORTED BUFFING POLISH, though intended for aluminum, works well on brass when applied with a cloth.

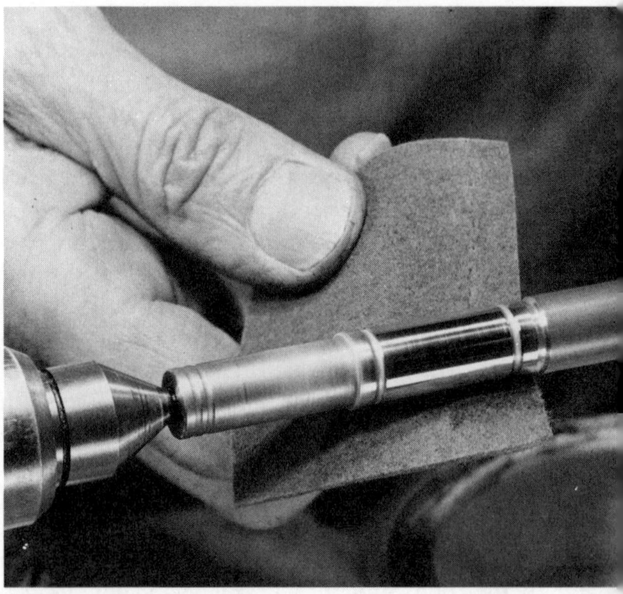

TO DEVELOP A LUSTER after polishing, use a piece of felt from an old hat to remove any dried compound.

some recommenders had in mind man-made aluminum oxide (such as Aloxite), or even silicon carbide (such as Carborundum) which is suitable for polishing hard, brittle materials. (Aluminum oxide seems preferable for tough steels and the like.)

One polishing procedure is to glue or staple a strip of the abrasive-coated material to a flat wooden stick, and use it like a file—dry or sulphurized, or with machine oil as with an oilstone.

Whether abrasive cloth, paper or loose grit or powder is used to smooth turned work, the accepted sequence is to start with a certain size grit (for example, medium No. 150, or 4/0) and proceed by steps to finer and finer sizes. The first grit polishes out tool or file marks; subsequent grits remove scratches caused by the preceding, coarser grit. The second grit might be fine, No. 180 or 5/0, followed by extrafine, No. 220 or 6/0; and then finer polishing could be done with buffing compounds or commercial polishers. In the end, there may still be polishing scratches—but so fine they can't be seen without magnification.

The precise grit sizes to use can be found by trial. Usually, in home-shop work, a sufficiently smooth surface can be developed in two or three

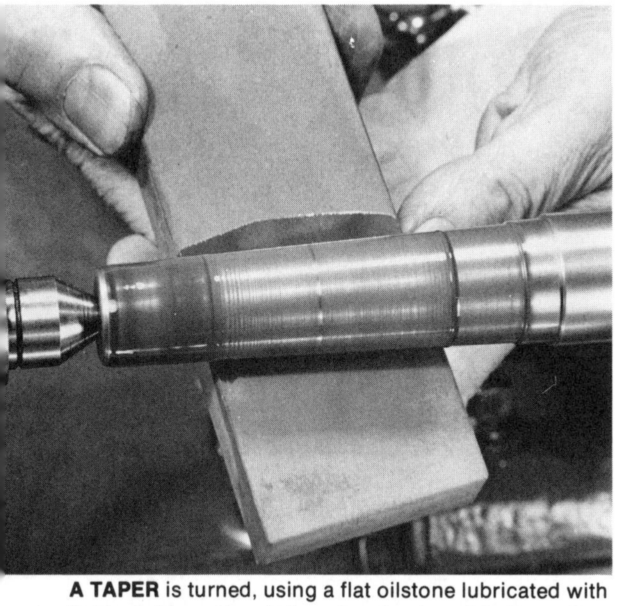

A TAPER is turned, using a flat oilstone lubricated with light oil. Move the oilstone in a back-and-forth motion.

A SMOOTH FINISH is given an oiled brass tubing with a diamond-tip grinding-wheel dresser used as a burnisher.

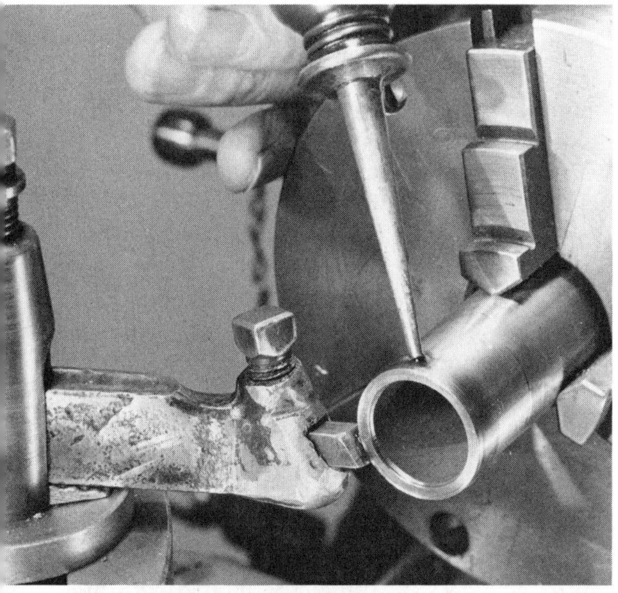

A HIGH-SPEED LATHE BIT can be used as a burnishing tool. Be sure that the work is kept well oiled.

A HAND-HELD KNURLING TOOL gives a fine, cross-hatched texture when held in the lathe.

polishing steps.

A worthwhile economy in the shop is to never throw away a piece of abrasive cloth that still holds together. The longer it's used, the finer it cuts; eventually it may produce a shine equal to that from the finest new material.

Instead of a stick to support the abrasive cloth or paper, you can shape various blocks, pads of felt, plastic foam, leather and the like to polish rounded shapes, including grooves.

• *Buffing, honing, and burnishing*. Buffing removes flaws left by previous polishing. Buffing compounds usually consist of finely divided material mixed with a binder (dry powder in oil or other fluid). In normal lathe work, you probably would be more likely to buff brass, copper, aluminum or silver than steel.

A buffing compound designed for "cutting" is intended to be used first, followed by final buffing with a "coloring" preparation. Tripoli is a typical cutting material in buffing, while rouge (producing a burnishing rather than a cutting action) is used to bring out the final luster.

The buffing compound can be used on work spinning in a lathe by spreading it on a block or pad serving as the tool. The pad may be of

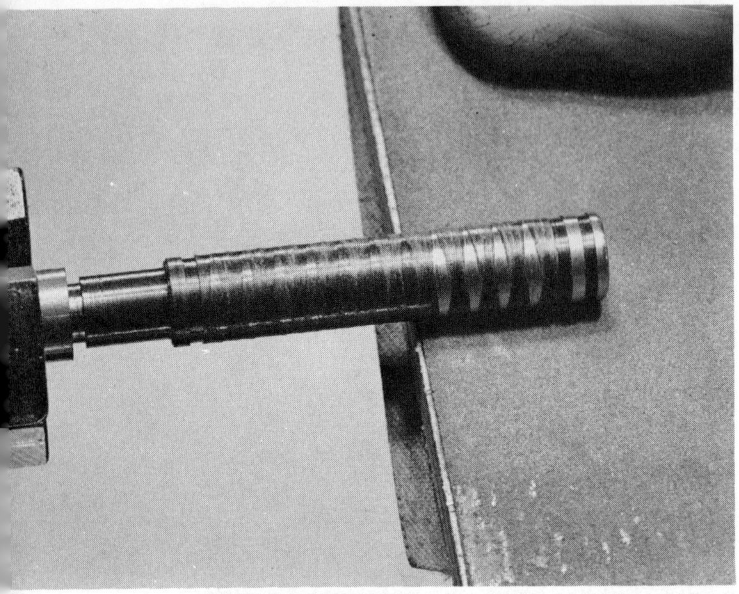

A DESIGN IS BIT-CUT in a blued-steel handle, and then polished with an abrasive cloth for a two-tone effect.

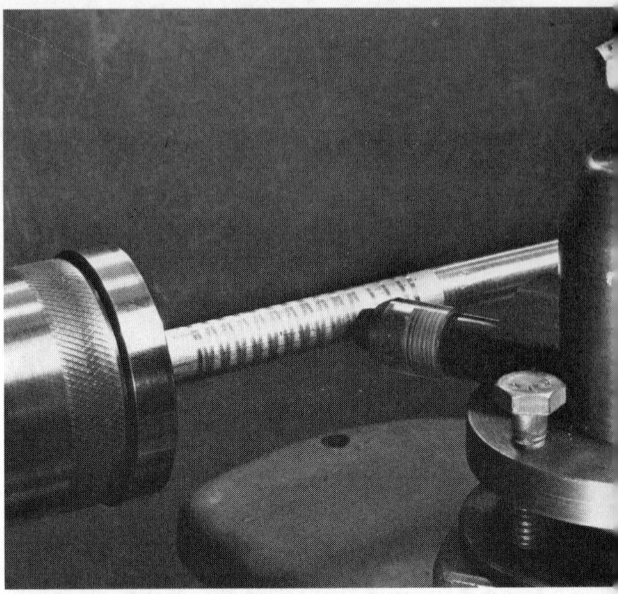

A DOUBLE-SPIRAL DESIGN was turned in aluminum by an abrasive-rubber pencil mounted as a "lathe tool."

leather, felt or plastic foam.

Of course, a piece can be polished on a conventional buffing wheel after removal from the lathe. Such a wheel, made of cloth or felt and charged with compound, might be mounted on a toolpost grinder and used to buff revolving work. Finally, buff with an uncharged wheel.

In oilstone lathe honing, an abrasive stone is held against the revolving work, primarily to grind down any metal points that might be projecting. Machine oil or special oilstone oil is the lubricant. The stone generally is moved back and forth parallel to the work axis, in circles or in figure-8s. "Superfinishing," a process attributed to David A. Wallace of the Chrysler Corp., is a form of honing with moving stones. Lathe headstock spindles operating in solid bearings are among parts on which superfinishing may be used.

Since a honed surface generally has a duller finish than a polished one, it can form a basis for subsequent polishing.

Lapping is an operation performed (often by hand rather than power) with abrasive grains plus oil or other fluid, to achieve close fitting of parts, bring gauges to precise size, even out surfaces and so on. Thus, you might lap a taper shank into a taper hole. Some lapping compounds are designed to break down readily to make their action self-limiting, and thus prevent "overlapping."

Lathe burnishing is simply a rubbing operation with a hard, highly polished tool pressed against the revolving, lubricated surface. Its desirability is best found by trial, for sometimes a similar smoothness can be produced readily by other methods. A sort of burnishing can be achieved with a diamond-point grinding-wheel dresser by adjusting it for light rubbing contact, employing fine feed and keeping the work well-oiled. But, some diamonds may prove too rough for a satisfactory result.

Sometimes the use of a commercial metal-polishing compound as a final finishing operation will develop on brass, aluminum, and the usual metals, a shine comparable to that achieved by wheelbuffing. Apply the polish to the spinning work with a small cloth or felt, manipulate the pad in contact for a while, then clean and polish with another cloth or felt. Always use a small cloth and check for roughness on the work that might snag it.

• *Texturing and "inlay" patterns.* Texturing consists of producing on the surface of turned work a pattern of lines or grooves that blend into a pleasing appearance. One way is to hand-hold a knurling tool lightly against the revolving work—preferably after polishing. Keep knurling pressure at a minimum, and frequently lift knurls from the surface and replace them, so they do not tend to follow a repeat path (as would occur in conventional knurling).

For metal tool handles and levers to be grasped, an interesting, nonskid effect can be produced by first knurling or cross-threading the surface, blueing the piece if it is steel or applying

DECORATIVE CONCENTRIC RINGS are also produced by rubber. Space rings with the aid of a cross-feed scale.

COUNTLESS CONCENTRIC SCRATCHES made with abrasive-charged cloth give a starlike light reflection.

colored lacquer if it is another metal, then filing and polishing it to remove color from the high spots while leaving it in depressions. Steel can be blued chemically or by heating until the desired oxide color develops.

• *Pattern polishing.* Selective polishing with an abrasive rubber eraser (or with Brightboy stick) can produce interesting effects. The surface to be decorated should not be highly polished, but preferably a dull finish such as that developing on aluminum over a period of time.

Spiral patterns on cylindrical work can be produced by mounting the abrasive pencil like a regular lathe tool and using a coarse-thread setting, such as 4 t.p.i. (threads per inch), to control tool movement. Tracing right and left-hand overlapping "threads" produces a lattice effect. A series of bright bands or rings can be made with abrasive hand-held or in the toolpost.

By mounting the abrasive pencil as you would a conventional bit for a facing operation, you can produce concentric circles, spirals, or lattice designs on the flat surfaces or knobs, push plates and other items.

Those striking, circular-diffraction-grating-like effects you sometimes see on the front of transistor radios can be achieved on doorknobs, push plates and the like by mounting the item on a lathe faceplate or in a chuck and holding against it, as it spins, a fine-grit abrasive paper or cloth or a felt pad charged with fine abrasive powder.

• *Loose abrasive grits.* Almost any abrasive, if finely divided, can be used for polishing lathe work. It's fun to try different materials—such as aluminum oxide or silicon carbide grains and powders, pumice, Damascus ruby powder, rottenstone, valve-grinding compound, various abrasives used by rockhounds—and even household cleaning materials such as Bon Ami. Generally you can mix the abrasive with oil and use it to charge a pad or stick held against the spinning work. It's a good idea, when using any abrasive that could fall on the lathe, to cover the carriage and bed.

• *Grinding.* A toolpost grinder can produce a smooth finish on both hardened and unhardened metal. While grinding is often used primarily to bring the work to a definite dimension, or work metal too hard to cut with tool bits, the proper abrasive wheel can produce a very smooth finish. Recommendations for wheel choice can be obtained from suppliers of grinding materials and equipment.

There exists a considerable array of materials for producing smoothness and brightness, or achieving novel effects. In many cases, the best way to find out what is most suited for the job is to do some experimenting—to polish or treat some scrap pieces before tackling the main one.

Sources for various polishing and buffing supplies include William Dixon, Inc., Box 99, Newark, NJ 07101; also various abrasive manufacturers such as Norton Co., 50 New Bond St., Worcester, MA 01606 and the dealers who handle their products.

Turn plastic on your lathe

By WALTER E. BURTON

■ IF YOU'RE WEARY of turning steel and brass on your home-shop lathe, you can find diversion and challenge in working with an interesting nonmetal material—rigid PVC (polyvinyl chloride). It comes in various forms including sheet, pipe and fittings. In addition, there are other plastics rigid enough to be machined—such as acrylics (Plexiglas).

Shapes readily handled on the lathe, which can be used as good starting points in making various items, include pieces of rigid plastic pipe and such items as couplings, male and female adapters, cleanout plugs and fittings. Many local building-supply stores handle them, sometimes in a choice of colors such as white, gray, and ivory. Also, local distributors and fabricating shops often can provide sheet stock and scrap pieces of plastic materials they handle.

From such odds and ends, you can make various ornaments and novelties; even useful items such as washers and shade pulls. Or a trivet or trinket box (made from a Tepco fitting and plug) as shown in the drawing at right. The photos show a few lathe-turned items produced from random plastic parts (mostly of rigid PVC) found at local stores and in a shop scrapbox.

In production machining of rigid plastic materials, specially sharpened tools often are used. Some plastic compounds are so abrasive that tungsten-carbide tools are needed. But for limited machining of rigid PVC on a home-shop lathe, tools normally used for metals will do.

First, in turning plastics be sure that the workpiece is securely mounted in the lathe—that

SEE ALSO
Metal-lathe accessories . . . Plexiglass projects . . . Tools, hand

STOCK ITEMS are easily handled on lathe. Two black couplings in foreground fit plastic pipe.

TO PREVENT WALLS from being crushed, simply cut a plug from ¾-in. plywood to fit pipe's i.d.

USE PARTING or grooving bit to cut decorative grooves in future jewel box.

REMOVAL IS EASIER if all but a few turns of threads at top are machined off jewel-box cover.

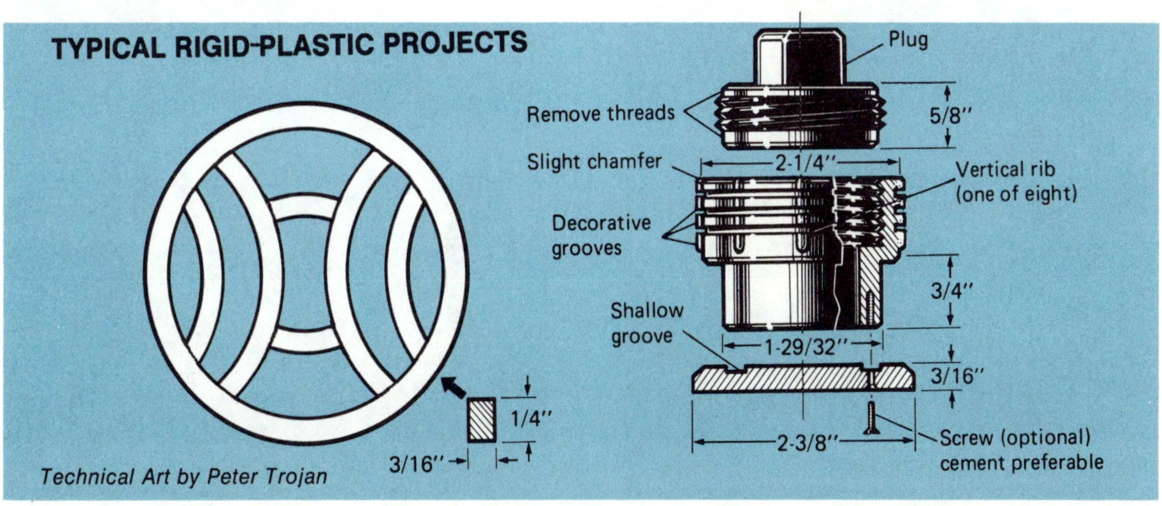

CUT BOTTOM FOR BOX from sheet plastic using a cutoff tool. Next, cut scrap away by hand.

FASTEN DISC to the chucked wooden mandrel using contact cement with a piece of paper between.

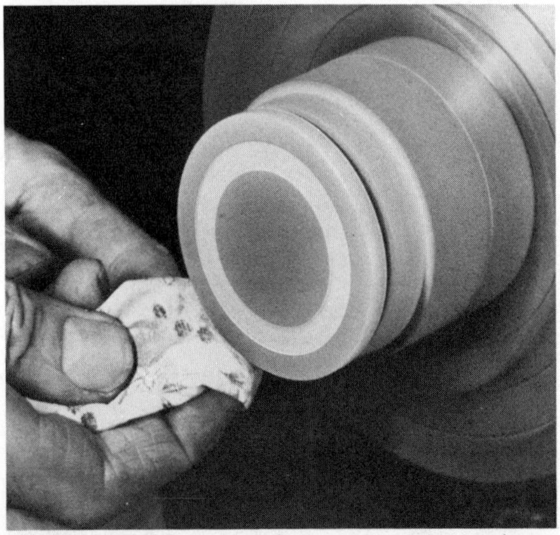

TO POLISH DISC, use a soft rag and powder (such as Bon Ami). Groove receives round wall.

PLASTIC COUPLING of the type used to join flexible plastic pipe is soft but still machinable.

AS YOU DRILL HOLE in the end of the cast-resin rod, chips are almost white—though rod is amber color.

IN THREADING END of rigid PVC pipe, with aid of a center rest, use regular threading tool.

chuck jaws grip it firmly and that there is no unsupported overhang that is likely to cause trouble. Keep cutting tools sharp. Until you get the "feel" of the material and operation, it's good to use slow spindle speeds and a careful feed. Then judge whether you will gain by increasing speed and feed. Don't let chips accumulate.

In doing the work illustrated, ordinary lathe tools ground for machining brass and steel were used and worked well. Edges were kept keen by frequent honing. Tools generally were set with cutting edges in line with the workpiece center, as in threading. Those ground with zero or slightly negative rake and plenty of clearance seemed to work well in many cases.

In cutting the key-chain links with a thin-blade parting tool, the lathe was run at the lowest of its four direct (nonback-geared) spindle speeds. This produced free-flowing chips and a cut surface having a good finish that required little further treatment other than knocking off sharp edges.

Chips often come from the tool in long, uncurled ribbons and may collect in loose bunches which have to be cleared at intervals. Chips from any plastic accumulating on or near the lathe, should be removed frequently. Besides being messy, they might be a fire hazard. If the plastic produces a nose-irritating dust, use a breathing mask.

Some stringy chips may wind around the work, like thread on a spool, and have to be removed when they become a nuisance by obscuring the cut or tool. When rounding sharp edges with a file (single-cut files are preferred), a by-product may be very fine, clinging "whiskers." To rub them off, hold a piece of felt against the revolving work. All lathe work on the items in the photos was done without use of cutting fluid.

grip work carefully

Mounting work in lathe: Under chuck-jaw pressure, a tubular piece can distort so readily that it is impossible to get a firm bite on it. A remedy is to insert a wooden plug in the end gripped by the chuck. For a large diameter, this can be a disc of ½ to ¾-in. plywood jigsawed or turned to a light drive fit. For a small pipe or tube, a dowel may do. Rigid plastic materials can be marred by rough chuck (or vise) jaws; a layer or two of masking tape or other padding around the o.d. where the jaws will bite is advisable.

Unsupported projection of a workpiece from a chuck should be kept as small as feasible. For threading and other operations near the ends of somewhat long tubes, rods and pipe sections, a center rest with jaws as near the outer end as possible is a good bet. Tubes and pipe sections can be center-supported like rods if their i.d. is not greater than the diameter of the pointed portion of the center; or they can be plugged and mounted between centers, like metal rods. Centers are lubricated with oil.

Corners, edges and surfaces can be smoothed with fine abrasive sheet. The degree of polish obtainable is best found by tests on the material being worked. Some plastics will require more polishing to bring out a desirable sheen. Merely burnishing with a wooden stick or one charged with an abrasive may be sufficient; this is one way of smoothing bottoms of deep grooves and the like. Bon Ami powder on a cloth or felt pad will polish some plastics spinning in a lathe; it was used for the base of the trinket box shown. Other polishes, such as those for brass or aluminum, could be tried. It's fun to experiment on scrap with various abrasives.

decorating plastic

Finished plastic can be decorated with paints or lacquers. Hobby shops usually carry paints for the plastic-model trade. A gold paint was used in the grooves turned on the trinket box.

An attempt to knurl a rigid PVC pipe resulted in a shallow pattern consisting essentially of grooves in cross-hatch arrangement. The material tended to give under knurl pressure, and well-formed diamonds could not be produced. However, the resulting diamond-hatch of lines was attractive and could serve as a slip-resistant grip surface.

Off-the-lathe treatment of turned items may include cutting, drilling, boring, milling, filing, bending and cementing. In the home shop, rigid PVC can be worked successfully enough with ordinary on-hand, "nonlathe" tools intended for wood or metal. For hand-sawing, try a dovetail saw or small hacksaw; for splitting rings to make the key chain, a jeweler's saw is preferable.

Because rigid PVC is not a good thermal conductor, the frictional heat generated by drilling or another operation may build up rapidly in a tool. Drill bits and other cutters should be watched for signs of overheating. As suggested earlier, tools should be sharp so that they produce less friction. Plastics containing fillers dull edges rapidly. A drill bit may seem to cut easily and penetrate with little resistance, but it should

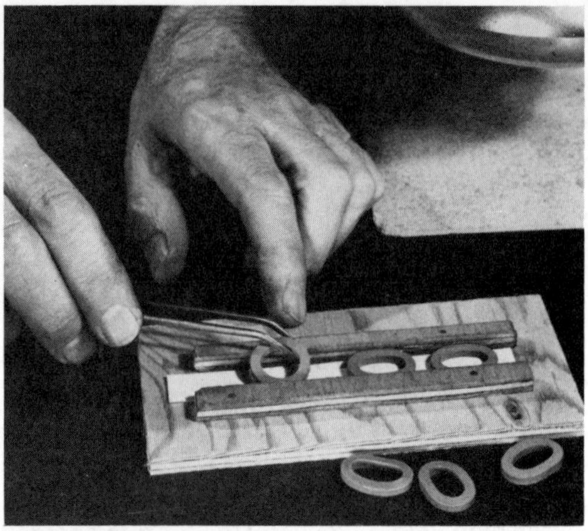

ELONGATED LINKS were formed by heating with lamp, then letting them cool between wood strips.

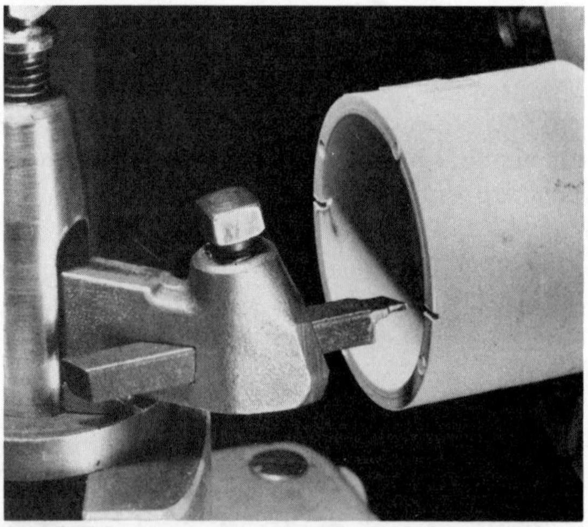

GROOVES can be cut in plastic using lathe as shaper. Here cross-slide is moved to and fro while side-mounted cutoff bit plows grooves in edge.

EXAMPLES of lathe-turned plastic: Black couplings were machined to slide together like telescope tube; trinket box was made from cleanout plug; oversize key chain is of two diameters of rigid pipe.

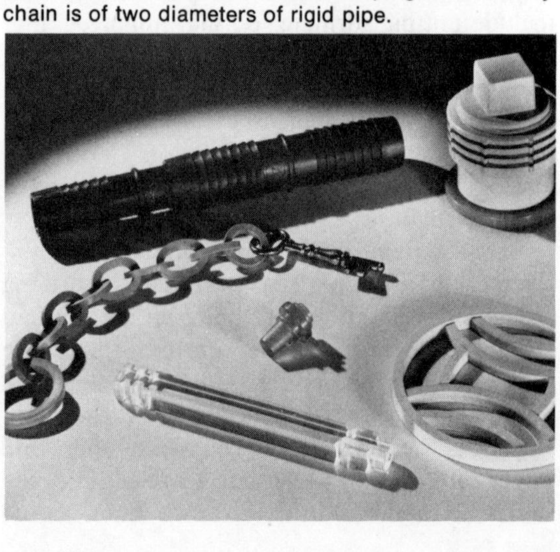

be withdrawn frequently, especially from a deep hole, for cooling and chip removal. Well-polished bit flutes offer less resistance.

For a threaded hole in a plastic material, you may use a slightly larger drill than for metal, to prevent excessive thread height. When there is a great deal of threading to be done, you may grind the tap (or die) teeth to a slightly negative front-angle rake.

If necessary, a plug can be installed to stiffen the wall of a pipe or tube for lathe-threading. Such threading may weaken the material; if the wall is thin, joining parts with cement generally is preferable. Suitable cements are sold by sources of rigid pipe and fittings.

shaping with heat

Rigid PVC, a thermoplastic material, can be heat-softened. In its soft state, it can be bent, stretched or otherwise modified; upon returning to room temperature, it will be rigid again. For example, rings cut from a rigid Koroseal pipe for making the oversize key chain shown were softened by placing them a few inches from a 250-w. reflector heat lamp for a minute or so. Then they were made into elongated links by squeezing them between two parallel wooden strips. Alternate links were split with a jeweler's saw, snapped through adjacent links, and rejoined by cementing.

Softened PVC should be handled carefully so that its surface is not damaged; if cooled against a rough board it may show the embossed texture of the board surface.

Though rigid PVC was used mostly in the sample projects, other plastics can be worked on a lathe, among them cast or molded resins. Some tough, somewhat softer plastics, such as those used for couplings for bendable polyethylene pipe, can be machined, but you may have to guard against a tendency for them to bend too readily. PVC stock pieces may vary in properties; there are extra-rigid grades for severe service. When turning such materials, the lathe operator usually has little difficulty in detecting differences in their response to tool action.

But whatever the particular piece of PVC or other plastic, it is interesting to determine what can be done with it on a lathe. The venture can be useful, for rigid plastic parts, besides being somewhat easier to obtain and easier to machine than metal ones, may have certain properties that no metal can boast—such as a desirable resistance to oils, grease, water, weather, as well as most chemicals likely to be encountered.

A shop forge you can build

By MORTON E. MILLIKEN

■ I MADE this $30 forge with a cast-off barbecue grill, legs from an old kitchen stool, some firebrick and a sheet-metal hood. I purchased the blower (electronics supply houses usually carry them) and a length of flexible exhaust pipe to fit the inside diameter of the blower outlet. The squirrel-cage blower is mounted on a metal flange attached to one leg. Wires from the blower pass through an outlet box containing a dimmer switch.

I secured the flexible pipe to the bottom of the barbecue grill by attaching a 90° pipe elbow to the grill with a U-bolt. Then I added a nipple to the elbow to accept the flexible pipe. The grill was mounted on the stool legs with ¼-in. bolts.

I made the hood from sheet metal, a length of vent pipe and an elbow. I used Pop rivets to fasten the hood sections together.

To use your forge, fill the grill with sand level with the opening of the pipe elbow. Start the fire with lighter fluid. Then run the blower at low speed. Soon coals nearest the air inlet will glow red, then light orange. Increase blower speed and, using tongs, place the workpiece into the center of the almost white-hot coals.

SEE ALSO

Crucible furnaces . . . Metal casting . . . Sheet metal . . . Tin-can crafts . . . Torches

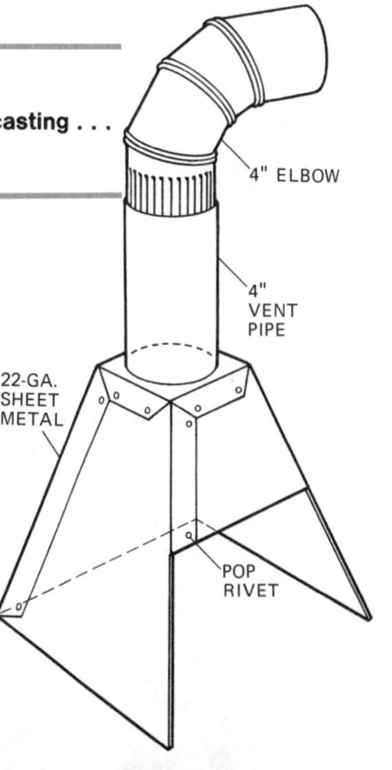

FASTEN 90° elbow to bottom of grill with U-bolt.

ADD SAND, level with elbow, then set four firebrick on edge around hole.

MOUND FIREPIT with handfuls of briquets; light with fluid and match.

USE LIGHT-DIMMER switch to control blower speed, regulating air to firepit.

KEEP BLOWER at low speed until most coals glow bright red.

DO-IT-YOURSELF fireplace cover, made of aluminum, offers energy-saving and safety advantages.

Build an energy-saving fireplace cover

■ THIS EASILY-MADE fireplace cover prevents heat loss up the chimney. It's a boon to those who hate to go to bed with the damper left open.

Cut the aluminum bar stock with a hacksaw. Aluminum sheet can be cut with tin snips. Lay out the scrolls on parts C. To start a scroll, clamp a ½-in. tip of the bar in the vise and bend. Next, install the slotted pipe in the vise and complete the bend. Taper tips slightly.

TO MAKE jig for bending scrolls in bar aluminum, cut slots in one end of ¾-in.-dia. pipe; clamp pipe in vise. Reposition bar as needed to shape. Test on scrap to see how bend occurs.

SEE ALSO

Cutoff machines . . . Energy, saving . . . Fireplaces . . . Power hacksaws . . . Sheet metal . . . Torches

After scrolls are made, grip the straight part of C in the vise—where it will bend at a right angle (near the bottom scroll). Hammer the bar as you bend it. Repeat on second bar.

Make the offset bends on parts B as shown. Cut and bend tabs on pieces D. Lay out the frame, check it for square and apply C-clamps at the four corners. Locate, center-punch and drill the corner holes. Assemble temporarily with stovebolts. Next, mark and drill evenly-spaced rivet holes. Align the sheet with the bar frame and clamp. Use holes in the bar stock as a guide to drill rivet holes through the sheet. Permanently assemble corners; rivet sheet to the frame. Finally, attach D.

File edges. Clean with steel wool and mineral spirits. Use metal primer and finish. Apply Snap Caps.

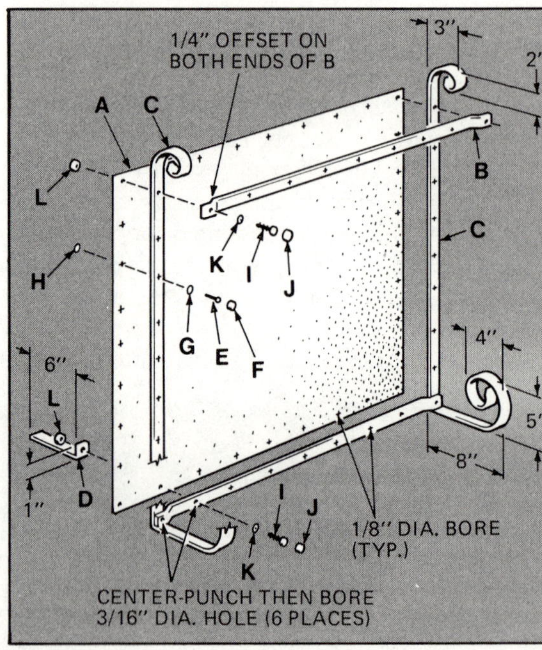

MATERIALS LIST—FIREPLACE COVER

Key	No.	Size and description (use)
A	1	Leather grain embossed sheet aluminum ¼" less than each o.d. of frame (cover)
B	2	¼ x 1" aluminum bar; length equal to width of fireplace opening plus 2"
C	2	¼ x 1" aluminum bar; length equal to height of fireplace opening plus 1", plus 8" (top scroll), plus 21" (bottom scroll)
D	2	¼ x 1 x 7" aluminum bar (back foot)
E	(as reqd.)	⅛"-dia. x ½" Pop Rivet
F	(as reqd.)	small Snap Cap to fit rivet
G	(as reqd.)	Small Snap Cap washer
H	(as reqd.)	Back-up plates to fit ⅛"-dia. rivets
I	6	8-32 x ¾" rh stovebolt
J	6	large Snap Cap to fit bolthead
K	6	large Snap cap washer
L	6	8-32 nut

Misc.: 00 steel wool, mineral spirits, metal primer and finish coat (such as Rustoleum).

Frosty metal door

The door to my patio from the family room is metal framed. When cold, it's covered with frost. During the day this often melts and runs down on the floor. The moisture is on the inside. How does it get in and how can I prevent it from forming the frost?—T.R., Ky.

It doesn't "get in," as you put it. It's already inside the room. You're looking at condensate that forms on the surface of the metal that's at a lower temperature than the air with which it is in contact; so much lower that frost forms on cold days and nights.

I assume the door is weatherstripped and closes tightly. A tight-fitting storm door would probably minimize the formation of condensate to the point where it is no longer damaging. Some homeowners with this trouble on both metal sashes and doors apply adhesive tape to the exposed metal frames. This usually prevents the trouble. Even colored tape does not enhance the appearance of window sashes or doors but perhaps it is better than mopping water off the floor.

If your home is heated by a gas-fired furnace, especially one of the floor type, make sure it is adequately vented to prevent excessive moisture inside the house. Other sources of moisture are uncontrolled furnace humidifiers, boiling teakettles, frequent showering, unvented washers and dryers.

Replacing sash cord

I have old-type sash with cords and balancing weights. The cords need replacing. I can see how to replace them on the lower sash, but how do I replace those on the upper sash? That is, how is the upper sash removed?—C.R., Utah.

After you've removed the lower sash you have to pry out one of the two parting strips you'll see between the sashes. On an old window frame these strips may have been "painted in," and you'll have to proceed very carefully to get one out without breaking it or splintering the frame. Perhaps the best way is to break the paint seal on both sides of the strip by tapping the edge of a chisel in lightly at the point where the strip meets the sash frame. Do this at spaced intervals along the exposed length of the strip on both sides. Then tap the edge of the chisel into the strip and pry *very lightly* until it loosens at the lower end. Repeat this along the length until the strip loosens sufficiently for you to lift it out with your fingers. Be especially careful in this step not to break the strip or, worse, splinter the frame. Once the strip is out the sash can be lifted clear without removing the strip on the other side of the frame.

Basement wall 'leak'

I have an outside entrance to my basement. There are drops of water on the concrete-block wall near the floor—even when weather is dry. What could cause such a leak?—G.R. Waud, Elmira, N.Y.

I don't think it's a leak; I'm quite sure it's condensate. If you place your hand on the wet surface, you no doubt will find that it's noticeably cold. Moisture condenses here because of the variation in temperature. Though it is hard to diagnose from this distance, it is also possible that these drops of water are caused by sweating cold-water pipes overhead. If so, you can correct the problem by wrapping the pipes with a pipe insulation that comes in rolls, and is carried by well-stocked hardware stores.

Removing fabric stains

I spilled chocolate topping on my sofa, but didn't notice the stain until it had hardened. How can I remove it?—J. Hansen, Beatrice, Neb.

Since you didn't identify the fabric, I can't guarantee to give you the correct procedure. Generally, however, dry-cleaning fluids are safe on most common fabrics. Just twist a ball of cotton on the end of a small dowel—or handy stick or sliver of wood—and sponge the stain lightly. Follow with a warm, damp cloth, rubbing lightly away from the center. Repeat the procedure if necessary.

Pinpointing roof leak

Shingles on my home are laid over a low-pitch plywood deck. I've just discovered a leak and don't know how to locate it. About halfway down the ridge, it shows as a discoloration at a joint in the deck. How can I pinpoint it?—D.W., Nev.

It's going to take some rather blind sleuthing. You're reasonably certain that water is coming through at a point more or less directly above the discoloration at the joint in the plywood deck. You also know this point can't be more than 4 ft. above the stain. So, drive back the projecting ends of the roofing nails across the width of the plywood sheet directly above where the stain appears. Then go up on the roof and gently lift the loosened shingles until you locate the cause of the leak.

This may turn out to be a split or broken shingle tab, a bent nail hammered inadvertently through a shingle, a not-fully-seated nail, permitting rain to creep under a shingle, or other damage. Once you've found the cause, the remedy should be quite simple: replace a defective shingle or seal a break with roofing cement. Drive all nails back in place.

Learning to live with the metric system

By ED NELSON

Will the conversion to metrics simplify—or complicate—our lives? Must we give up our miles-per-hour, our quarter-pounder sandwiches, and even our 10-gallon hats as we inch (centimeter?) along toward the metric system? Here's what you should know about the Big Switch—plus a wealth of easy-to-use tables that show you how to convert virtually any measurement to or from metrics

THE UNITED STATES is going metric. Many of us have heard that statement since childhood.

We've also been told that the metric system will simplify our lives.

Indeed, as this is written, there is a change underway—even though anti-metric pressure groups are fighting it bitterly. These traditionalists, who feel that any measurements good enough for their forefathers are good enough for them, have won skirmishes here and there. Their voices were loud enough to stop, at least temporarily, the conversion of highway signs from miles to kilometers. Members of Congress have been amazed at the bitterness of the opposition to the metric system.

But slowly and inexorably the United States is being "metricized." We now are buying soft drinks and liquors by the liter, weathermen are telling us the temperature in degrees Celsius, and the waist sizes of all our kids' Levis are stamped in centimeters as well as inches.

Will this conversion to metrics simplify our lives? Probably not as much as we've been led to believe, but there certainly are big advantages to the metric system. (Big disadvantages, too, holler the traditionalists.)

Just what is the metric system? Where did it come from? When? More important, why?

The metric system is a precisely defined body of weights and measures accepted by international authority.

SEE ALSO
Calipers . . . Measurements . . . Tools, hand

where they came from

It's quite correct to say that there have been several different metric systems, since some measurements have undergone a series of modifications. But for the most part these were only small refinements. Many of today's metric units aren't greatly different from the uniform units of measurement demanded by Talleyrand after the French Revolution.

Another name for metric units is "SI" units. That's the abbreviation bestowed on metrics by the General Conference on Weights and Measures, an international body that met for years to make revisions which for the most part were miniscule. Such revisions and simplifications finally were completed and accepted in 1960, and the entire body of measurements was named the *Systeme International d' Unites*. The conference decreed "SI" as the official abbreviation in all languages. (However, the U.S. Department of Commerce still prefers to call it the International Metric System.)

Throughout man's history, he has required familiar, consistent and easily available units of measurement. The Biblical *cubit* was the length of the forearm from the elbow to the end of the middle finger (in ancient Egypt that amounted to approximately 20 of our modern inches). And consider the inch itself; our inch came from the early British measurement, which was defined as "the length of three barleycorns, round and dry."

forearms won't do

As man learned to master his environment and to build his machines, such imprecise measurements no longer served him adequately. Neither forearms nor barleycorns are uniform, and no system of measurements is useful unless the units mean the same thing to all who use them. In fact, confusion in regard to exact meaning can lead to chaos.

Furthermore, the standard to be agreed upon must be available to all who use it. The distance from the tip of King Henry's nose to the end of his thumb—the official basis for the English *yard*—may have been totally consistent all the time the King was on his throne, but few Englishmen had access to it.

The length of the *mile* has been elastic, too. Our word *mile* is a descendant of the Latin *milia passum,* or one thousand paces. The Roman *mile* had a very precise definition; it was one thousand paces measured from the point where the heel of one foot strikes the ground to the point where the same heel strikes the ground again. A precise definition all right, but a highly imprecise measurement. A Roman legionnaire built like Mickey Rooney would count off a good many more miles than one measuring up to Charlton Heston.

sailors and problems

Nautical miles, another oldtime measurement, have never had anything to do with paces. How can you walk on water? A *nautical mile* was defined as one minute of the Earth's circumference—1/21,600th of the way around the world. This, again, may appear to be a very precise measurement. And it *was* precise until it was discovered that the Earth isn't perfectly round, so a one-minute arc doesn't mean the same everywhere. As a result, the *nautical mile* has been redefined in feet; to be exact, a *nautical mile* measures 6076.1 feet.

Then along came aviation. Fliers use long-distance navigation methods developed by sea captains, but most early flying was done over land. As a result, U.S. aviators use both *statute* and *international nautical miles*. Sounds confusing, eh? However, so adaptable is the human brain that pilots and navigators quickly learn to convert, almost automatically, from one kind of mile to the other. No doubt aviators will be happy to settle, eventually, on the *kilometer*. However, this experience demonstrates how rapidly we can learn to shift from one measurement system to another, and do it without much difficulty when the need arises.

The metric system has had its share of ambiguities, too. In the 1700s the Paris Academy of Sciences thought it was pinning its basic unit of measurement—the meter—to one of nature's most constant realities; surveyors established the sea-level distance from the North Pole to the Equator, and the *meter* was defined as one 10-millionth of that length.

Ha! That, too, soon developed flaws. The average guy trying to measure the distance from the North Pole to the Equator, and then fractionate it, was no more successful than the English serf who sought to measure the distance from King Henry's nose to the end of his Royal Thumb.

decimal convenience

Disregarding the Royal Thumb, the metric system offers one tremendous advantage over any other system ever invented. It's the same advantage that the United States coinage system had, until recently, over most other coinage systems since the early days of the Republic. This major advantage is *the decimal relationship of one unit to another*. If you can multiply by 10, or 100, or 1000, you can easily manipulate the system.

This is most helpful to those of us who desperately try to avoid multiplication and division. In the metric system, in most cases, a specific unit is 10 times the size of the next smaller unit, and 1/10th the size of the next larger unit.

Take the measurement of land, for example. (We ordinarily are accustomed to measuring in *acres* or *square miles*—units which can have no logical relationship to one another.) In the metric system, the basic measurement of land area is the *are* (rhymes with bare). An *are* is defined as an area of land equivalent to a square measuring 10 meters on each side, or 100 square meters. A *hectare (hecto-* is a prefix signifying 100) is 100 times the area of an *are*, or 10,000 square meters. The system obviously lends itself to rapid mental

turn the page →

calculation. Thus an area of 235 *square meters* is equivalent to 2.35 *are* and to .0235 hectare.

Compare that calculation with the arithmetic necessary to convert 4,367 square feet into square yards, square rods and acres!

Most other metric elements are just as regular in their decimal consistency. *Milli-* is the prefix for one one-thousandth, so a *milliliter* is a thousandth of a *liter*. This metric relationship is somewhat comparable to the number of cubic inches in a gallon in our customary system, except that there's no logic to our customary system. Well, how many cubic inches *are* there in a gallon? The answer is 231, but how many of us can be expected to know that, or even know how to compute it?

The relationship of cubic inches to gallons isn't the only example of our customary measuring units that fit together so clumsily they scarcely seem to fit at all.

a foot is a foot?

Take something as familiar as the *foot*. No, the foot isn't always the same throughout the United States, and in our technological society even minor differences can be critical. In the U.S. there are two slightly different "approved" definitions for the *foot*, and the British offer still a third "approved" definition. The American Standards Association (now the American National Standards Institute) stated that a foot is precisely 0.3048 meter. The National Bureau of Standards says the foot is precisely 1200/3937 meter (which in decimals is about 0.3048006096).

Until deciding to go metric, the British, with their usual aplomb, said the foot was precisely one-third of the Imperial *yard*, and then defined the *yard*. The result didn't match our own two clumsy feet.

The three different feet are close in size. Their relative lengths are in this ratio:

914,400:914,402:914,399

But why should there be any difference at all? Can't we all talk about a *foot*—or any other unit of measurement—and mean precisely the same thing?

whose quart counts?

Now take a look at the quart, which is one of the most familiar and comfortable old measurements we've known since we hit the refrigerator as kids. A *quart* measures volume, and it shouldn't matter whether that volume is filled with corn likker or corn flakes. So how much is a quart? A U.S. *liquid* quart is 57.75 cubic inches; our *dry* quart is 67.0062 cubic inches. There's a difference of 16 percent between the two.

In 1864 Great Britain, facing somewhat the same problem, consolidated a number of various-size quarts into one quart for all uses. It amounts to about 69.35 cubic inches—bigger than either of our quarts. Until recently, if you bought a quart of Irish whiskey in Great Britain you'd get considerably more to drink than if you bought a quart of Kentucky bourbon in the United States.

Even some writers are traditionalists, and thus are apprehensive about giving up the old measurements. Some of us, observing the march toward metrics, feel a chill 11-centimeter hand squeezing our hearts. What will happen to our cherished figures of speech? Instead of saying, "Give him an inch and he'll take a mile," will we now be stammering, "Give him a centimeter and he'll take a kilometer?" Or, more precisely, "Give him 2.54 centimeters and he'll take 1.60934 kilometers?" Horrors! Have the metricians become morticians? Are they burying our language?

(Actually, John Heywood's original remark in the early 1500s was, "For when I gave you an inch, you took an ell." The ell was a cloth measure; in England it equalled 45 inches—or thereabouts. Old John didn't even mention miles.)

914-mm pin-up girls

Will we be ogling the girl whose millimeter measurements approach the metric ideal of 914-610-914? (No, that's not her phone number; it's her mathematical description.)

Will we be trying to shed 4.761 kilograms by living on a daily diet of 4200 joules? Will we have centimeter worms instead of inchworms, will our sailors be forced to give up their beloved knots, and will we ask at the fruit stand for 8.810 liters of apples, instead of the beloved and old-fashioned peck? As columnist Erma Brombeck asks, will we be saying, "Peter Piper picked a hectoliter of pickled peppers?"

Instead of walking "a million miles for one of your smiles" will we hike 1,609,300 kilometers for the same reward?

Are 10-gallon hats gone forever?

Levity aside, we *are* going metric. Many observers felt it would be much more difficult to get industry to accept metrics than to persuade the public. In many respects, the reverse has been

HOW TO CONVERT ALMOST ANYTHING TO—OR FROM—METRIC

Here are the factors to use in converting customary units to SI and *vice versa.* Most are approximate. To convert British nautical miles to meters, for example, a *precise* answer calls for you to multiply by 1853.184. But multiplying by 1850 would introduce an error of only about 17/100 of 1 percent. So our "approximate" factors still give you good, solid conversion figures.

This is how you use the table:

In starting with terms from the first column, multiply by the conversion factor in the second to find the equivalent in the SI units from the third column. Follow the arrows in the opposite direction to change from an SI quantity to its equivalent in customary units.

To make it easier to read long decimals, we follow the American National Standards Institute suggestion. We put digits in groups of three separated by spaces.

Multiply→ To get←	→by→ ←by←	→To get ←Multiply
ACCELERATION		
feet per second per second	→.304 8→ ←3.281←	meters per second per second
feet per second per second	→.109 7→ ←9.113←	kilometers per hour per second
inches per second per second	→.025 4→ ←39.37←	meters per second per second
miles per hour per second	→1.609→ ←.621 4←	kilometers per hour per second
AREA		
acres	→.4047→ ←2.471←	hectares
square feet	→.092 9→ ←10.76←	square meters
square inches	→6.452→ ←.155 0←	square centimeters
square miles	→2.59→ ←.386 1←	square kilometers
square yards	→.836 1→ ←1.196←	square meters

FORCE

SI units use kilograms only as units of mass ("weight" in popular usage). Force has a basic SI unit of its own, the *newton,* based on the force of inertia, not the force of gravity. One newton is the force that, if applied to a free body of 1 kilogram mass, will accelerate it at a rate of 1 meter per second each second. A newton, in customary terms, equals about 3.7 ounces of force.

kilograms force	→9.807→ ←.110 3←	newtons
ounces (avoirdupois) force	→.278 0→ ←3.702←	newtons
pounds (avoirdupois) force	→4.448→ ←.225 1←	newtons

true. The change of highway signs to kilometers was attempted at a speed that the American people didn't find comfortable. There had been no consistent campaign to inform the public before kilometer signs suddenly appeared wherever the motorist was driving. The public hollered, and the government backed off.

Nearly half of the nation's thousand largest companies, on the other hand, are converting their specs to the metric system, or are inching (centimetering?) toward it.

A change in industry can be much more precisely planned. For example, leading torque wrench manufacturers, such as Sturtevant, have added metric calibrations to their wrenches (although instruction manuals still use customary units). Manufacturers use a special blue background for metric dials. Many users now accept newton-meters as the units they use, while others still choose pounds-feet (or less properly, foot-pounds) because they've lived with that unit all their measuring life.

ounces of turmoil

Now we plunge into an area of confusion. We have had a tendency in the past to use a single measuring unit for a variety of purposes. An *ounce,* for example, has been our unit for measuring troy weight, for measuring avoirdupois weight, and for measuring liquids. Yet these measuring systems are basically incompatible. The units are called *ounces,* but they're far from equal. We have used *pounds* for weight, and *foot-pounds* for energy—a combination of terms born of our assumption that the force of gravity is uniformly constant. Confusion!

Since the force of gravity *isn't* uniformly constant, the two measuring systems really require different terms. The *kilogram* thus becomes the

turn the page →

HOW TO CONVERT ALMOST ANYTHING TO—OR FROM—METRIC

ENERGY (including Work)

The *joule* is the SI unit of energy or work. It is the work done (or energy expended) when a 1-newton force displaces a body for 1 meter in the direction of the force.

British thermal units (mean)	→1055→ ←.000 948 7←	joules
calories (mean)	→4.190→ ←.238 7←	joules
ergs	→1 x 10^{-7}→ ←1,000,000←	joules
foot-pounds	→1.356→ ←.738←	joules
kilowatt hours	→3,600,000→ ←.000 000 277 8←	joules

LENGTH

caliber	→.025 4→ ←39.37←	millimeters
chain (surveyor's)*	→20.12→ ←.049 71←	meters
chain (engineer's)*	→30.48→ ←.032 81←	meters
inches	→25.4→ ←.039 37←	centimeters
mils (.001 inch)	→25.4→ ←.039 37←	microns (.001 mm)
miles (U.S. nautical)	→1.852→ ←.54←	kilometers
miles (U.S. statute)	→1.609→ ←.621 4←	kilometers
rods	→5.029→ ←.198 8←	meters
yards	→.914 4→ ←1.094←	meters

* A surveyor's chain, 66 feet, equals four 16½-foot rods or 100 7.92-inch links. An engineer's chain equals 100 12-inch links.

MASS (Weight)

carats	→.2→ ←5←	grams
grains	→.064 79→ ←15.43←	grams
ounces (avoirdupois)	→28.35→ ←.035 27←	grams
ounces (troy or apothecary)	→31.10→ ←.032 15←	grams
pounds (avoirdupois)	→.453 6→ ←2.205←	kilograms
short tons (2000 pounds)	→.907 2→ ←.068 52←	kilograms

POWER

Btu (thermochemical) per hour	→.292 9→ ←3.414←	watts
calories (thermochemical) per hour	→4.184→ ←.239 0←	watts
ergs per second	→.000 000 1→ ←10,000,000←	watts
foot-pounds (force) per second	→1.356→ ←.737 6←	watts

metric system, continued

metric unit for measuring mass (scientists prefer the term "mass" to "weight"). And the *newton* thus becomes a unit for measuring force—the force needed to overcome inertia and accelerate a one-kilogram mass to a speed one meter per second in one second.

But even in industry there has been some confusion. Sturtevant officials find many a purchasing agent unfamiliar with the distinction in measuring terms. Orders come in calling for torque wrenches calibrated in meter-kilograms, instead of newton meters.

conversion success story

For an area of change with a slightly different history, take a look at the pharmaceutical industry. Early in the 1960s, major drug companies opted for metric measurements. They moved fast, and even the public found the switch surprisingly painless.

Early on, manufacturers decided to change only what was necessary. Since the pharmaceutical industry deals mainly with weights and volumes, there was little concern about length measurements (inches or meters). Most of the processing machinery was amenable to change; scales, for example, could get by with only a new dial, new weights, or a new beam. Volume measuring gear took somewhat more modification, but still was not too difficult to alter.

Retraining workers turned out to be relatively easy; it went more rapidly than expected.

What about customers? At first, the metric quantities were added to the labels in parentheses after the customary quantities. Later, the metric quantity was printed first, followed by the customary quantity in parentheses.

The whole process went surprisingly fast. One of the largest pharmaceutical firms switched completely to metrics in about one year, and a spokesman says it could have been done even faster.

horsepower (550 foot-pounds per second)	→.745 7→ ←1.341←	kilowatts

PRESSURE

The pascal (Pa), adopted as the special name for a unit of pressure, is a newton of force per square meter. (See Force for a discussion of the newton.)

atmospheres	→101,325→ ←.000 009 869←	pascals
kilograms per square centimeter	→66.5→ ←.000 010 2←	pascals
pounds per square foot	→47.88→ ←.020 89←	pascals
pounds per square inch	→6894.75→ ←.000 145←	pascals

SPEED

feet per minute	→.005 08→ ←196.9←	meters per second
feet per second	→.304 8→ ←3.281←	meters per second
knots (international)	→1.852→ ←.539 96←	kilometers per hour
miles (U.S. statute) per hour	→1.609→ ←.621 4←	kilometers per hour
miles (U.S. statute) per minute	→94.41→ ←.010 59←	kilometers per hour

TORQUE

ounce-inches	→.007 062→ ←141.6←	newton meters
pound-feet	→1.356→ ←.737 6←	newton meters
pound-inches	→.113→ ←8.851←	newton meters

VOLUME

acre-feet	→1233.→ ←.000 810 7←	cubic meters
bushels (U.S.)	→.035 24→ ←28.38←	cubic meters
cords	→3.624 5→ ←.275 9←	cubic meters
cubic feet	→.028 32→ ←35.31←	cubic meters
cubic inches	→16.39→ ←.061 02←	cubic centimeters
cubic inches	→.016 39→ ←61.02←	liters
cubic yards	→.764 6→ ←1.308←	cubic meters
gallons (U.S. dry)	→4.405→ ←.227←	liters
gallons (U.S. liquid)	→3.785→ ←.226 4←	liters
ounces (U.S. fluid)	→29.57→ ←.033 81←	milliliters
ounces (U.S. fluid)	→.029 57→ ←33.81←	liters
pecks (U.S.)	→8.81→ ←.113 5←	liters
quarts (U.S. dry)	→1.101→ ←.908 1←	liters
quarts (U.S. dry)	→1101→ ←.000 908 1←	milliliters
quarts (U.S. liquid)	→.9464→ ←1.057←	liters
quarts (U.S. liquid)	→946.4→ ←.001 057←	milliliters

By the mid-1970s, food packages were working well into the first of these same two steps—printing metric measurements on the label after customary measurements.

Detroit moves fast

Car builders were joining the parade in earnest. A Chevrolet service bulletin on weatherstripping calls for "additional cement . . . down each side and around the lower corners approximately 152 mm (6 inches)." In regard to trunk locks, assembly mechanics were told, "Torque the attaching bolts to 10-14 Nm." At that point they weren't even told that this meant about 7.4 to 10.3 pounds-feet.

So now we're smack in the middle of metrics.

Regardless of how you feel about it, the wait for metrics has been a long one. 'Way back in 1821 John Quincy Adams told Congress that metrics offered "the ideal perfection of uniformity applied to weights and measures." But he added that the time wasn't yet ripe in the United States to adopt the decimal system. It has ripened very slowly.

while we hung back

The rest of the world moved steadily toward metrics while we, clinging to our feet and yards, our ounces and pounds, our pints and gallons, were left alone among the great industrialized countries. As this is written, the list of countries *not* committed to metrics is unimposing, as far as industry goes: Barbados, Burma, Gambia, Ghana, Jamaica, Liberia, Muscat and Oman, Nauru, Sierra Leone, Southern Yemen, Tonga and Trinidad.

It seems inevitable that metrics eventually will become universal. But it's likely that in 1999 we'll still bet on horse races measured in furlongs, McDonald's may still be featuring a quarter-pounder rather than a 0.113398 kilogrammer, Erskine Caldwell's classic will not have been renamed *God's Little 0.4047 Hectare*, and the announcer at the Superbowl will not be saying, "First down and 9.144 meters to go."

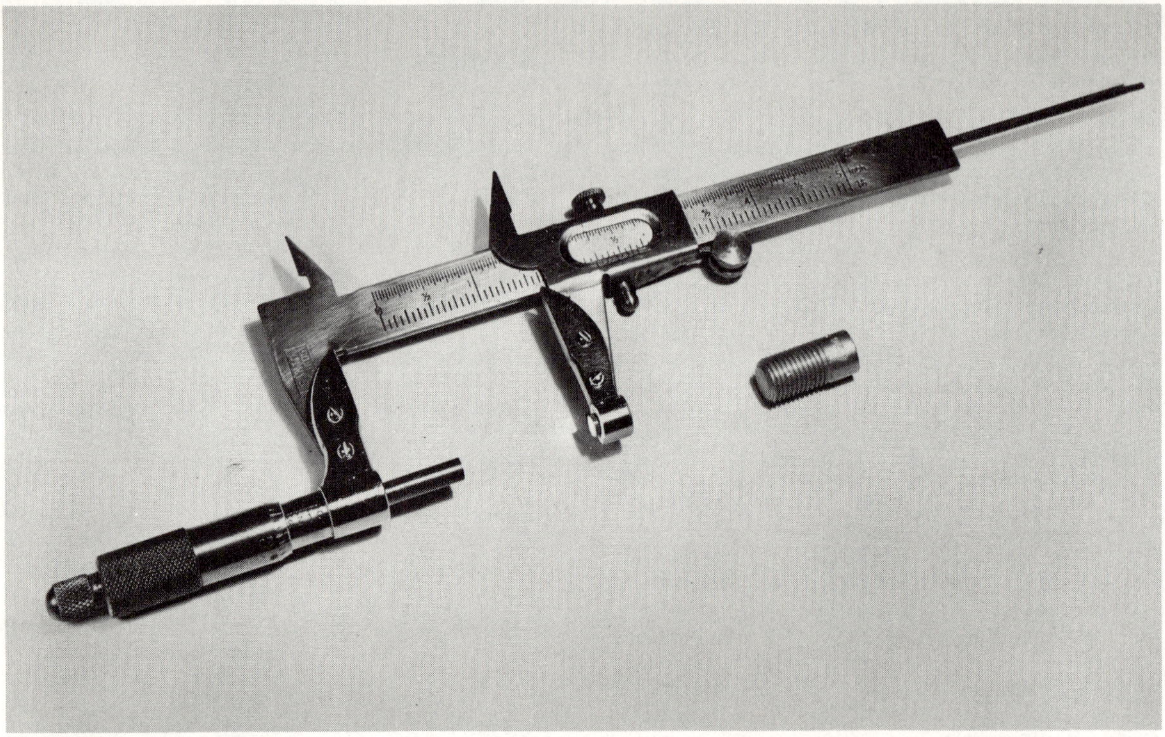

IF YOU BUILD this hybrid tool, you can turn your small 1-in. micrometer into a precision instrument that has up to four times its original capacity.

How to 'enlarge' your micrometer

By JOHN F. DRYER

■ MARRY A VERNIER caliper to a micrometer and increase the accuracy of the former and the capacity of the latter. This hybrid, accurate to .001 in., eliminates the need for a larger, more expensive micrometer. My enlarged micrometer is made with a 1-in. micrometer and 5-in. caliper, but select the size combinations that best suit your requirements.

Begin by opening the caliper jaws slightly to align the micrometer as shown. Then clamp the micrometer tightly to the caliper jaws and drill four holes through both tools using a No. 50 bit.

SEE ALSO
Caddies, tool . . . Calipers . . .
Combination squares . . . Measurements . . .
Metric system . . . Shop tools . . . Tools, hand

For calipers with surface-hardened steel, use a small, high-speed grinding tool to penetrate the surface. A good bit will then drill into it. If the bit doesn't deliver chips, grind more. Tap threads in the caliper holes for No. 2-56 machine screws and enlarge micrometer holes with a No. 43 bit to accommodate the screws. Use a hacksaw to cut out the middle section of the micrometer. Screw the remaining anvil and spindle ends to the caliper as shown.

To measure, set the micrometer's handle gauge at 0 and slide the caliper jaw to bring the anvil snugly against the spindle. On our prototype, the jaw stops at 1-7/32 in. At this "standard" setting, lengths from 0 to 1 in. are measured by placing the work between the anvil and spindle of the micrometer and adjusting the micrometer gauge to obtain a reading. For larger measurements, slide caliper jaw in 1-in. increments away from spindle

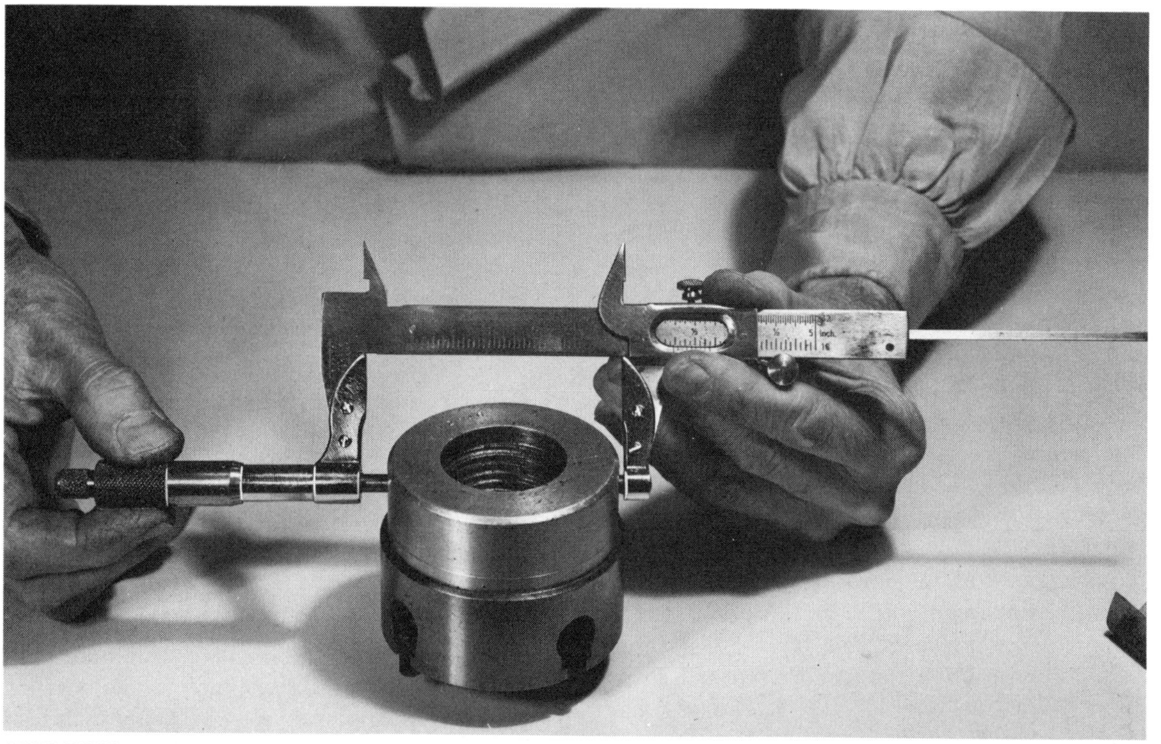

NEW TOOL measures lengths up to 4¼ in. using a 5-in. vernier caliper. You may want to remove the depth gauge tongue seen projecting at the right on the caliper.

(e.g. to measure between 2 and 3 in. with micrometer, set caliper at 2-7/32 in.; between 3 and 4 in., set caliper at 3-7/32 in., and so on).

Apply the same pressure on all readings to insure accuracy. Using a larger caliper increases the range of the micrometer. However, accuracy will be no better than the finest unit on the micrometer gauge.

FOR ACCURATE alignment, drill holes and fasten micrometer to the caliper jaws to test fit before cutting off the middle section of the micrometer frame.

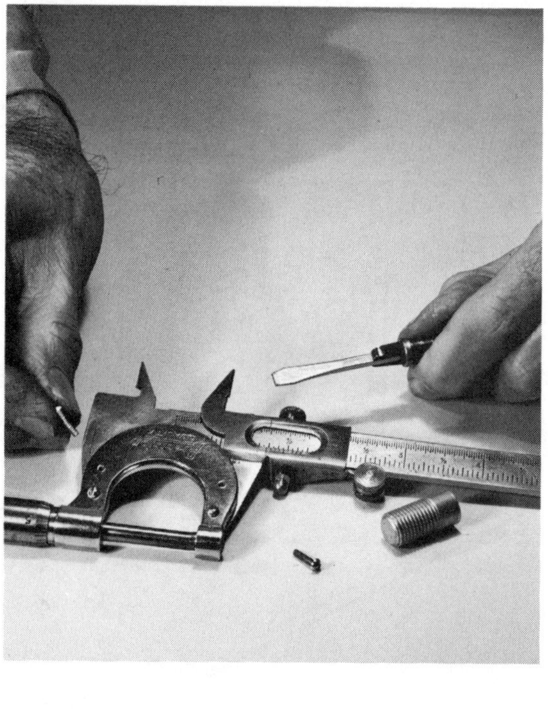

CLAMP MICROMETER in a vise and cut out the middle section. When assembling, align anvil and spindle accurately as if frame still connected them.

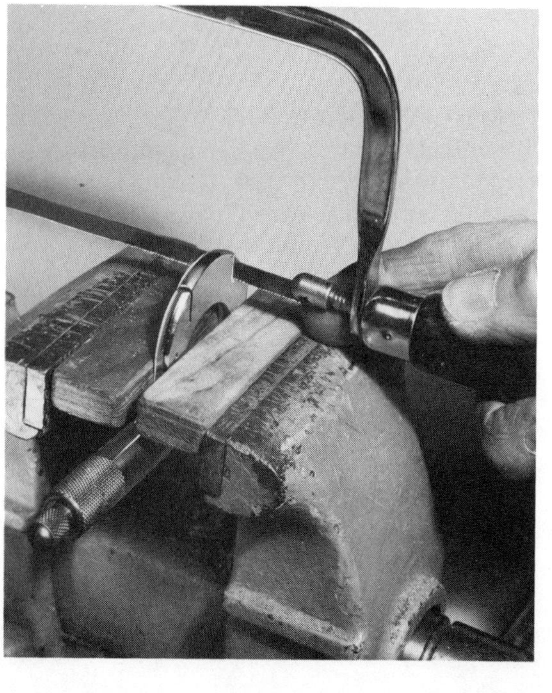

An enchanting dollhouse

■ WELCOME TO the world of miniatures by way of our Victorian dollhouse.

The dollhouse might well become an heirloom in your family. Certainly any girl of almost any age would be proud to own it.

The exterior is premade clapboard painted white. Shingles are made from chipboard strips. The sloping roof over the porch is made from three pieces of wood attached to a subroof.

materials

To make the house, you'll need two 4x8 sheets of finished plywood, one ¼-in. thick and one ½-in. thick. You'll also need: 8 ft. of 1x2-in. pine strips for the exterior trim and porch trim; 8 strips of 22x5⁄16-in. molding for the baseboards and livingroom ceiling trim; one strip ½-in. wide of decorative molding for the top of the pillars and porch; 16 windows; one door; white glue for gluing joints; rubber cement for gluing wallpaper; ¾-in. brads for nailing the exterior molding; finishing nails for attaching partitions to the ceilings; 1x8 flathead wood screws for joining the outer shell of the house; metal filigree trim for the rooftop (available at lamp stores); piano hinge 24-in. long (a 30-in. hinge is easily cut); two caster bearings for ease in opening the house front; three sheets 22x30-in. chipboard for shingles; paint; wallpaper; 18 sheets of 3½x22-in. clapboard siding; latch.

steps for assembling

First cut the pieces out, making proper spaces for your windows and door. Use the layout diagram for the arrangement of parts, but follow the dimensions given for cutting.

Attach sides and back with screws in predrilled holes. Join the porch according to the exploded drawing and attach it to the house front. Construct the roof. Glue the roof trim and paint it black. Install painted windows and door. Paint and paper the interior.

SEE ALSO
Children's furniture . . . Dump trucks, toy . . . Gifts, Christmas . . . Jewelry boxes . . . Toys

installing inner walls

The inner walls are installed a floor at a time. Glue first-floor walls to the floor. Insert the second floor and nail it to the first-floor walls. (You'll have to retouch the nail holes.) For additional strength, predrill from the exterior and screw the second floor to the house shell. Continue until all floors are installed. Then nail on the painted clapboard.

furnishings and accessories

You can represent virtually every detail in life in miniature form. Many of the materials needed are right at hand. The standard scale when working with miniatures is one inch to the foot.

■ Books and magazines: Check book club ads for pictures of tiny books. Cut these out and paste them to a piece of wood. The rows of books in our Victorian house bookcase were drawn on strips cut from file folders, folded and glued to form a hollow rectangle.

■ Bookcases: The bookcase in our Victorian library was made from ⅛-in. beechwood joined

FIREPLACE in our town house was made from balsa wood cut to the above dimensions. Brick paper was glued to the wood (don't forget the inside) with rubber cement. Try your own design if you wish.

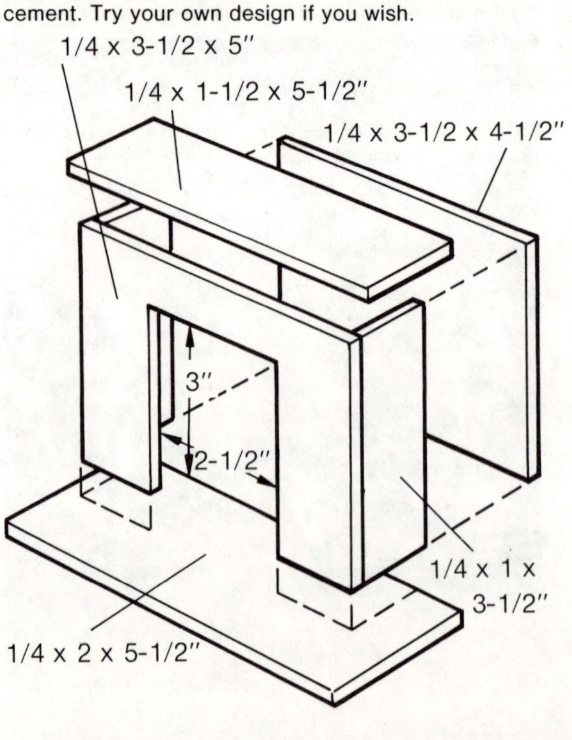

with white glue and decorated with narrow molding.

■ Chandeliers: Crystal chandeliers can be made from tiny beads glued or wired together.

■ Curtains: The curtains for our houses were cut from material that doesn't ravel, gathered at the top and tied back with bits of yarn. You can glue them to the house.

■ Floor coverings: Magazine illustrations of carpet and parquet can be glued to the wood floor, then lightly varnished.

■ Food: Modeling clay painted with enamel and varnished makes delectable pastries, vegetables, fruit and breads. Or use bits of wax crayons to make fruit.

■ Stairs: Precut stringers of thin hardwood to which you can glue treads and risers are available.

continued

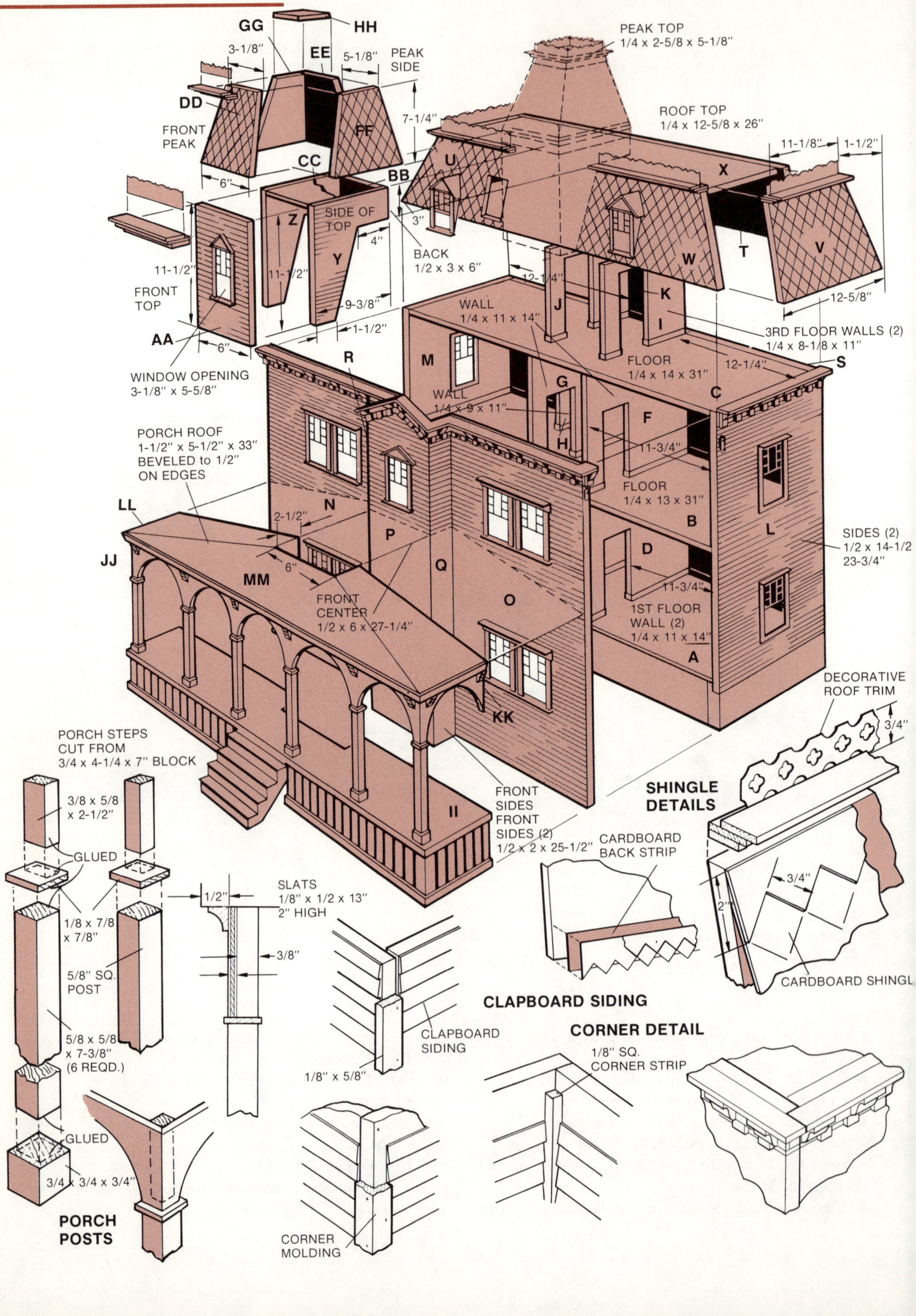
GG
HH
EE
3-1/8"
5-1/8"
PEAK
SIDE
PEAK TOP
1/4 x 2-5/8 x 5-1/8"
DD
FRONT
PEAK
FF
7-1/4"
ROOF TOP
1/4 x 12-5/8 x 26"
11-1/8"
1-1/2"
CC
6"
BB
U
X
SIDE OF
TOP
Z
3"
4"
BACK
1/2 x 3 x 6"
T
V
W
Y
11-1/2"
11-1/2"
FRONT
TOP
9-3/8"
12-1/4"
K
J
12-5/8"
WALL
1/4 x 11 x 14"
I
3RD FLOOR WALLS (2)
1/4 x 8-1/8 x 11"
AA
6"
1-1/2"
M
FLOOR
1/4 x 14 x 31"
12-1/4"
S
R
WINDOW OPENING
3-1/8" x 5-5/8"
G
WALL
1/4 x 9 x 11"
C
F
H
PORCH ROOF
1-1/2" x 5-1/2" x 33"
BEVELED to 1/2"
ON EDGES
11-3/4"
FLOOR
1/4 x 13 x 31"
LL
N
2-1/2"
B
JJ
P
L
SIDES (2)
1/2 x 14-1/2
23-3/4"
6"
D
MM
Q
11-3/4"
FRONT
CENTER
1/2 x 6 x 27-1/4"
O
1ST FLOOR
WALL (2)
1/4 x 11 x 14"
A
DECORATIVE
ROOF TRIM
3/4"
KK
PORCH STEPS
CUT FROM
3/4 x 4-1/4 x 7" BLOCK
SHINGLE
DETAILS
3/8 x 5/8
x 2-1/2"
FRONT
SIDES
FRONT
SIDES (2)
1/2 x 2 x 25-1/2"
II
GLUED
CARDBOARD
BACK STRIP
1/2"
SLATS
1/8" x 1/2 x 13"
2" HIGH
3/4"
1/8 x 7/8
x 7/8"
2"
3/8"
5/8" SQ.
POST
CARDBOARD SHINGL
CLAPBOARD SIDING
5/8 x 5/8
x 7-3/8"
(6 REQD.)
CLAPBOARD
SIDING
CORNER DETAIL
1/8" x 5/8"
1/8" SQ.
CORNER STRIP
GLUED
3/4 x 3/4 x 3/4"
PORCH
POSTS
CORNER
MOLDING

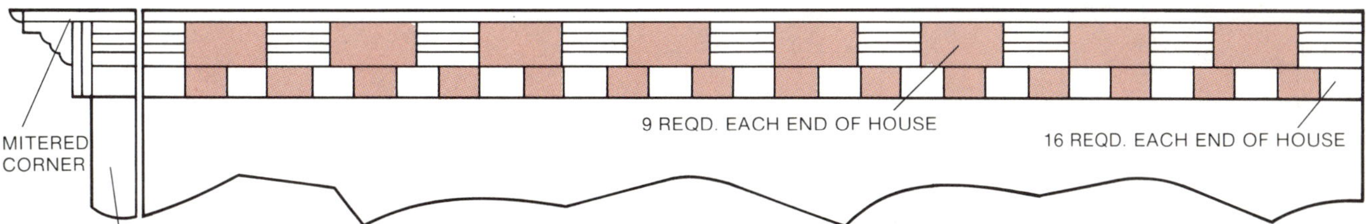

ROOF MOLDING LAYOUT

DECORATIVE MOLDING AND TRIM DETAIL

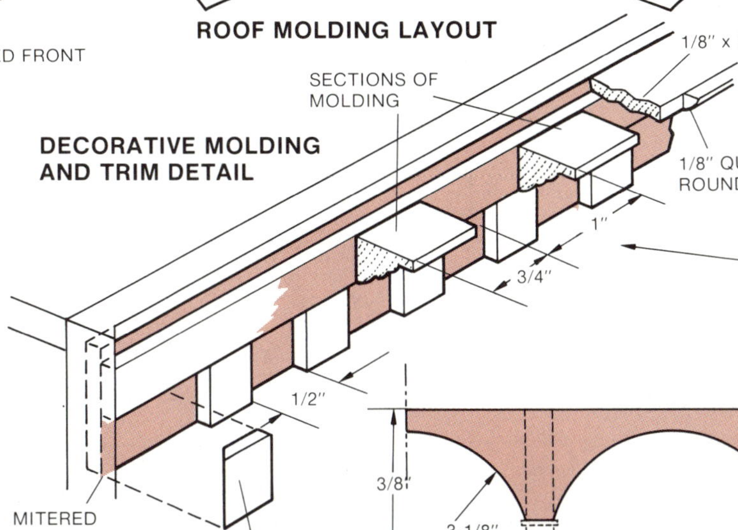

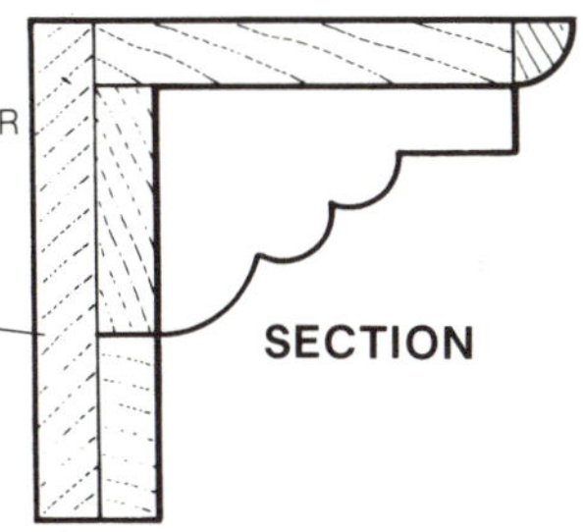

SECTION

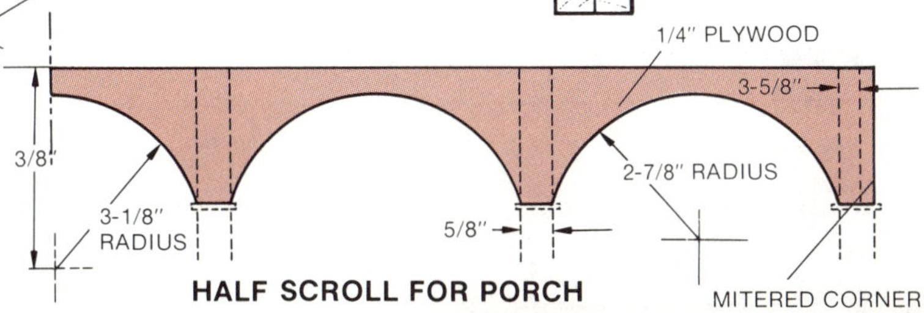

HALF SCROLL FOR PORCH

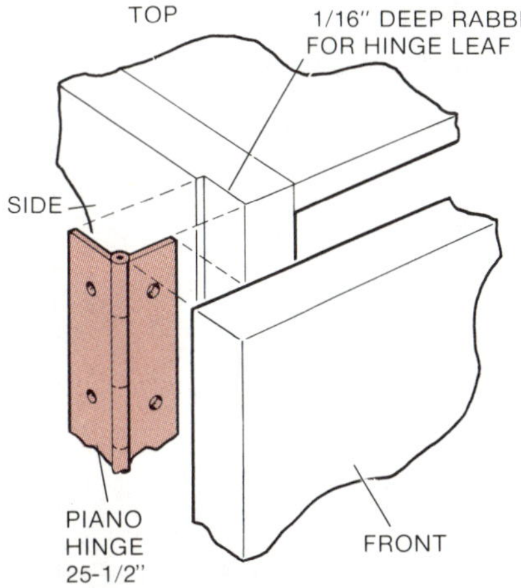

HINGE DETAIL

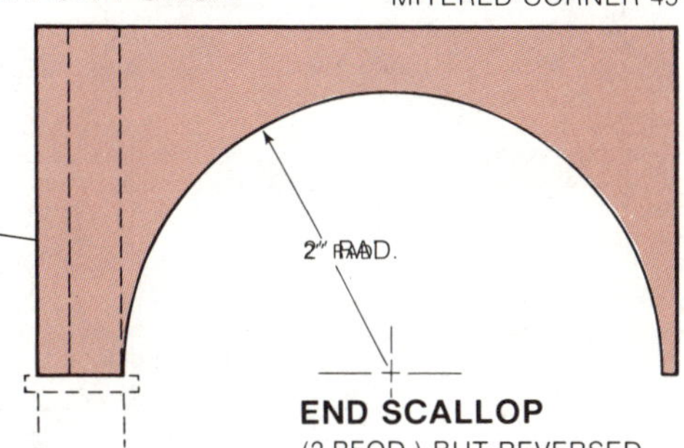

END SCALLOP
(2 REQD.) BUT REVERSED

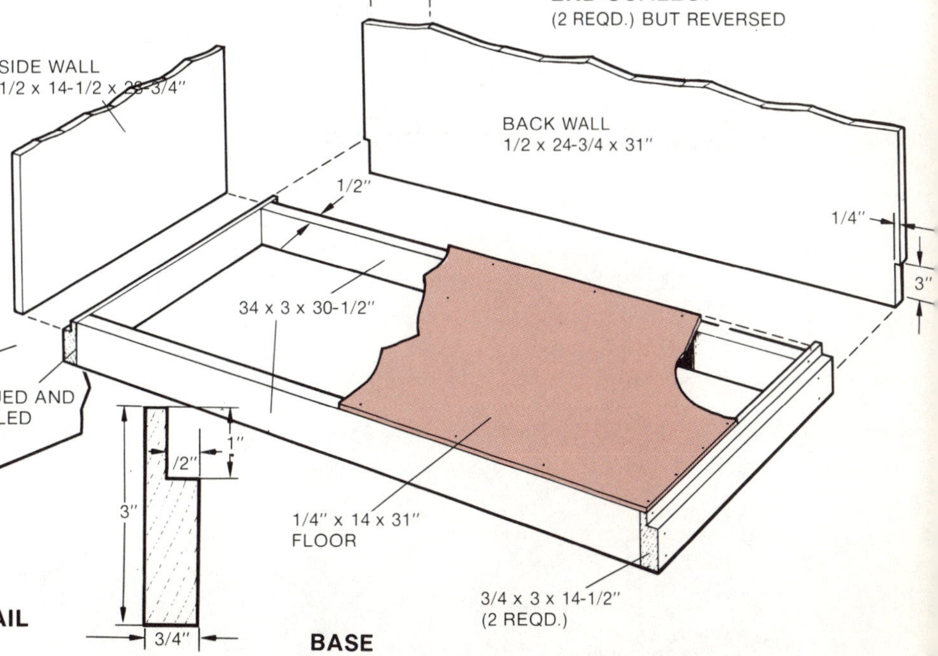

BASE

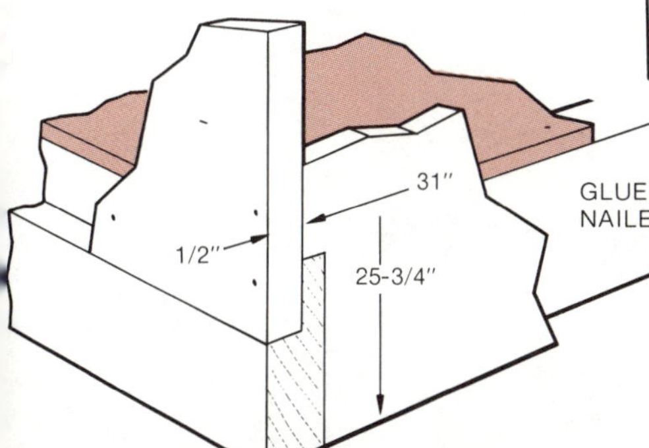

REAR CORNER DETAIL

continued

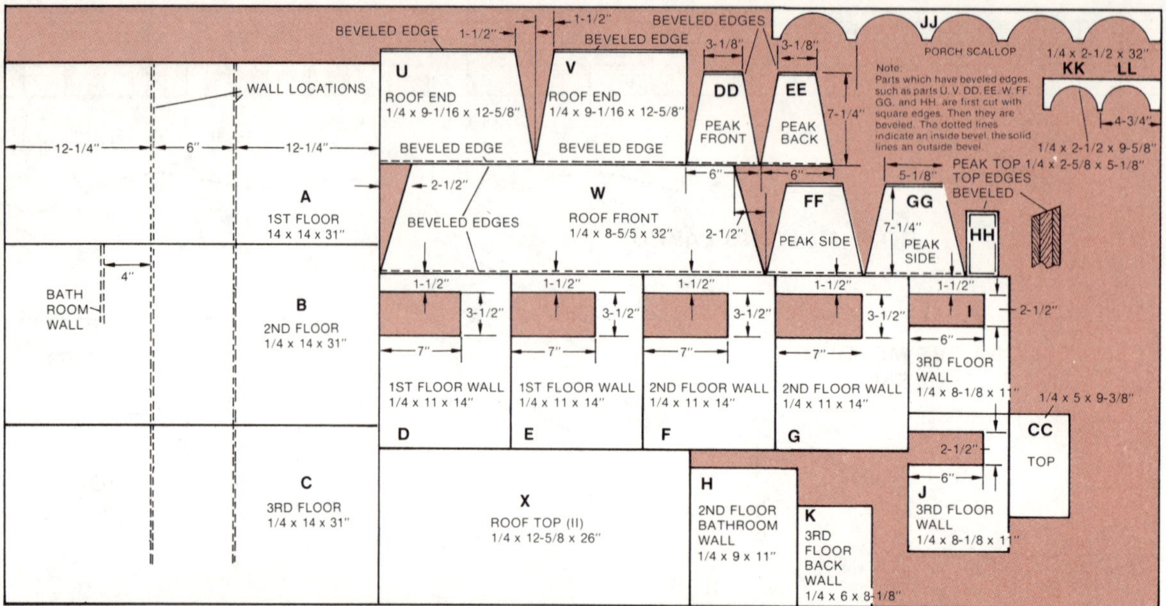

1/4" PLYWOOD, GOOD BOTH SIDES. ONE SHEET REQUIRED.

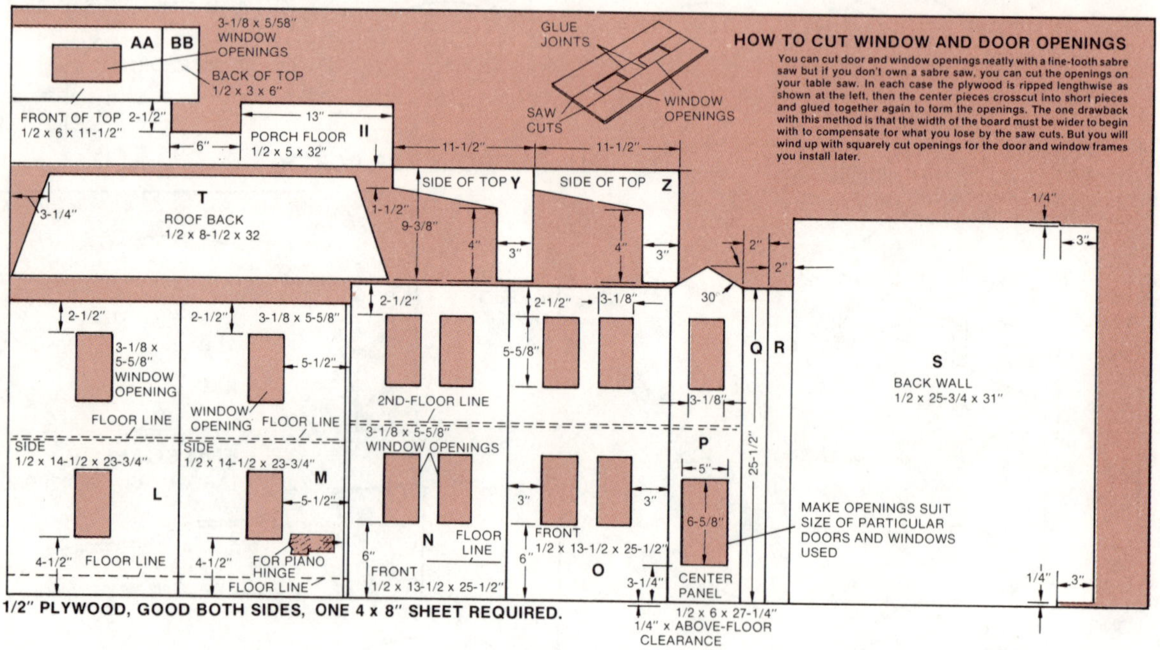

HOW TO CUT WINDOW AND DOOR OPENINGS

You can cut door and window openings neatly with a fine-tooth sabre saw but if you don't own a sabre saw, you can cut the openings on your table saw. In each case the plywood is ripped lengthwise as shown at the left, then the center pieces crosscut into short pieces and glued together again to form the openings. The one drawback with this method is that the width of the board must be wider to begin with to compensate for what you lose by the saw cuts. But you will wind up with squarely cut openings for the door and window frames you install later.

1/2" PLYWOOD, GOOD BOTH SIDES, ONE 4 x 8" SHEET REQUIRED.

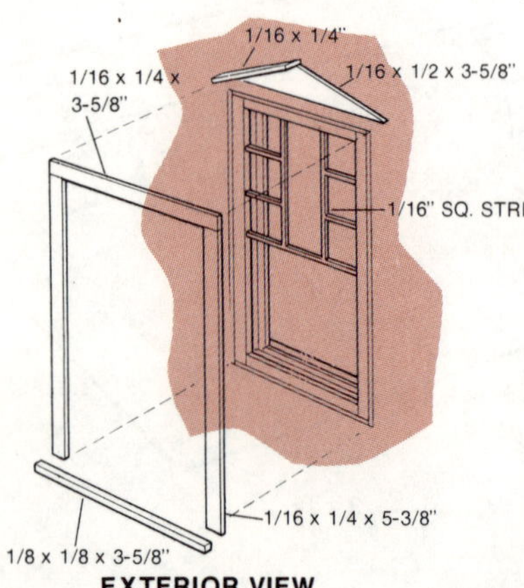

EXTERIOR VIEW

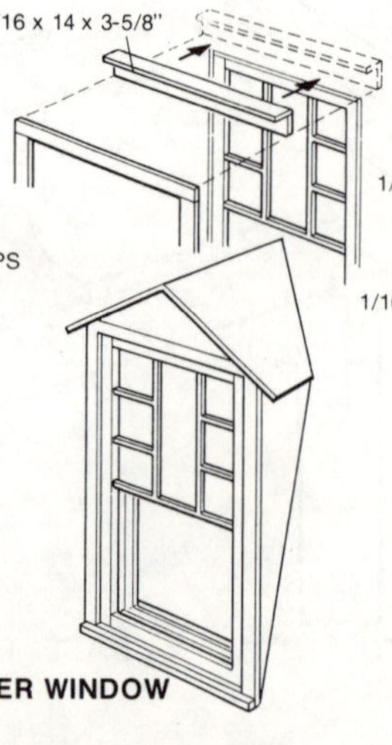

DORMER WINDOW

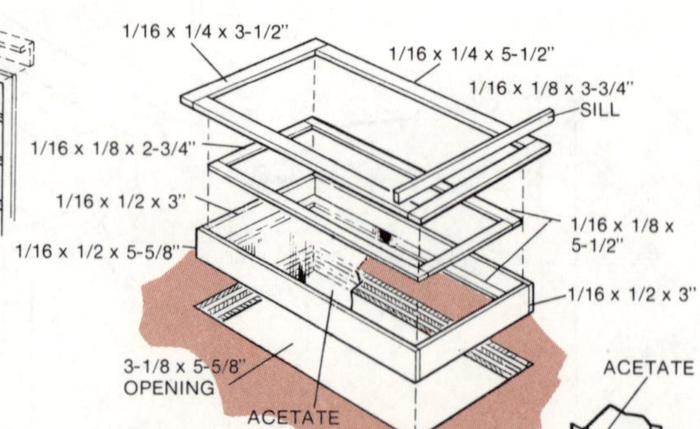

INTERIOR VIEW

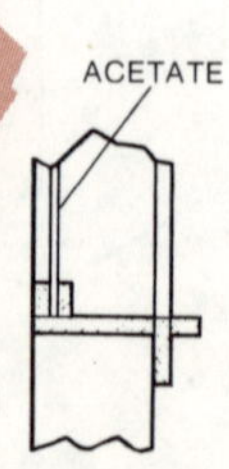

SECTION

WHEN USING A DISC SANDER on a painted floor, I found the paper became so paint clogged before it was worn it was no longer effective. By using paint remover and cleaning off softened paint I got more mileage.—*B. W. Ervin, Kent, OH.*

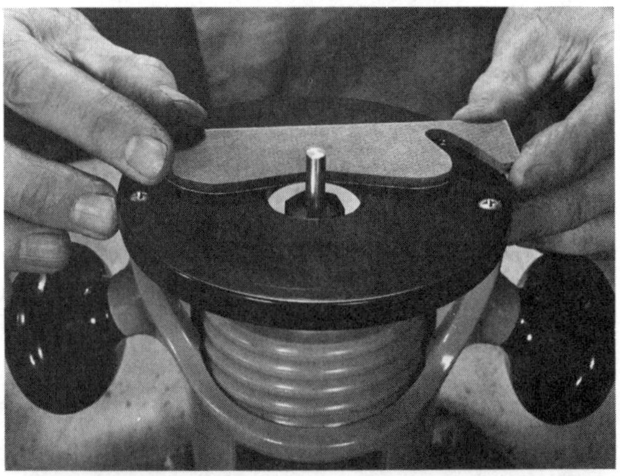

BY CLAMPING A ROUTER upside down, you can use it as a stationary tool to burnish scroll workpieces. Insert a short length of ¼-in. steel rod in the collet, tighten and feed the work against the spinning rod.—*Walter E. Burton, Akron, OH.*

WHEN END-DRILLING some hardwood dowels in a lathe, I found the small drill bit tended to wander off center. After inserting the bit deeply into the chuck, I was able to drill the axial holes accurately.—*W. B. May, Oak Park, IL.*

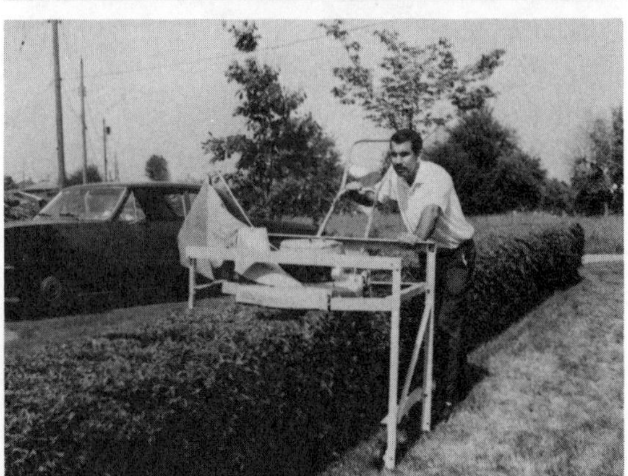

BY BUILDING the rolling gantry , left , I reduced my hedge-trimming time from eight to two hours. The rig, a welded angle-iron frame, supports my rotary mower. The ground on which the setup rolls must be level to produce a neat cut.—*Louis P. Bruno, Cheswick, PA.*

Modernize your old minibike

By DOUG RICHMOND

A new motorcycle engine can turn that worn-out, garden-variety machine into the hottest bike in the neighborhood!

THERE ARE COUNTLESS MINIBIKES sitting in basements and garages because of wornout engines or power trains. These bikes are equipped with industrial-type power plants and torque-converter transmissions. They've caused so many problems that they're regarded as more trouble than they're worth.

Most of these old minibikes have perfectly usable chassis, and would require only new engines with motorcycle-type transmissions to turn them into exciting "new" machines. The problem with doing this has been in the mounting: Motorcycle engines are specifically designed to be installed in a given chassis, and putting one in a different frame can be well-nigh impossible. However, Pacific Basin Trading Co. (the Hodaka people) produces the Fuji "Phoenix," an engine designed with a universal-mounting system.

I bought a Phoenix F480, an 80-cc engine with a four-speed transmission, added a Taylor Products Model 800 muffler and installed them in a Bonanza chassis. Total installation time was about eight man-and-boy hours. Although there is an almost infinite variety of minibike designs, this chassis is pretty much typical of the platform-frame bikes.

With two-cycle engines such as the Phoenix, maximum power is obtained by means of an expansion chamber—one of the finest noise generators devised by the mind of man! In this installation we were primarily interested in a tractable, *quiet* machine, rather than having a super-fast, noisy one.

SEE ALSO

Bicycles . . . Engines, small . . . Motorcycles . . . Tune-up, bicycle

ENGINE THAT ADAPTS easily to platform-frame minibikes is the Phoenix F480 from Hodaka. The 80-cc two-stroke is complete with four-speed transmission and is compactly packaged. All you do is add a muffler and exhaust system and route it appropriately for your machine. The F480 engine can be obtained from your local Hodaka dealer or distributor. For the one nearest you, write to Hodaka Motorcycles, Box PM-327, Athena, Ore. 97813.

REMOVE OLD ENGINE from the minibike frame. At far left, the torque converter is being readied for removal. After all hardware is loosened and taken off, pull the unit off (left). Clean up the frame and possibly paint it before mounting the new engine.

ENGINE MOUNTS are shaped on a grinder (left) as necessary before you install the new engine. Align the new mill before tightening it in place: With rear wheel centered in the frame, align the sprockets. Check chain clearance with a straightedge or yardstick as shown at far left. Allow at least ¾-inch clearance between the drive chain and swing-arm cross member.

ENGINE MOUNTS (shown at right) should have all edges rounded. Note double-nutted mounting bolt. Engine mounting bolts should be double-nutted or secured with Loc-tite.

IN-LINE FUEL FILTER (far right) should be used with all mini-bikes since bikes are usually refueled from cans, often under undesirable conditions.

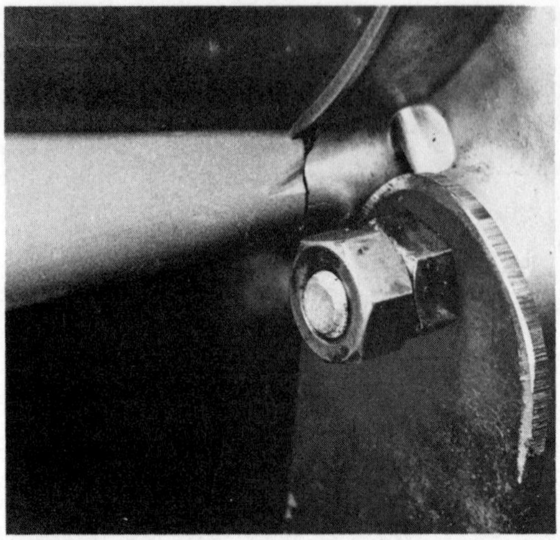

EXHAUST PIPE was fashioned from flexible steel tubing (right). Always run the exhaust tubing along the top of the frame, never underneath it where it would be damaged easily.

REPAIR LINKS often fail because they're installed dry. At far right, master link is lubricated with a Teflon-moly compound before the chain is installed.

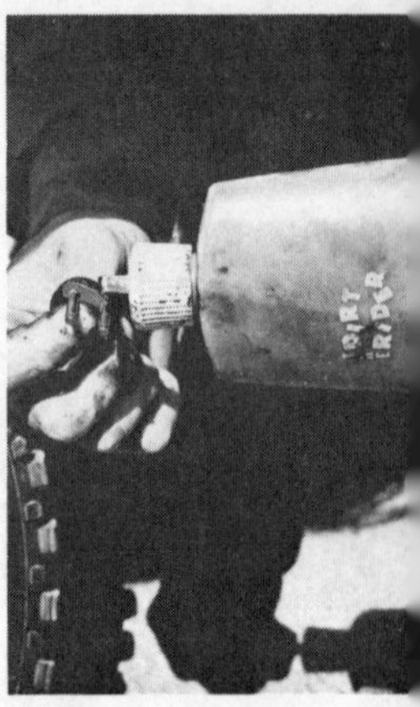

OLD JACKSHAFT can be left on the minibike, but if there's a possibility it may be used again, knock it out with a soft hammer, as shown at right.

CONVERSION COMPLETE, minibike is ready to ride. Note that the 0.4-gallon fuel tank is secured to the frame with silver duct tape, a practice common in motorcycle racing.

If you do the job, the toughest part will be with the exhaust pipe. The average automotive muffler shop is unable to cope with the 1¼-inch inside diameter pipe. We solved that by using flexible-steel exhaust tubing, obtainable at industrial-equipment outlets and better auto parts houses. Its only disadvantage is that it is not oil-tight and rather messy, although it seals itself fairly well after use.

Most minibikes had jackshafts in a crossover configuration, that is, power input on one side—usually the left—and output to the rear sprocket was on the other. When installing a Phoenix, every effort should be made to eliminate the jackshaft as a power-waster and maintenance headache. Usually the rear wheel can be turned around and the sprocket installed on the left side.

You can put the brake mechanism on the left, or just eliminate the rear brake. I prefer the latter and accomplish rear-wheel braking by downshifting the engine.

Paint failure

Why does paint fail earlier on the south and west sides of my house?—S.M., Iowa.

What you describe is not so much paint "failure" as ordinary day-to-day exposure to the elements. Paint on all houses, in any clime, will always have a shorter life on the sides exposed to the sun. If you take a good look at your roof, you will find the same holds true for asphalt shingles. If you are trying to cut down on the painting chore, your best bets are to use a high-quality paint and to give some thought to applying an extra coat to the south and west walls.

Paint-stained concrete

I accidentally spilled about a pint of green paint on the concrete floor of my breezeway. Of course, I mopped it up but that green stain won't come off. What to do?—E.H., Tenn.

A wash-off type of paint remover just might do it. Here you have to watch the remover closely after applying it to see that it does not evaporate to the point where it won't wash off readily. After rinsing with clean water you may need a second and possibly a third application.

Or, you can make a thin paste by adding trisodium phosphate (about a double handful to the gallon of water), spread and cover with a cloth. Scrub away just before the stuff dries completely and rinse thoroughly.

As another alternative, you might use a wire brush or masonry abrasive disc chucked in your electric drill.

Concrete floor slant

I'm replacing a wooden porch floor with concrete and disagree with my contractor when he says ½-in. pitch, or slant, of the floor, will be sufficient for drainage. I think it should be at least 1¼ in. Who's right?—O.T., Mass.

Standard pitch for water runoff is ¼ in. per running foot. Thus, if your porch is 8 ft. wide, the high end—at the house—should be about 2 in. higher than the outboard edge. If your personal taste rules out this much pitch, I would not recommend a pitch of less than 1 in. For your peace of mind, "positive" water run-off is a must.

Don't shake that varnish!

Recently I was told never to shake a can containing varnish, but my informant did not know why. There must be a reason. What is it?—Y.M., Wash.

In a can containing varnish from which some of the contents have been used, air is entrapped when you replace the lid. If you shake the can prior to use, tiny air bubbles will form in the varnish and these will be picked up by the brush and laid on the surface being finished. As the varnish dries these form tiny flecks you can feel when you pass a finger over the surface. Always stir—never shake—varnish.

'Splicing' carpet

My carpet dealer says that my room and a small, narrow hallway are too wide for one standard width of carpet and too narrow for the next larger width; and that he can save me money by splicing on a strip to the required size. Can he make an invisible or nearly invisible splice? He insists he can but I'm doubtful.—Benjamin Ord, Alton, Ill.

Experienced carpet installers can splice, or patch, wall-to-wall carpeting in looped, sheared or shag texture so skillfully that you'd never guess it had been done. I would assume the dealer is thinking about a saving of waste material as well as money.

The floor over which the carpet is to be laid should be in good condition, and you should insist that your dealer renail the floor all over to catch any developing squeaks while you have the chance. I'm also assuming that the left-over strip from the room is to be used to patch out the carpeting in the hallway.

Paint peeling from concrete

Poured-concrete foundation walls of my 10-year-old home were originally painted above ground. Last year I repainted them with latex. This has peeled off in large sheets from ground level to top of the concrete, leaving the original paint. Can you tell me why, and advise what I should do?—John Rutherford, Washington, D.C.

The original coat must have been an oil-based exterior paint. Latex-based paints do not always bond solidly to the smooth oil-paint surface. If the original coating is still in relatively good condition, adhering solidly to the concrete, I suggest that you scrape off all loose material with a wire brush, wash and rinse the surface, let it dry thoroughly and apply an oil-based masonry paint. If you want to use latex instead, prepare the surface by removing as much loose material as possible with the wire brush, then applying a surface conditioner such as Glidden's Y-40 Spred Spar Varnish mixed with naphtha or mineral spirits (follow directions appearing on the can) before painting. Sandblasting is an (expensive) alternative.

ANTIQUE buffs will welcome the opportunity of reproducing the his- and-her mirrors of Abraham and Mary Lincoln. Through the courtesy of the Illinois State Historical Library in Springfield, we are able to show you how to reproduce these personal mirrors that were used in the Lincoln's Springfield home.

CUT OUT uprights with bandsaw or jig-saw. Shape with spokeshave and rasp.

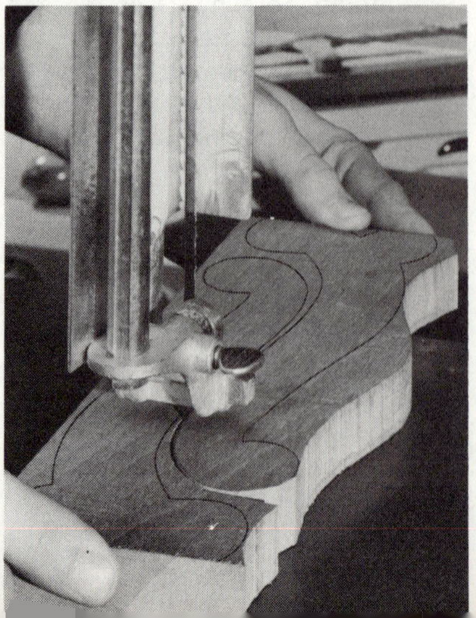

SEE ALSO

Antique reproductions . . . Butler's tables . . . Clocks . . . Comb boxes . . . Desks . . . Gifts, Christmas . . . Letter racks

Two mirrors: authentic Lincoln reproductions

PM received permission for our craftsman to measure two mirrors from the Lincoln Springfield house: Abraham's shaving mirror and Mary's vanity mirror. We've drawn the plans so you can build accurate reproductions out of mahogany or some other fine hardwood

By DAVID WARREN

THESE HOMEMADE reproductions will reward their present-day creators with a sense of the past that is often missing from spiritless, manufactured reproductions. The original bureau mirrors represented here were used in the Lincolns' Springfield, IL, home.

FACE FRONT edge of shaving mirror base with veneer cut so grain runs vertically. Leave 1/16-in. excess on each edge, apply glue, and sand flush.

When the President-elect and his wife, Mary, were preparing to move to Washington in 1861, Mr. Lincoln gave his shaving mirror to his family's seamstress as a memento for her service. She gave it to her niece, who in turn gave it to her brother. It was then sold to its present owner, the Illinois State Historical Library. Mary Lincoln's niece inherited the vanity mirror and later willed it to the same library.

MATERIALS LIST—SHAVING MIRROR

Pcs.	Size (Use)
1	1 1/8 x 6 7/8 x 14 in. (Base)
1	3/4 x 6 x 8 3/4 in. (Uprights)
1	3/8 x 3/4 x 50 in. (Frame)
1	1/4 x 1-1/32 x 40 in. (Molding)
1	1/4 x 1/2 x 50 in. (Back strips)
1	1/2 x 10 x 12 1/4 in. (Filler panel)
1	3 sq. ft. (Veneer, plain striped)
2	1 3/4 x 1 3/4 x 8 in. (Feet)
2	1 1/4 x 1 1/4 x 3 in. (Knobs)

Misc.—1/4-in.-dia. x 4-in. dowel, 3/8-in.-dia. x 4-in. dowel, 2 wood washers (use scraps), 2 2-in. No. 8 fh wood screws, 1/8-in. mirror cut slightly shy for easy fitting, plastic resin glue, contact cement, mahogany stain (or lye), orange shellac, linseed oil.

WOOD screw on knob is threaded with woodcutting die, holds mirror at angle.

UPRIGHTS are glued, doweled and screwed to base.

CAUL, hollowed with rounding plane, will insure tight bond of veneer.

Your reproduction will also become a coveted heirloom—and would make a fine gift for someone right now.

Both projects are constructed of Honduras mahogany, which is available by mail from Craftsman's Wood Service, 1735 W. Cortland Ct., Addison, IL 60101, and other wood supply companies.

building the shaving mirror

Begin construction by sanding out any jointer marks on the upper surface of the base stock. Draw the serpentine front using the scaled-down grid in plans and cut with a bandsaw. Smooth concave curves with a drum sander and convex ones with a disc sander or Sand-O-Flex.

Next, cut a veneer strip for the front edge (see photo). If 15-in.-wide veneer isn't available, use two pieces. To do so, select a pleasing grain pattern for a centered butt joint. Then overlap the two strips and cut through both at the point selected to get a joint that butts perfectly. Use contact cement to fasten veneer to the serpentine front. Sand edges of veneer flush, stroking sandpaper toward the base to avoid splintering the veneer.

For all other glued joints, use plastic resin. Plastic resin oozings will accept stain reasonably well if they are wiped clean with a hot, damp cloth before the glue sets.

Now, lay out two uprights on ¾-in. stock and cut out as shown. Shape and smooth the sides and edges. To join uprights to the base, bore ⅜-

MATERIALS LIST—VANITY MIRROR

Pcs.	Size (Use)
1	⅜ x 6⅛ x 6⅝ in. (Case bottom)
1	⅜ x 6⅜ x 6¾ in. (Case top)
2	⅜ x 2⅝ x 5⅞ in. (Case sides)
1	⅜ x 2⅝ x 5⅜ in. (Case back)
1	1¼ x 1-5/16 x 6¼ in. (Case front)
1	¼ x 5¾ x 6¼ in. (Compartment bottom)
1	⅝ x ⅝ x 25 in. (Mirror frame)
1	3/32 x 3⅝ x 5⅝ in. (Backing)
2	1¼ x 1¼ x 6 in. (Uprights)
1	1 x 1 x 6 in. (Feet)
1	1¼ x 1-5/16 x 5-5/16 in. (Drawer front)
2	⅜ x 1-5/16 x 5¼ in. (Drawer sides)
1	⅜ x ⅞ x 4-9/16 in. (Drawer back)
1	¼ x 4-15/16 x 5⅞ in. (Drawer bottom)

Misc.—2⅜ x 1-in. brass hinges, 1⅜-in.-dia. brass pull, 2 1-in. No. 5 rh brass wood screws, ⅛-in. mirror cut to fit, plastic resin glue, white glue, mahogany stain (or lye), orange shellac, linseed oil, 10 x 10-in. piece of green felt.

ABRAHAM LINCOLN'S SHAVING MIRROR

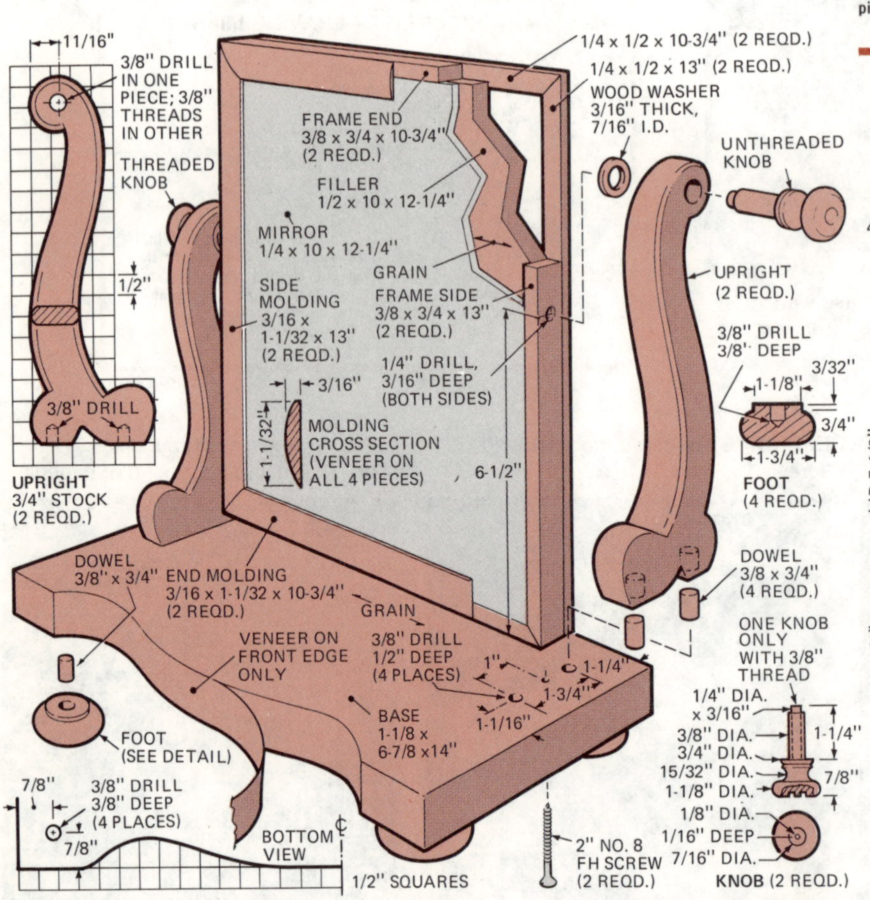

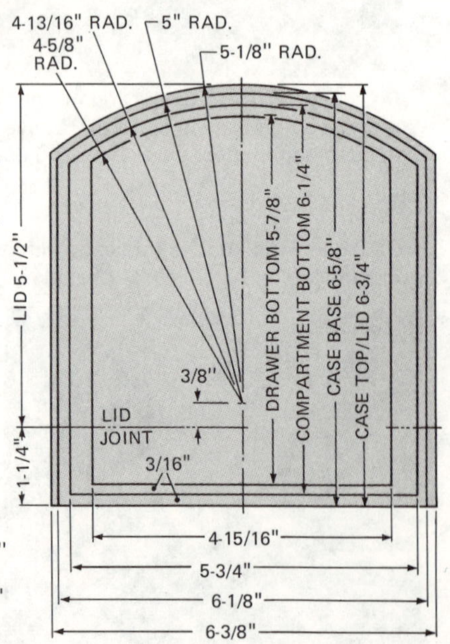

RADII DETAIL

MARY TODD LINCOLN'S VANITY MIRROR

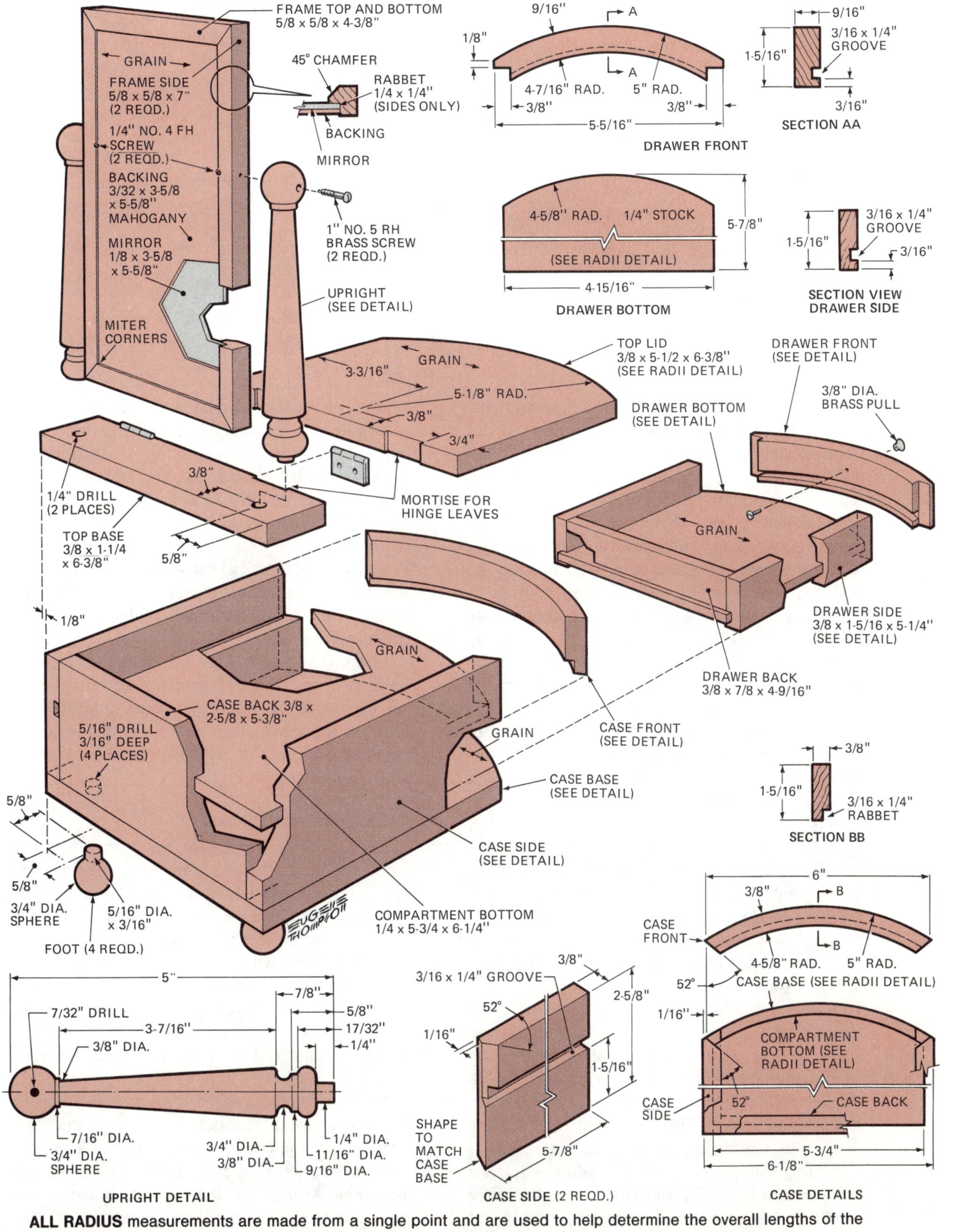

ALL RADIUS measurements are made from a single point and are used to help determine the overall lengths of the rounded components and to insure a consistent curve. Use the radii detail shown on the opposite page.

ASSEMBLE cabinet with resin glue and brads. Clamp, let dry overnight.

NEXT, use disc sander to remove saw marks, smooth curved cabinet front.

in. blind dowel holes in top of the base and corresponding holes in bottom of the uprights. Cut four dowels to fit. Bore 5/32-in. shank holes through the base. Assemble uprights dry and mark corresponding pilot holes in bottoms of the uprights with a nail. Then bore 7/64-in. pilot holes in uprights. Glue and screw uprights to base. Complete base/upright assembly by turning the four feet and fastening them with dowel pegs.

To accommodate angle-adjusting knobs, bore 3/8-in. pivot hole in right upright. Bore a 5/16-in. hole in the left upright and tap with a 3/8-in. wood-cutting tap. Cut 3/8-in. threads on the end of the left knob. (After you start threads, you must remove the cone-shaped front guide in order to cut threads to the base of the knob.) If it is impractical to obtain woodcutting taps and dies, a good alternative is to use a tight friction fit at pivots.

Construct the mirror frame by cutting stock to length, mitering corners and gluing them together with picture-frame corner clamps. Cut backing board to the same size as the opening in the mirror frame. Make 1/4x1/2-in. strips to hold mirror and backing in the frame, and miter these corners, too.

Form a molding for the frame by shaping strips with a flat-soled jack plane as indicated in cross section. Sand smooth. This operation requires that molding strips be temporarily reinforced with 3/4x1-in. scrap before clamping between bench dogs. Hold scrap to the molding with 7/8-in. brads nailed up through the scrap.

Gluing veneer to the frame molding requires a caul formed from a scrap 2x4 to accept the curve of the molding face. (See photo, page 1840.) Cut the veneer strips slightly oversize with the grain running in the short direction. Then apply plastic resin glue to a dampened veneer. Bend the veneer over the molding by clamping a sandwich of caul, wax paper, veneer, molding and cover with a flat 2x4. Let this dry 24 hours before removing clamps. Sand veneer with the grain using 150-grit paper and miter four veneered pieces to length. (The veneer is fragile at the point of the miter. To lessen its tendency to splinter, saw it on the pull stroke or use a miter-trimmer.) Glue molding to the frame.

Insert the mirror into the frame and place backing board over it. Fasten mitered strips over the backing with 1/2-in. brads. Finally, drill 1/4-in. holes in the mirror frame and mount the frame between the uprights with two wooden washers and knobs as shown.

building the vanity mirror

Begin construction of the case by cutting the sides and back. Note that the angle of the edge where the sides and front join is 52°. Groove the sides for the compartment bottom. Cut the curved front piece with a bandsaw and smooth the inside curve with a drum sander. Next, rout a rabbet on the bottom inside edge of the front piece. To do this, clamp parallel fences of scrap wood on the drill-press table. Chuck a 1/4-in. router bit and feed the piece through, removing about 1/16 in. of stock with each pass.

Cut out top/lid and base pieces according to the drawing and radii detail. To assure matched graining on top, cut the two pieces as one, allowing for thickness of the saw kerf. Then rip off the back end. Mortise for the butt hinge leaves and assemble the top. Cut out the compartment bottom (see radii detail).

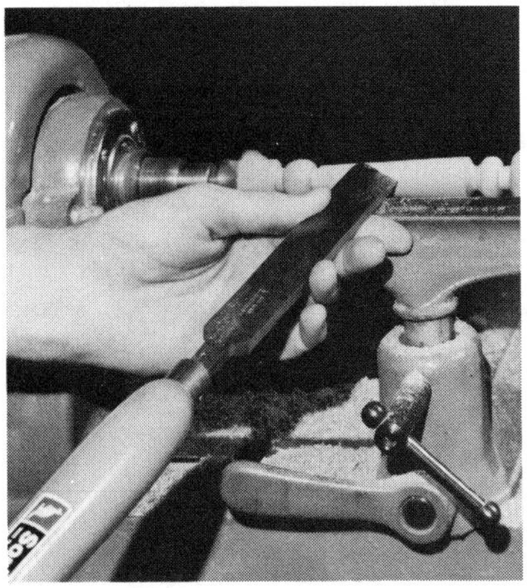

SLIGHT variations in lathe-turned parts can be expected.

HAND PLANE chamfer on edge of wide board. Then rip ⅝-in. molding for frame.

TENONS on feet should be a push fit. Be sure they sit flush before gluing.

After all pieces have been cut and sanded (except the upper front, which may be left rough-sawn), assemble the cabinet with glue and ½-in. finishing brads. Clamp and let dry overnight.

making the drawer

To make the drawer, first cut out sides, back and front. Use a bandsaw to cut the front, making it just over 9/16 in. thick to allow for sanding. Smooth the inside curve with a drum sander. Next, rout a groove in the front on a drill press the same way you routed the rabbet in the cabinet front. Then rout grooves in sides of the drawer so the bottom can be fitted.

When laying out the drawer bottom, let it protrude from the back to act as a drawer stop. Plane it down later for the final fit. Chamfer all edges of the drawer bottom about 1/16 in. so it will fit snugly into the 3/16-in. grooves. Glue the drawer together; check it for squareness and let it dry overnight.

When the cabinet is glued, and the drawer fitted, smooth the front curve of the vanity on a disc sander until saw marks are removed and all elements are flush. Paper wedges inserted on either side of the drawer will hold it tightly in its opening while you're sanding. Turn two uprights and four feet on your lathe following specifications in the drawing. After sanding, burnish all turnings with wood shavings held against the revolving work. Bore 7/32-in. screw holes in the top sphere of each upright for mounting the mirror.

Make the mirror frame molding as shown in photo and cut rabbet for mirror and backing. Miter corners of the molding to length and assemble with glue. Install the mirror and cover it with 3/32-in. backing. Hold backing with ¾-in. finishing brads or screw wedges as shown. To complete the assembly, mark and bore holes in the bottom for feet and in the top for uprights. Glue feet and top base in place. Then glue uprights to the top. Hold mirror in place between the glued uprights while they dry. After they are dry, mark location of screw-hole locations on the mirror frame, bore the holes and install screws.

Apply the finish except for the inside compartment. (See next section.) Then line the jewelry compartment with green felt. Cut the felt sides to the 1/16 in. below the upper edge. Hold the felt in place with white glue applied sparingly to complete your reproduction.

finishing the mirrors

Seal all exposed end grain with oil and stain the pieces a traditional mahogany color. A typical mid-Victorian way to stain mahogany is to brush on a lye solution (about one part lye to four parts water). Wait about 10 minutes, or until you reach the shade of red desired. (The stronger the lye solution and the longer it is left on, the darker it gets.) Then wash off the lye solution with clear water. If the red shade is too deep, wash it with vinegar in order to neturalize the lye and reduce the redness.

(*Caution:* Use extreme care when you're working with lye. Wear safety goggles and gloves, and wash up carefully afterward.)

When the finish is dry, sand it lightly with 220-grit sandpaper, then use a 4/0 steel wool pad to polish in several coats of a 70/30 solution of orange shellac and linseed oil. When this is dry, buff on carnauba wax. In due time, the natural oxidation will impart the fine patina on the originals.

TO FIND CAUSE of engine misfire, start with the air cleaner; replace if dirty and clogged.

Tracking down engine misfire

By MORT SCHULTZ

■ "WHERE DO I START?" That's a question do-it-yourself—and even professional—mechanics ask themselves when faced with troubleshooting engine misfire.

You start by defining misfire, putting the problem in perspective so it doesn't seem overwhelming.

Engine misfire occurs when the fuel charge in one or more cylinders fails to ignite. The condition generally results from lack of spark, a fuel-

SEE ALSO
Autos, maintenance . . . Carburetors, auto . . .
Chokes, auto . . . Dieseling, auto . . .
Engines, auto . . . Fuel systems, auto . . .
Ignition systems, auto . . . Noises, auto engine . . .
Sparkplugs . . . Tune-up, auto

TIME IGNITION SYSTEM. If timing cannot be set, suspect the distributor, assuming that breaker-point dwell is set correctly. You'll need a timing light.

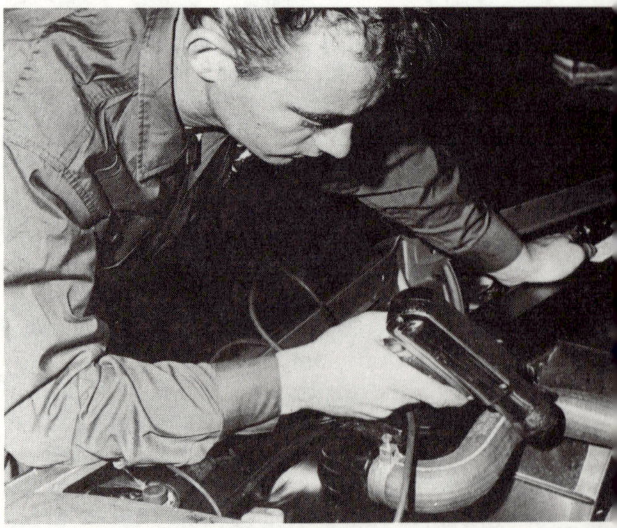

REMOVE SPARKPLUGS. Check wide gap, electrode deposits, worn electrodes or other damage.

REMOVE DISTRIBUTOR. Check carefully for signs of wear on the distributor shaft.

system problem that results in an excessively lean or rich fuel charge, or internal engine damage.

Misfiring wastes gasoline, causes a loss of power and increases exhaust emissions. An engine can misfire at idle or running at lower speeds, at higher cruising speeds (no load), or under load (hard acceleration or a tough pull up a hill).

what causes misfire?

To judge whether an engine is missing, warm it

CHECK FUEL FILTER. Replace if dirty or crimped. The filter is found at the carburetor inlet as indicated by the arrow in the photo below.

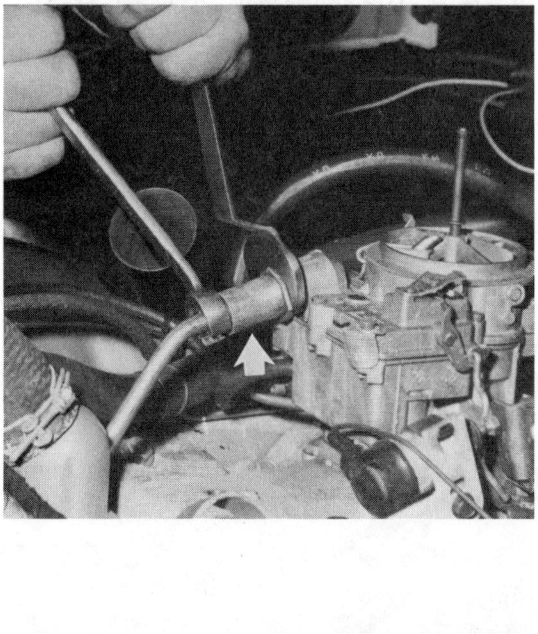

ANOTHER TYPE of fuel filter is found in line between the fuel pump and carburetor. You'll find this on some Ford and most Chrysler and AMC models.

CLEAN CARBURETOR using a product that's commercially available (above, left). If carburetor is dirty, disassembly and complete cleaning are necessary.

up. A cold engine frequently doesn't run smoothly, only because it is cold.

Engine missing makes the car kick or lope every time the affected cylinder (or cylinders) skips a beat. To uncover the reason, check the following in the order given:

1. Remove the carburetor air cleaner and examine the filter element. Replace the filter if dirt-clogged.

2. Examine the choke butterfly plate with the engine warmed up. The plate should be wide open.

If partially closed, free the plate by cleaning choke linkage and applying carburetor cleaning solvent to the plate's pivot points. If the plate doesn't function now, the trouble is a misadjusted choke or a bad part in the choke system.

3. Look down the carburetor barrel and move the throttle lever by hand once or twice. Gasoline should squirt forcefully into the carburetor. If it doesn't, odds are the fuel filter should be replaced.

4. Two types of fuel filters are used. Most GM and some Ford Motor Co. models have the filter positioned inside the carburetor inlet. Most AMC and Chrysler Corp. cars, and other Ford models, have the fuel filter visible in the fuel line between fuel pump and carburetor.

If you're dealing with an internal filter, let the engine cool and place a rag under the fitting to absorb gas that may drip. "Break" the connection, removing the fuel line and retaining nut. Take out the filter (paper or bronze) and the spring behind it.

Replace a paper element. Clean a bronze filter in kerosene or carburetor cleaner.

Install a new or cleaned element, using the old spring, and reattach the fuel line tightly.

If your car uses a visible inline fuel filter, wait for the engine to cool. Using pliers, slide off retainers holding the filter to the fuel line. Pull the filter from place and install a new one.

5. Activate the throttle lever by hand again and see if fuel flow is now strong. If not, the carburetor probably requires cleaning.

To try to avoid a big job, you first attempt to restore the carburetor by using a commercially available carburetor cleaning kit. It contains a can of carburetor cleaning solvent and a tube that attaches to the carburetor inlet.

With the engine running, the cleaner flows into the bowl, through the needle valve seat, through passages and into venturis through jets. If the carburetor isn't too badly clogged, the method should work.

If it fails, you'll have to disassemble the unit, clean it by letting parts sit in a tub of cleaning solvent, install replaceable parts from a rebuild kit which you can buy at an auto parts supply store for your model of carburetor, and make such internal adjustments as float level and accelerator pump stroke.

6. Speaking of carburetor adjustments, it's possible that if your engine-missing problem is occurring at idle it's being caused by an incorrect slow (curb) idle-speed adjustment. Connect a tachometer and get the correct adjustment specification which, if your car is a '68 or later model, is given on a decal in the engine compartment.

If your carburetor is equipped with an idle-stop solenoid, idle speed is adjusted by turning the adjusting nut on the solenoid. If the carburetor has no idle-stop solenoid, the adjusting screw will be found protruding from the carburetor.

7. Missing at idle and slower speeds is frequently caused by vacuum loss around the carburetor-intake manifold joint. Prepare a mixture of one part SAE 20 motor oil and one part kerosene. Pour the mixture into a squirt-type oil can.

With engine running, spread the mixture around the joint. If idle smooths out (the mixture may be pulled into the joint), tighten carburetor mounting bolts and test again. If missing prevails, replace the carburetor mounting gasket.

8. Another cause of engine missing at idle and slower speeds is a vacuum leak in the crankcase ventilation (PCV) system. Start the engine and remove the PCV valve from the rocker arm or valve cover. Hold your thumb tightly over end of the valve. You should feel very strong suction. If suction is weak or doesn't exist, examine PCV hoses for cracks. Replace a bad hose and retest. If vacuum is still weak, replace PCV valve and recheck system.

9. If your car was built in 1973 or thereafter (1972 in California), it probably has an exhaust-gas recirculation (EGR) system. A vacuum leak in this system can cause engine misfire at idle and slow speed.

Essentially, the EGR system has an EGR valve and hoses. Inspect hoses leading from the valve for cracks and loose connections.

Warm up engine and pull off the hose attached to valve's stem. With the engine idling, pinch the hose closed gently with pliers. If missing stops, the trouble is likely a leaky EGR valve diaphragm. Replace valve.

10. Examine each high-tension cable closely (all cables from distributor to sparkplugs and the distributor cap-to-coil tower cable). If insulation is cracked and brittle, replace all cables.

11. Take off the distributor cap, wipe it clean inside and out, and inspect it for cracks. A carbon path along the cap signifies a narrow crack. Replace a cracked cap.

Examine terminals inside the distributor cap for carbon that signifies arcing and the fact that cables weren't seated firmly in the distributor-cap towers. Clean terminals; if they are badly burned, replace the cap.

12. Remove the rotor from the distributor, and inspect it for cracks and an eroded terminal. If the rotor is damaged, you should replace it.

13. Make sure distributor breaker points are properly aligned, with one point meeting the other squarely.

14. Test spring tension of the movable distributor breaker point by attaching a spring scale to its arm and pulling with a smooth motion. The breaker point should part company with the stationary point when the scale reads 17 to 21 ounces. If this requirement is not met, replace points. Weak tension causes point bounce, causing a misfire at higher speeds.

15. Condenser connections should be attached firmly to the breaker points.

16. Button up the distributor and connect a dwellmeter/tachometer. See that distributor point dwell is adjusted to specification (check the decal).

Note: Cars with electronic ignition do not have distributor breaker points, so you guys can forget about checks Nos. 13 through 16.

17. Remove and examine every sparkplug. Fouled, cracked, worn or improperly gapped sparkplugs are a major cause of engine misfire.

18. Test the engine for compression. If you find compression in one or more cylinders about 70-percent lower than that of the highest-reading cylinder, pour some SAE 20 engine oil into the cylinder and test again. If compression does not improve, missing is being caused by defective valve(s) serving the cylinder, such as a weak valve spring or a burned valve. Internal repairs are needed.

19. Reinstall plugs and connect your timing light. See that ignition timing is set to specification.

If you can't set timing properly, the distributor may have a worn shaft or a camshaft lobe may be worn. In any event, you have at last found the cause of missing.

20. If everything to this point checks okay, and the engine misses at higher speeds or under load, suspect that the ignition coil is breaking down under load. You can't test a coil unless you have an ignition-coil tester.

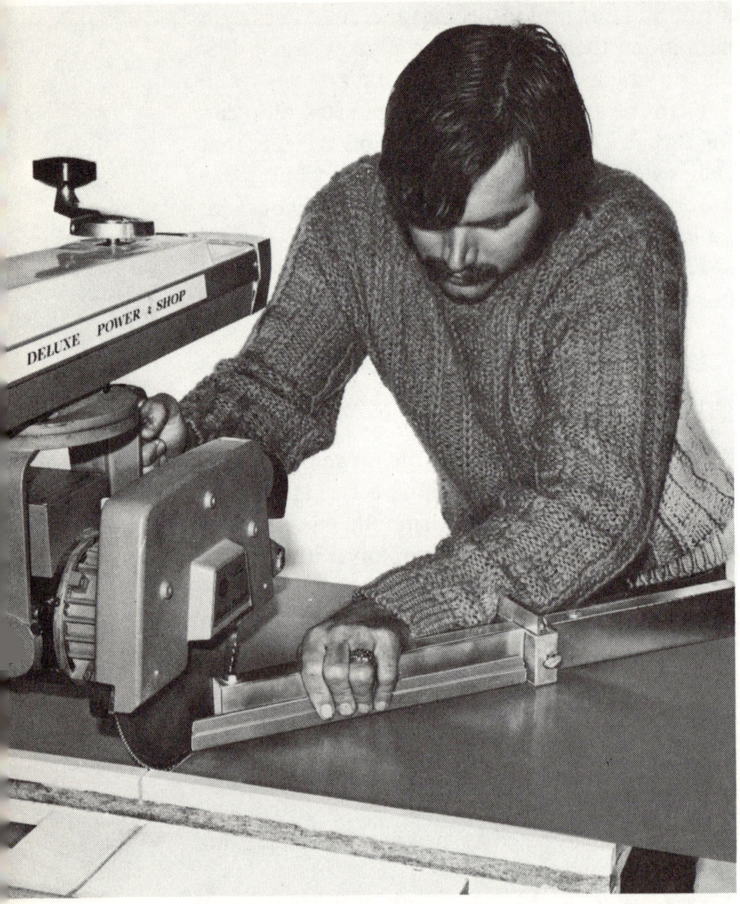

SLIP-ON JIG for radial-arm saw lets you cut miters while leaving the blade set at 90°.

JIG MAKES fast work of many angles including standard 45° miters and 15° and 30° cuts.

FENCE POSITIONS are gauged with arm protractors positioned tightly against flat of the blade.

TWO MITER BOARDS

RADIAL-SAW MITER BOARD

By WILLIAM G. WAGGONER

HERE'S AN auxiliary table with an adjustable fence that lets you cut 15°, 30°, 45°, and 90° angles with the radial-arm saw in the 90° position. Other angle positions can be added to the jig if desired. Cutting may be done from either side of the jig's adjustable fence (E). This enables you to choose the straight, nonrounded side of the work for holding against the fence while making the cut.

Construct the jig as shown in the plans. You may want to add a stop block to the board underside. Locate the block so the miter board will reposition in exactly the same place each time it is used.

The holes bored through the adjustable fence should be made using a drill press or a portable drill in a portable-drill guide. Bore one (pivot hole) near the end of the fence. Bore second hole at a point which falls above miter-board surface in all positions, 0 to 45°.

Next, mark the pivot hole in miter board and align with pivot hole in fence. Using the latter to guide hand-held drill, bore hole in board. Install Teenut at bottom of pivot hole and fasten the miter fence to the board with a bolt.

Clamp fence in each angle position and use the near hole in fence to guide drill through miter board. Counterbore for Teenuts in the board's

SEE ALSO

Angles, compound . . . Dovetail joints . . . Drawers . . . Frames, picture . . . Joinery . . . Miter joints . . . Shop techniques . . . Workbenches . . . Workshops

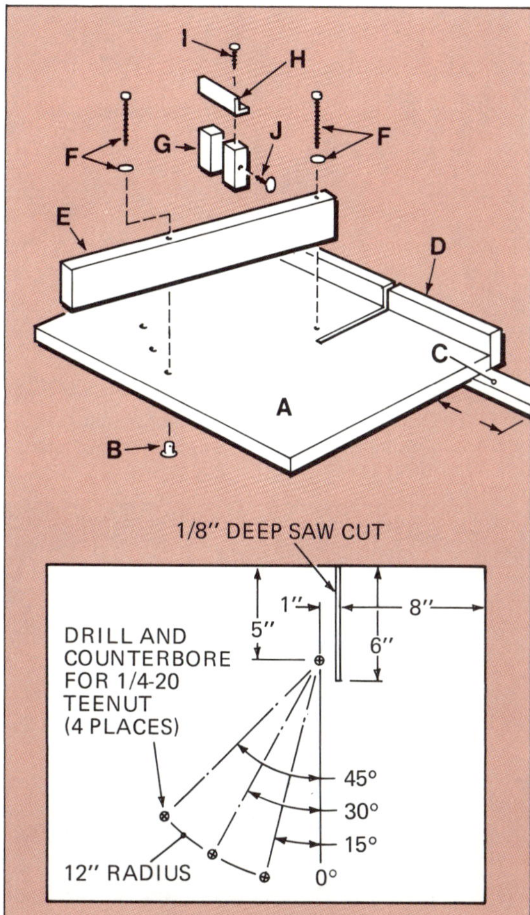

DETAIL OF PART A

underside and then tap them in. Determine the fence angles, using an arm protractor or by using some simple trigonometry. (See text for table-saw jig on next page.)

The guide-fence stop is optional, but handy for production cuts. The thumbscrew acts as a setscrew and will secure the stop in any spot along the fence.

The same jig design can be adapted to your bandsaw. With the bandsaw miter board, however, the board moves with the work into the saw blade. A slide must be fastened to the miter-board underside, so it will ride snugly in the saws's miter groove. The most convenient operating position, in this case, is to stand behind the blade and pull board and workpiece toward you. In this manner, it's easy to see where the blade will enter the workpiece. A drawer pull fastened to the board for righthand use makes the action easy and balanced.

MATERIALS LIST—RADIAL-SAW JIG

Key	No.	Size and description (use)
A	1	¾ × 18 × 24" countertop scrap or plywood (table)
B	4	¼-20 Teenut*
C	1	⅜ × ¾ × 29" or to suit
D	1	¾ × 2¼ × 24" pine (fixed fence)
E	1	5/4 × 2 × 18" hardwood or bend from sheet metal (adjustable fence)
F	2	¼-20 × 2¾" hex hd. bolts, washers
G	2	1 × 1 × 2" hardwood, aluminum or steel (stops)
H	1	⅛ × 1 × 1 × 3⅛" angle iron or aluminum
I	2	¾" No. 8 machine screw (or rh wood screw if stops are made of wood)
J	1	¼-20 × 1½" thumbscrew

*Available from The Woodworkers' Store, 21801 Industrial Blvd., Rogers, Minn. 55374.

TABLE-SAW MITER BOARD

By JOHN A. HAASE

JIG TABLE was made from sink cutout, available at most cabinet dealers.

table-saw miter board, continued

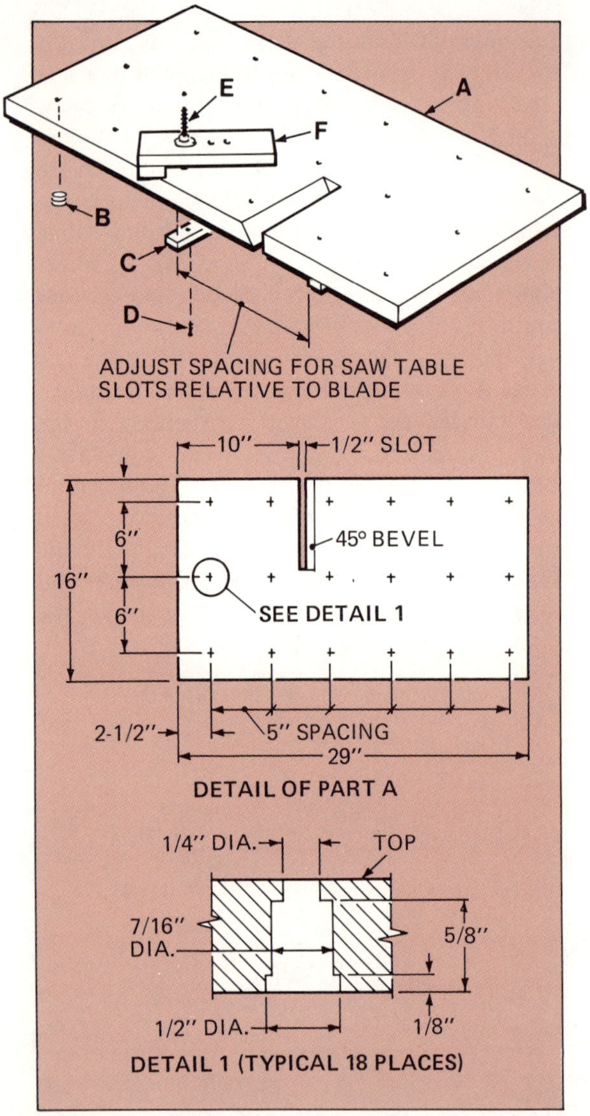

WITH GUIDES mounted in 45° positions, miters can be cut at both ends of molding without readjustment.

USE CLAMP to hold the work rigid. This is especially important when making compound miter cuts.

■ CONVENTIONAL MITER gauges are usually too small to allow a secure grip on large workpieces. Solid clamps, plus the large surface area of this sliding miter board, make cutting precise angles a sure thing.

Compound angle cutting is also possible, since the jig's blade slot is beveled 45° on the side toward which your blade tilts.

When building the jig, take care to make the slides, which fit miter-gauge grooves, absolutely perpendicular to the board's front edge. The workpiece-holding clamps are built onto the board and can be repositioned as the task demands.

Angle-cutting positions must be measured with an arm protractor. Commonly used angles can be marked on masking tape or permanently scribed on the surface of the board.

A good way to determine accurate fence positions is to use simple trigonometry. The tangent function will give you the ratio to locate appropriate sets of coordinates for any angle 0 to 90°. To do so, look up the tangent function for the angle in question. The tangent of 60°, for example, is 1.732. This means that for every inch you measure from the vertex along the line adjacent to the angle (blade's path), you should measure 1.732 in. to the right or left on a line perpendicular to the blade's path. If you measure 8 in. from the vertex on the blade's path, you should measure 1.732 in. x 8, or 13⅞-in. to the right or left from the 8-in. mark. Connect this point to the vertex, using a straight line to find the fence position for 60°.

MATERIALS LIST—TABLE-SAW JIG

Key	No.	Size and description (use)
A	1	¾ × 16 × 29" plywood or countertop scrap (table)
B	18	¼-20 thread inserts*
C	2	¼ × ¾ × 16" pine
D	6	¾" No. 8 fh screw
E	as reqd.	¼-20 threaded rod, washer, nut
F	as reqd.	¾" stock (clamps)

*Available from The Woodworkers' Store, 21801 Industrial Blvd., Rogers, Minn. 55374.

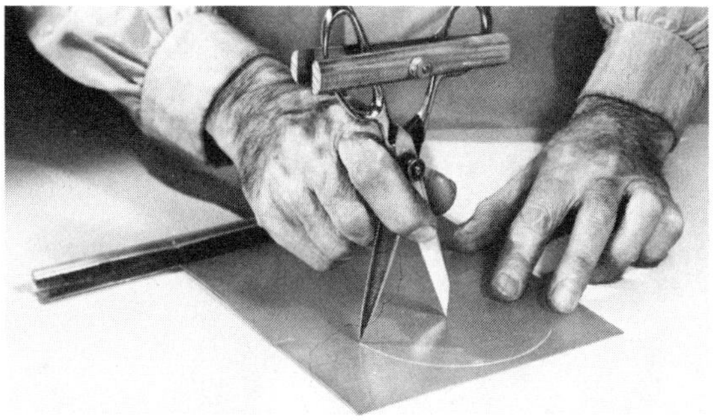

A SIMPLE clamping arrangement converts a pair of sharp-pointed scissors into a compass divider. The clamp consists of two stiff wood strips connected by a bolt with a wingnut through their centers. Install it across the handles as shown or across the blades when point separation is adequate. Clamp strips shown are 4½ in. long.—*E.B. Walters, Chicago.*

WHEN REPLACING plastic webbing on patio chairs and the like, ordinary cutting and hole-punching techniques leave frayed and raveled edges on the fabric. Run the hot tip of your soldering iron across the webbing where a cut is needed; the fiber ends will melt and join together so that you'll find it easy to make a neat cut.—*Charles Hardy, Whittier, CA.*

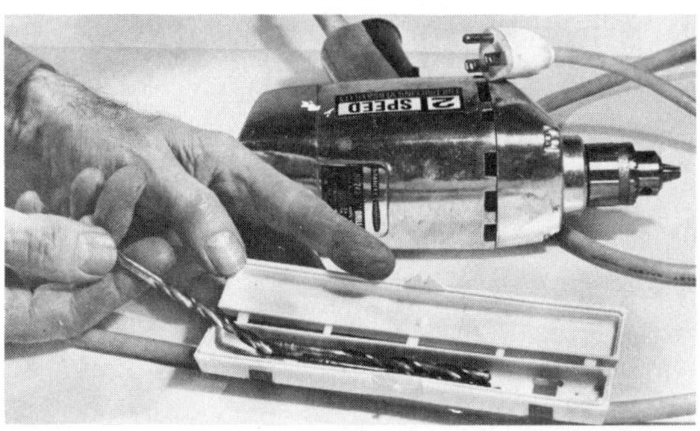

AFTER TRYING several methods without success for keeping drill bits neatly corralled by my drill, I came up with the idea shown at left. I simply taped a plastic toothbrush case to my drill's line cord for use as a drill-bit holder. Since I implemented my idea, I have never had to search for a drill bit when using the drill.—*Louis C. Davis, Albany, GA.*

WHEN LABELING workshop jars, apply three labels equally spaced around each jar's circumference, and you can identify the contents of a container no matter what position it was returned to its shelf. If you use rectangular or square jars for small-parts storage, apply a label to each side to achieve the same results.—*W. B. May, Oak Park, IL.*

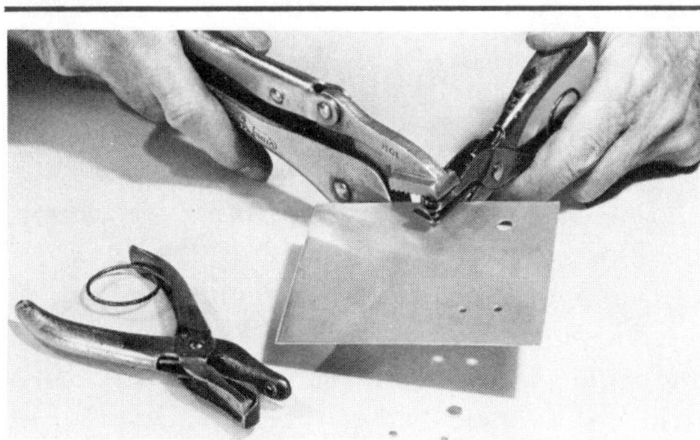

A PAPER PUNCH can be used for making holes in material heavier than those for which it was designed, such as cardboard and soft-sheet aluminum. To do it, give the punch an assist by using a toggle-type wrench. The wrench is adjusted so it will squeeze the punch jaws together just enough to penetrate the material.—*B. W. Ervin, Kent, OH.*

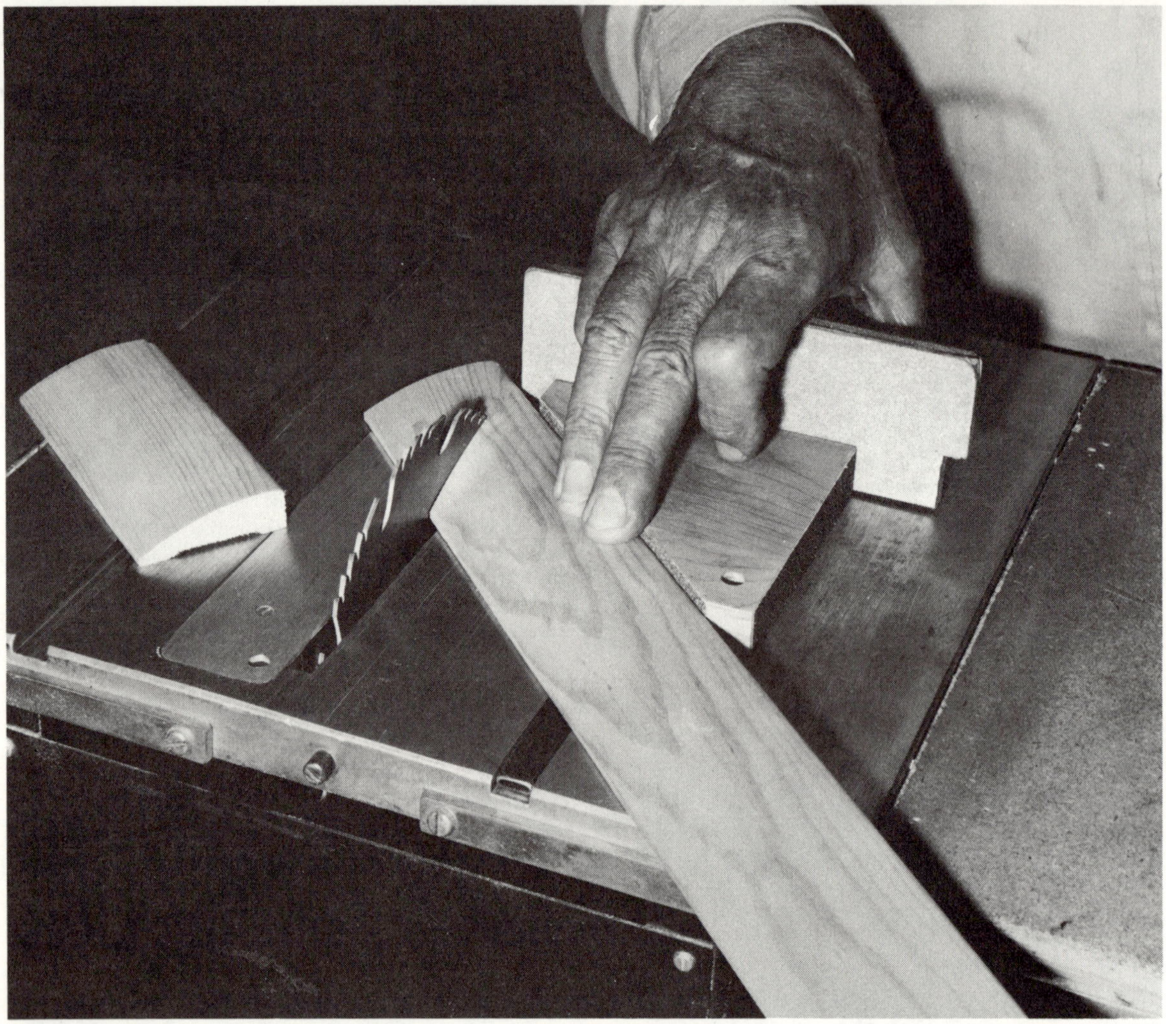

ANGLE BLOCKS save time, assure accuracy. Blade guard is removed for photos.

Make angle blocks for miter cuts

Use these on either a table saw or a radial arm saw to save yourself time and aggravation when cutting various angles

By FRANK H. DAY

SEE ALSO

Angles, compound . . . Dovetail joints . . . Drawers . . . Frames, picture . . . Joinery . . . Miter boards . . . Shop techniques . . . Workbenches . . . Workshops

■ MITERED JOINTS demand accuracy. Even a slight miscalculation will inevitably compound itself into a conspicuous, wedge-shaped gap in your finished work. Not only is this frustrating and shoddy-looking, but it's also expensive if you choose to try again and redo it.

A set of blocks for common angle cutting will take only half an hour to make from scrap plywood. They'll help you minimize waste and save hours of job time. No longer will you have to adjust and readjust your miter gauge every time you change from making a right-hand to a left-hand cut. Set it at 90° and move the miter gauge and block from one side to the other—or remove the block to cut at 90°.

The photos show how to hold and use the blocks. *Note: The blade guard has been removed for photo clarity only.* Be sure the block does not contact the blade—the garnet paper will dull it.

GARNET PAPER edging helps keep block and workpiece from slipping or "creeping" as you cut.

FOR TRUE angles on the blocks, use draftsman's triangles to set the miter gauge for cutting.

SAFELY POSITION fingers when mitering narrow picture-frame moldings as shown here.

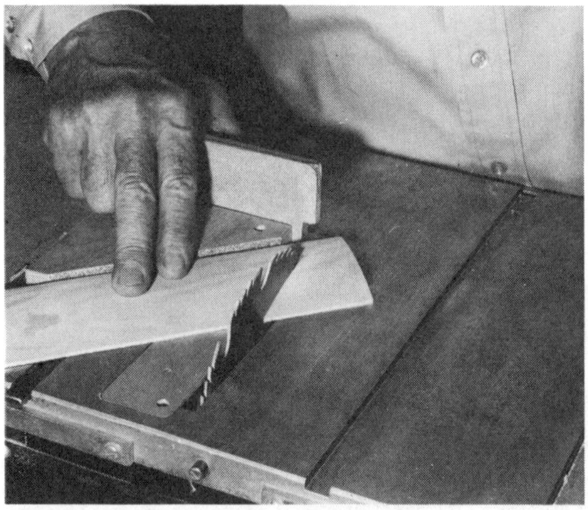

THE 45° ANGLE block makes mitering door or window casings quick, easy and accurate.

To make the blocks, cut a 6x8-in. rectangle and a 6x6-in. square from ¾-in. plywood. Make certain one corner of each is a true right angle. The easiest place to get a perfect 90° corner is from the mill-cut corner of a plywood sheet. Lacking that, set your gauge with a dependable square and cut your own. Also check your blade with the square to be certain you are making a true vertical cut.

reset gauge

Next, reset your miter gauge to the block angle you intend to cut first (45° or 30°). Use the appropriate draftsman's triangle with its long side butted against the fully exposed width of your blade (see photo). On a set-tooth blade, where teeth alternately point in opposite directions, be certain that contact is made at equivalent points on two teeth pointing in the *same* direction. The miter gauge is then set flush to the opposite side of the triangle as shown above.

Proceed to make your cuts. Trim ¾ in. off all acute angle corners to provide additional clearance between block and blade while cutting. Use contact cement to adhere ⅝-in.-wide strips of 80-grit garnet paper to edges. Finally, drill a hole in one corner of each block for hanging near your saw where they can be easily reached whenever you need them.

adapt for radial-arm saw

These blocks can also be adapted for use on a radial-arm saw. Simply place a board between the fence and the block to provide clearance for the cut-off end. The advantage is that you won't have to lift and swing the blade out of the 90° groove, then lower it into the angled groove each time the direction of cut is changed.

Mix your way to better sound

By BILL KANNER

Mixers have long been known to the serious audiophile, but you don't need a million-dollar system to use them. We tell you how to choose—and use—these often neglected audio components

THE TEAC MIXER/METER combination (top of page) solves all but the most complex mixing problems. There are inputs and outputs for nearly every purpose. The Audio-Kit 62 (above) is a build-it-yourself mixer.

SEE ALSO
Amplifiers . . . Cabinets, hi-fi . . . Cassette recorders . . . Cassette tapes . . . Hi-fi centers . . . Record care . . . Speakers . . . Television antennas

■ TO SOME PEOPLE a "mixer" is something you put in a highball, while to others it means a certain kind of fraternity party. But mention the word "mixer" to a dyed-in-the-woofer audio buff or a well-biased recordist and it means something else entirely. To them a "mixer" is a junction box for microphones and line inputs.

A typical mixer has sliders, buttons, knobs and often meters. It also has the remarkable ability to send into rapture any dedicated audio enthusiast. But why the ecstasy over something that's basically a junction box?

A mixer takes a signal, alters it only slightly and sends it on its way virtually unchanged. It simply takes a signal at the input and lets it out the other end as an output.

The answer is partly in the sex appeal of the sliders, knobs and meters and partly in what they allow you to control. With an ordinary stereo tape recorder, you can plug in two microphones and have one picking up signals for the left channel and the other for the right. On most machines, there is no provision for blending those channels or for adding other microphones. A mixer changes that. You can have a variety of microphones (or other input sources) giving you signals that you can blend together or keep relatively separate. You can alter the volume or "gain" of each input and even change the tonality of each independently.

mixing at home

A mixer is a necessity for the professional recording engineer, but why would the ordinary audiophile want one?

As sound equipment has gotten better, more and more people have been getting into the act. They either want to record themselves or they have friends in a band. Increasingly, audio gear that was originally intended for use by professional sound technicians has filtered down to the amateur.

With a mixer, a good set of microphones and a good tape deck, the enthusiastic hobbyist can make tapes that are virtually indistinguishable from a studio production. And with today's musical styles, you can always connect two turntables to your mixer and turn your next party into a disco.

Other than that kind of novelty, isn't a mixer an extravagance? Sure it is—unless you really intend to do some live recording. More and more audiophiles are finding that home studio-type recording is the next logical step for them. It provides a level of creativity not otherwise available. A mixer allows versatility and individual expression and need not be a big investment compared to the rest of the system.

A good open-reel tape deck (the kind most used for serious live recording and editing) will cost a minimum of $500. If that's the kind of equipment we're talking about, then the additional cost of a small mixer is, on a percentage basis, no great investment.

build it yourself

If you're willing to do a little work yourself, you can get a more than adequate mixer for under $300. AudioKit 62 is a British mixer kit distributed by AudioMarketing of Stamford, Conn. As the name implies, it's a 6-in/2-out unit. That means that you can take up to six high-impedance inputs, mix them as desired, and end up with two channels at the output. The 62 takes about eight hours to build.

The AudioKit 62 has a variety of controls and features. Each input channel has a gain control that acts as a microphone amp, bass and treble controls, as well as cue and echo controls. The last two are for external equipment and are connected to outputs on the back panel. Each channel has a pan pot, which can apportion each input to either or both channels. A slider controls the amount of signal going to the output stage.

In addition to the cue and echo outputs, the 62 has main and auxiliary pairs of outputs. The main set (which you connect to your tape deck) is controlled via slider and its level is reflected in V U meters. The auxiliary outputs are knob-controlled.

The AudioKit 62 is flat and can be carried in a briefcase. And while its optimum power source is its 24-volt d.c. power supply adapter, it can run successfully for hours on two 9-volt batteries.

Want to play with a few more output channels? Teac has just the item for you. Its Model 2A accepts microphone or line inputs of either high or low impedance and has a mike attenuate position that cuts the microphone amp's power. Each input has its own bass and treble controls. Color-coded pushbuttons allow you to assign any input to any or all outputs, and pan pots allow you to control the output of any input channel relative to the output.

The back-panel outputs are equally versatile. The quarter-inch microphone-inputs are supplemented by standard RCA-type line-input jacks. Above the line inputs are cue outputs that give you the signal before the input fader. They can give you a check and some insurance for another mix should you need a backup.

The dual set of line and auxiliary jacks both come after the last amplification stage—after the master fader. They give you the final signal. But the 2A also has patch points for auxiliary equipment.

The 2A has yet another set of jacks labeled "Buss In." This set can be used to gang or stack a series of mixers and control them via one master fader. You might find that the initial six inputs on your 2A are not enough and you want to use a larger mixer.

adding meters

You'll notice that while the Model 2A is a sophisticated piece of equipment, it has no meters. It's not that Teac feels meters are irrelevant. Quite the reverse. Teac makes the MB-20 meter bridge, which is basically a set of four VU meters with switching and inputs and outputs.

You can use the MB-20 quite effectively. Along with the 2A, it forms a control console. The mixer's line outputs feed the tape deck. A set of four tape-in jacks provide a monitor function (front-panel selection for each channel) and four jacks provide line signals for the mixer.

■ MOST electric food mixers are powered by motors of the universal type with carbon brushes. This type of motor develops high torque and speed, but is noisy and, because the brushes tend to spark, requires capacitors to prevent radio and TV interference. To deal with foods of different consistencies, the motor must turn at different speeds. The three common methods of speed control are a centrifugal switch, tapped field and adjustable brushes.

The centrifugal switch is a governor that keeps the motor at the desired speed by shutting off and restoring current. When the motor is off, its contacts touch (see page 1861). The contacts stay together until the motor reaches a speed at which centrifugal force overcomes spring tension and the contacts separate, breaking the circuit. The motor then slows until the spring can bring the

How to troubleshoot a food mixer

Many of the troubles of the electric mixer can be solved without even taking the unit apart. Whatever the difficulty, the comprehensive charts on these pages may help you diagnose and then solve the problem

TYPICAL MIXER COMPONENTS

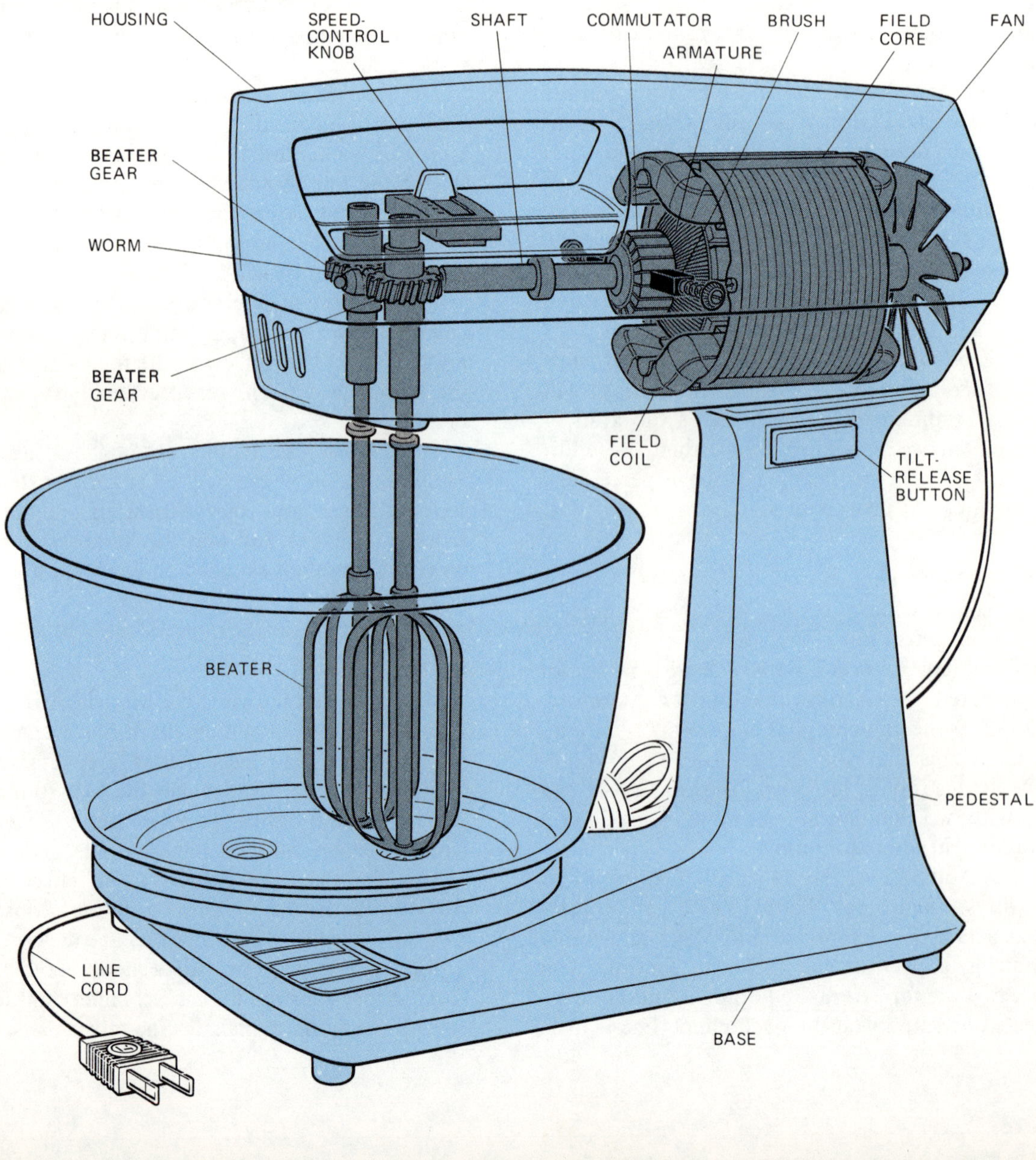

contacts together again. The cycle is short enough that the motor runs smoothly. Speeds are varied by moving the adjustable contact.

With tapped-field control, parts of the field coil are cut out of the motor circuit, giving it lower resistance and producing higher speed. At low speed, the entire coil is used. A medium setting, using part of the tapped coil, provides moderate speed.

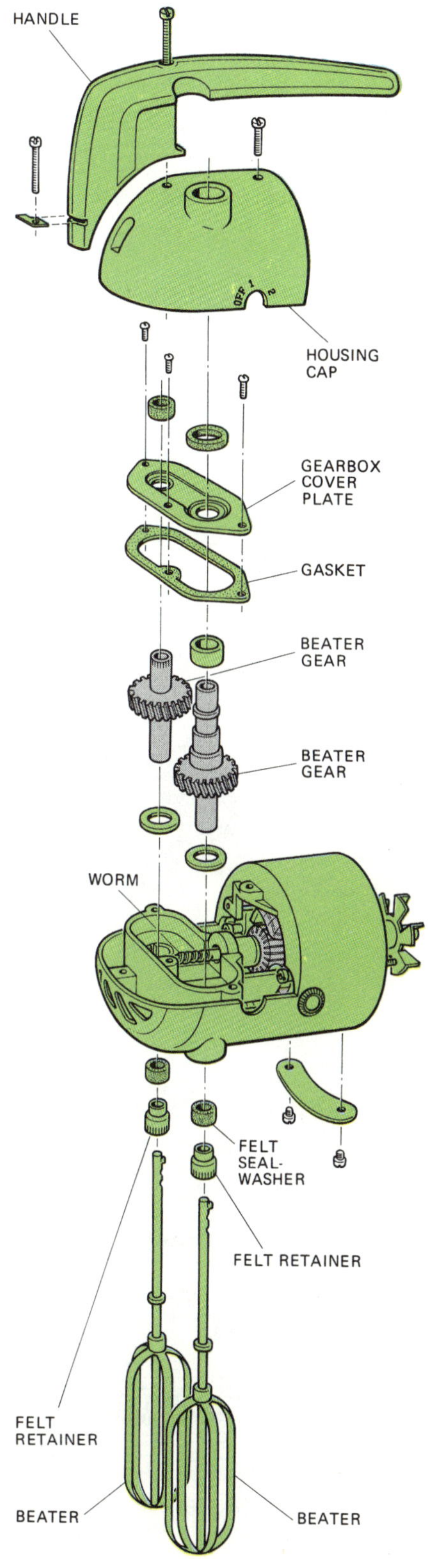

PEDESTAL MIXER: GEARBOX

Motor does not run

POSSIBLE CAUSES	WHAT TO TRY
1. No power.	Check for power at wall outlet with 115-v. test lamp. If there is no reading, replace line fuse or reset circuit breaker.
2. Defective cord.	Disconnect cord from outlet and then from motor casing. Test wires in cord for continuity. If either gives no reading, replace cord.
3. Worn brushes.	Remove brush caps from mixer housing. Pull out carbon brushes. If they have worn down to ¼ in. or less, replace them.
4. Defective on-off switch.	Remove switch and inspect contacts for pits or burned spots. Clean contacts with a fine file or sandpaper (do not use emery cloth). Test for continuity across terminals. If there is no reading with switch on, replace it.
5. Open field coil.	Test coil for continuity with one probe at wire junction of the cord, capacitor and field lead, other at lead from coil. There should be a reading. Also test between other coil lead and lead to brushes. There should be a reading. If there are no readings, replace field coil or check price of a new mixer.
6. Open armature winding.	Test for continuity across each segment of the commutator. Replace armature if any segment gives no reading. Test for armature short by placing one probe on commutator segment and the other on armature body. Replace armature if there is a reading.
7. Centrifugal switch stuck open.	Press switch closed. Clean all moving parts of the switch and put a drop of oil on the pivot point—do not over-oil.

SEE ALSO
Appliance repair . . . Food mixers . . . Food processors . . . Kitchens . . . Ranges . . . Toasters . . . Vacuum cleaners

continued

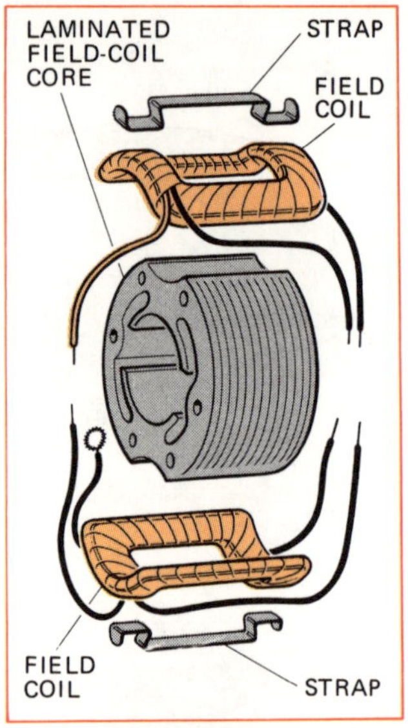

FIELD ASSEMBLY

Motor does not run, blows fuses

POSSIBLE CAUSES	WHAT TO TRY
1. Jammed bearings or spindles.	Remove gear housing. Apply penetrating oil to spindles; remove them at setscrews. Clean gear case, spindle holes with trichloroethylene solvent. Replace worn, broken gears. Grease gear compartment with proper lubricant, reassemble.
2. Jammed armature.	Disassemble mixer. Straighten or replace armature shaft. Spin armature by hand to check for clearance. Reassemble mixer.
3. Shorted line capacitor.	Test capacitor for continuity. There should be a reading for a split second. If no reading or if it is permanent, replace the capacitor.
4. Defective field coil or armature.	See preceding chart.
5. Shorted line cord.	Remove cord from outlet and then from motor casing. Test for continuity across plug prongs. If there is a reading, replace the cord.

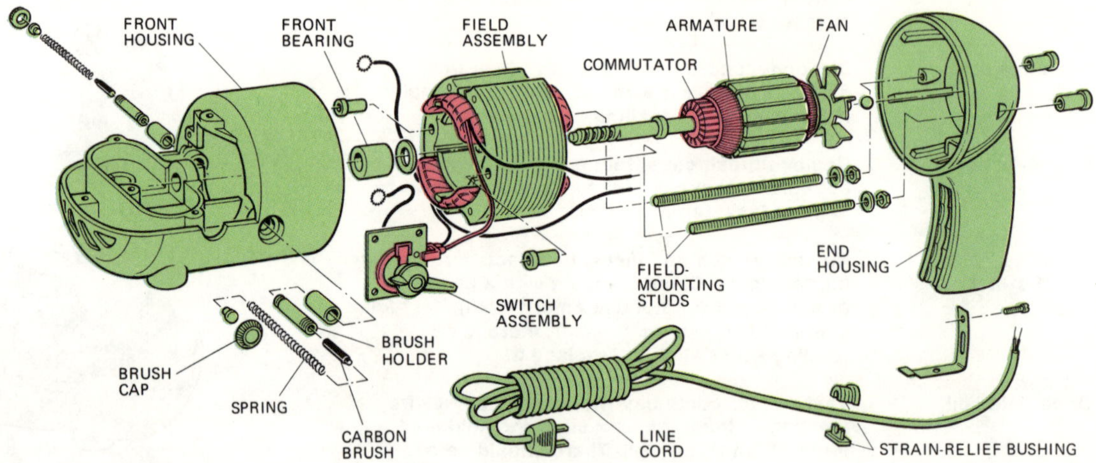

MOTOR ASSEMBLY

TYPICAL BRUSH ASSEMBLY

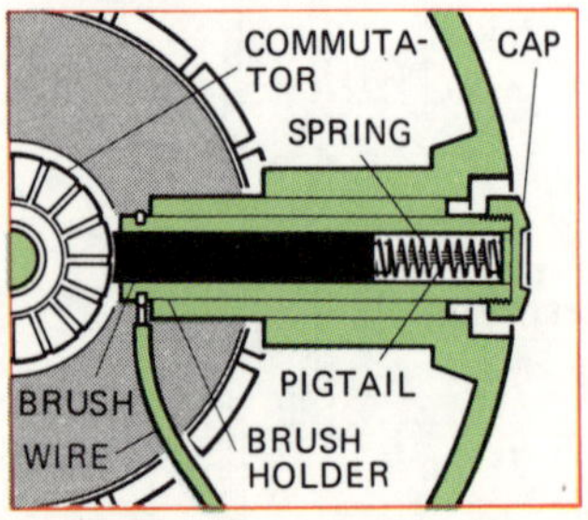

Motor overheats

POSSIBLE CAUSES	WHAT TO TRY
1. Centrifugal switch stuck closed.	Remove switch, separate contacts by hand. Check contacts for pits or burned spots. Clean with fine file or sandpaper (*not* emery cloth). Put a drop of oil on pivot point—do not over-oil.
2. Motor dirty.	Clean motor air intake with vacuum cleaner. Remove stubborn dirt with small toothbrush. Do not use solvents on internal motor parts.
3. Field coil or armature shorted or grounded.	Look for burn marks near edges of commutator segments, indicating a shorted or grounded winding. Test for continuity between commutator segment and shaft; a reading indicates a short or ground. Test field coil with one probe on coil lead, other on mixer housing. Replace any parts that produce readings.

Motor speed erratic

POSSIBLE CAUSES	WHAT TO TRY
1. Defective cord.	Test each side of cord for continuity while wiggling cord. Any variation in reading indicates a break. Replace cord.
2. Worn brushes.	See chart, "Motor does not run."
3. Loose connections.	Check all solder joints and wiring insulation. Correct any defects found.
4. Defective motor speed control.	See chart, "Motor overheats." Check tapped field by testing for continuity across resistor. Replace resistor if there is no reading. Test motor capacitor; see chart, "Motor does not run, blows fuses." Check adjustable-brush control by examining brushes; see chart, "Motor does not run."

continued

TAPPED—FIELD SPEED CONTROL

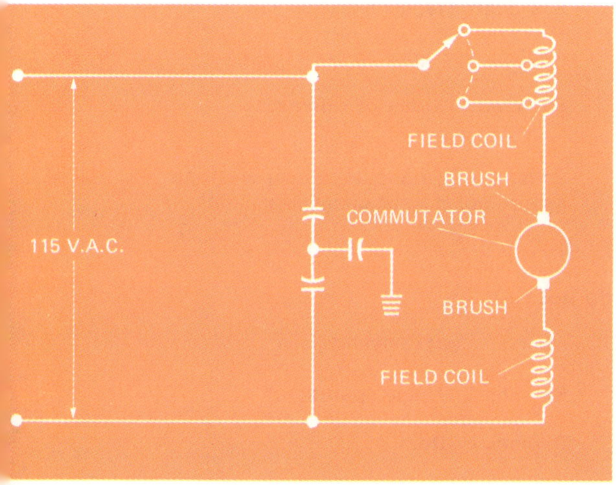

ADJUSTABLE—BRUSH SPEED CONTROL

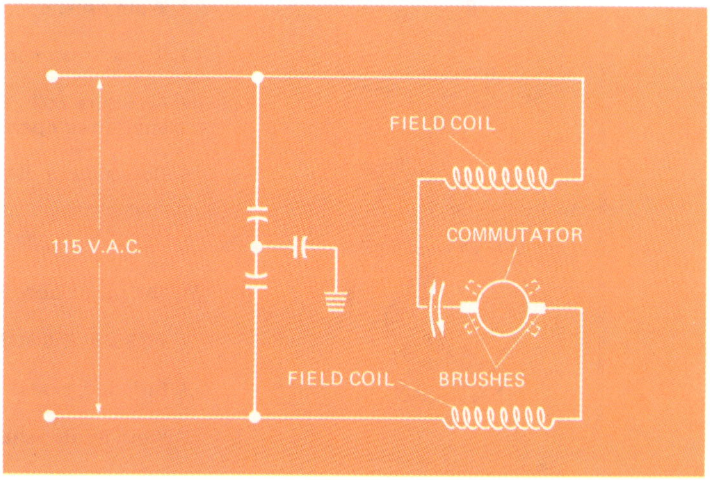

Noisy operation

POSSIBLE CAUSES	WHAT TO TRY
1. Worn bearings.	Tighten or replace bearings.
2. Play at end of rotor.	Shim rotor end with small thrust washers, .005 to .025 in. thick.
3. Motor dirty.	See chart, "Motor overheats."
4. Gears broken or dry.	Remove gear housing, check for chipped or broken gear teeth or lack of lubricant. Replace all worn or broken gears and grease with the recommended lubricant.
5. Bent beaters.	Straighten beaters so they clear each other.
6. Bent fan blades.	Straighten fan blades to clear housing.

CENTRIFUGAL—SWITCH CONTROL

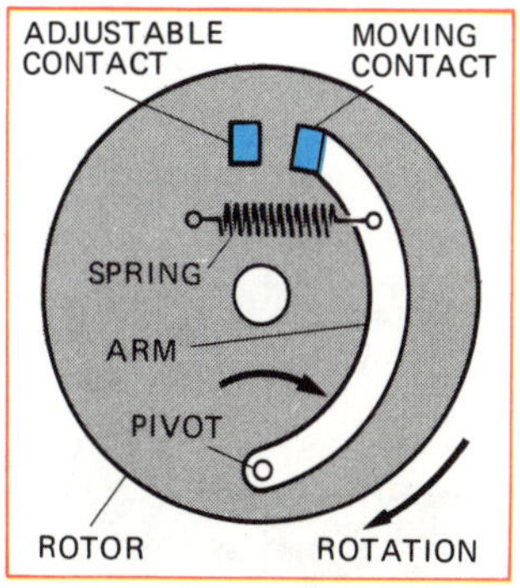

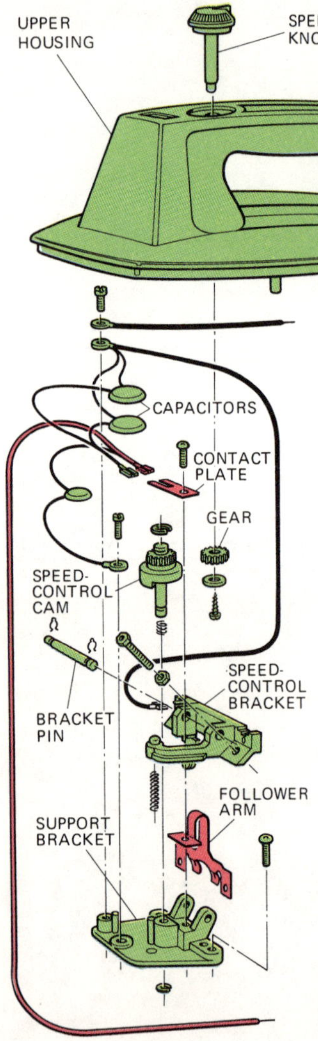

CAUTION: Be sure power is turned *off* before you handle components. Make all continuity tests with power *off*. When using a test lamp, keep power *off* while connecting and disconnecting the lamp. Use your manufacturer's manual to locate components, and use only replacement parts that meet his specifications.

Motor sparks at brushes

POSSIBLE CAUSES	WHAT TO TRY
1. New brushes.	Normal condition until new brushes wear to fit contour of commutator.
2. Worn brushes.	See chart, "Motor does not run."
3. Weak brush springs.	Replace springs.
4. Armature coil shorted or open.	See chart, "Motor overheats."
5. Commutator dirty.	Polish surface of commutator with fine sandpaper (do not use emery cloth).

Motor runs; beaters do not turn

POSSIBLE CAUSES	WHAT TO TRY
1. Stripped gears.	See chart, "Noisy operation."
2. Worn beater shafts.	Replace beaters.

HAND-MIXER: UPPER SECTION AND CONTROLS

MOTOR ASSEMBLY

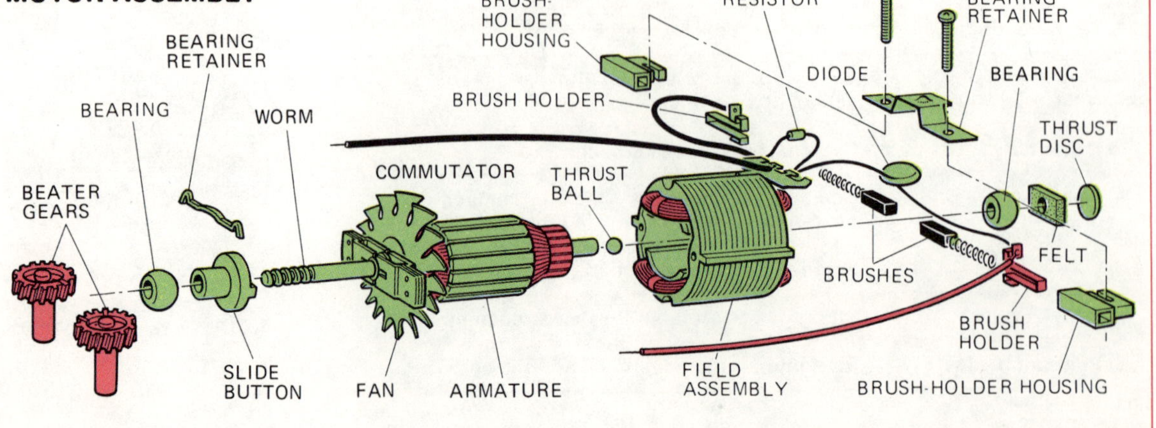

Motor runs slowly or lacks torque

POSSIBLE CAUSES	WHAT TO TRY
1. Wrong speed for load.	Change speed.
2. Load too heavy.	Not mixer's fault; don't use on unusually stiff mixtures.
3. Worn brushes.	See chart, "Motor does not run."
4. Rotor binding.	Check for proper end-play clearance—this clearance should be .005 in.
5. Centrifugal switch stuck closed.	See chart, "Motor overheats."
6. Field coil grounded to mixer housing.	Place one probe of 115-v. test lamp on mixer housing, other probe on known ground. If there is a reading, replace field coil or check price of a new mixer.

Motor runs continuously

POSSIBLE CAUSES	WHAT TO TRY
1. Switch dial broken.	Cam pin broken or worked loose. Replace.
2. On-off switch shorted.	Test for continuity across switch terminals with switch off. Replace switch if there is a reading.

Adjustable-brush control provides lower motor speeds by moving the brushes away from their position of maximum efficiency with respect to the commutator. This type of control reduces torque as it reduces speed, and for this reason is not commonly found on new machines.

At one time or another, a food mixer will require lubrication for proper performance. Some mixers have accessible oil holes or grease cups that permit lubrication without disassembly. If water or another liquid has found its way into the gearbox, all of the old grease should be removed and the compartment repacked with grease of a weight recommended by the manufacturer of the mixer.

Many mixer problems can be solved without taking the appliance apart. Stuck beaters can be loosened by squirting penetrating oil into their sleeves. Bent beater blades can be straightened, although a bent beater shaft usually requires replacement. If beaters slip in their spindles, the trouble is usually a worn shaft that should be replaced. Brushes are accessible through caps on the mixer housing. When you must take a mixer apart, keep careful track of the sequence of disassembly so that you can reverse the process with a minimum of difficulty.

LOWER SECTION AND GEARBOX

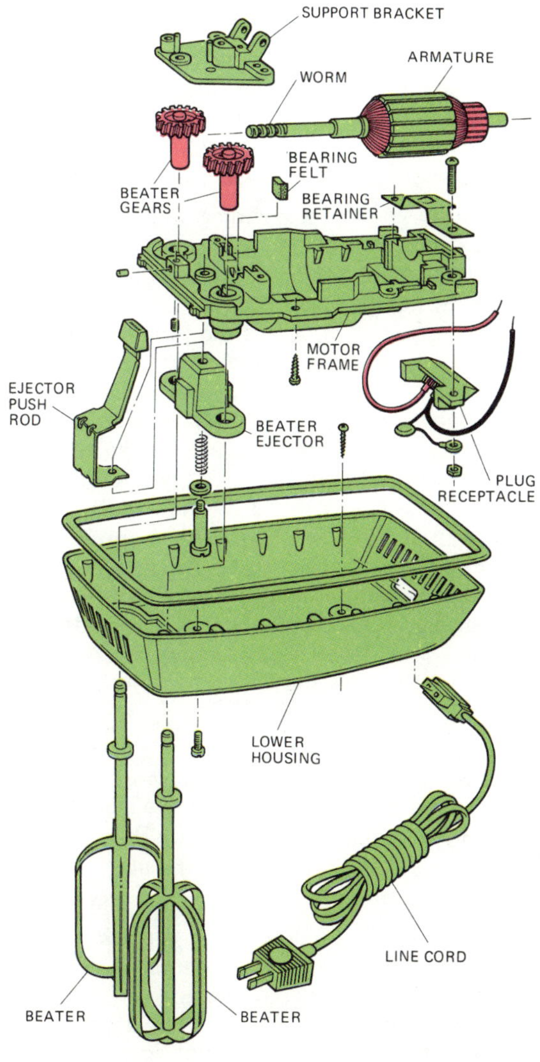

Seepage or condensation?

I have slight seepage in a corner of my basement. Drops of water appear on the wall just above the floor during the summer months. Should I plaster the area with cement-and-lime mix, or what?—A.W., Minn.

A cement-and-lime mix is not a waterproofer comparable to those especially compounded for the purpose. I don't think this is seepage; rather it is moisture from the air condensing on the surface of the affected area, which has a slightly lower temperature than the basement air. Adequate ventilation (windows open during cool, dry days) should dispel the condensate and prevent a recurrence.

Seedlings break through blacktop

Early last summer I had my driveway blacktopped. Within a month or so I noticed what appeared to be oak seedlings breaking through. I applied a weed killer and sealed what seemed to be a tiny opening. Now three other seedlings are coming through in different locations. What's the matter with the blacktopping? I thought it was impervious to any growth from underneath. Is there another way to prevent this?—G.B., S.C.

I don't know that anything is wrong with the blacktopping, provided it was properly put down over a tamped gravel fill. But seedlings can find their way through tiny openings or cracks. This leads me to suspect that the topping is settling due to inadequate fill or bedding, and that perhaps the topping is thin where the seedlings emerge. Or the topping may have been put down over the earth, without a fill. Not an approved practice, this might lead to early breakup of the material, with fine cracks developing. Before you take other corrective steps, try an application of the asphalt-base coating especially made for resurfacing old blacktop. It's readily available, is relatively inexpensive and might well turn the trick without resorting to more heroic measures. Be sure to follow the instructions in all details.

Feathering patcher

I've always had trouble troweling a concrete patcher when making a shallow patch. I can never get it quite flush, smooth and neat. How is this done?—J. Erickson, Moline, Ill.

Ordinarily, you don't trowel a patch when edges require shallow filling. Instead, smooth and level these edges with a brush as indicated. Use an old paintbrush or the coarser-bristle kind for masonry paint. Cover such a patch with coarse fabric and keep it damp for several days while the patching cures.

Walnut to fruitwood

The cabinet of my old sewing machine is made of solid black walnut and I'd like to give it one of the new fruitwood finishes. The old finish is in rather poor condition and must be removed. There also are a few minor nicks and dents but I do not care to correct them. How do I get the desired finish?—T.Y., Calif.

Any black-walnut cabinet in the solid wood is choice. Even if nicked, dented and worn it is still a first choice among the finest cabinet woods. For this reason I hesitate to go along with your suggestion of a fruitwood finish. It seems to me you would be better pleased in the long run to remove the old finish and refinish the wood in its natural color—about the simplest and easiest of all refinishing jobs.

However, if it must be a fruitwood finish, take off the old finish with a remover of the wash-off type. Permit the remover to work only through the old finish and not soften and remove the filler in the pores of the wood. Once the old finish has been softened to the wood, rinse thoroughly to remove all residues and then allow the wood to dry. Sand with a medium and fine abrasive to cut off any grain that may have been raised by washing off the remover. Then spray on the fruitwood finish (it's available in spray cans) and be careful to get it on uniformly without runs or sags. It is assumed you have first removed the sewing head, switch and all hinged parts.

Will insulation harm shingles?

I've built up the insulation in my attic from 3 to 7 in., the original 3 in. being batts. Now I'm told that this will greatly accelerate the deterioration of the composition roof shingles. If this is so, how?—Gene Cowdry, Dubuque, Iowa.

If I were you, I would continue to sleep soundly. Your attic will be colder in winter and perhaps hotter in summer without added ventilation, and there is an opinion that this will tend to shorten shingle life, but I doubt that this reduction would be more than three years on the average, if that much.

Best time to transplant tree

When is the best time to transplant a growing crabapple tree, spring or fall?—W. Leonard, Jefferson City, Mo.

I favor spring as the best time for open-root transplanting. This gives the transplant time to develop an adequate new root system and attain some growth before winter comes. Balled specimens can usually be transplanted any time, but even then, spring is best.

Mobile entertaining, indoors and out

ROLL THESE THREE mobile carts out on a deck or patio and you have, in effect, an "instant" outdoor playroom all set up and ready to go for family fun and party entertaining. A brand-new concept in flexible, go-anywhere furniture developed by our editors, the carts include a complete cooking unit with electric barbecue and built-in refrigerator (see below), a wet bar with sink and running water, and a self-contained stereo music center on wheels.

MOBILE COOKING CENTER is designed for use with electric barbecue from Char-B-Que and a Sears mini refrigerator. The compartment on the right side is for the storage of supplies.

SEE ALSO

Barbecues . . . Barbecue bars . . . Bars . . . Cookout bars . . . Firepits . . . Grills . . . Hi-fi centers . . . Modular furniture . . . Patios . . . Serving carts . . . Snack tables . . . Speakers

What's best about these versatile roll-abouts is that they're not limited just to outdoor use, either. There's no need to store them away between seasons while waiting for another summer to come around. Companion-styled with the smart good looks of fine furniture, they're as handsome and functional indoors as out. The cooking center, in addition to its barbecue and mini fridge, features swing-up extension wings

that make it ideal for doubling as a buffet server inside. The rolling wet bar and music center shown on these pages are match mates with hinged tops that swing down to conceal their contents when not in use. Closed, they look like sleek, modern credenzas ready for service in a living or dining area. On the next 13 pages, you will learn how to build these unusual pieces you can't buy anywhere.

1. Mobile cook-center

AT INDOOR BUFFET (above) cart becomes the center of attraction. For buffet use, a three-well food warmer replaces the barbecue setup shown on page **1865**. Compact refrigerator from Sears (below) holds food and drink for typical get-together. Storage area holds cooking and serving equipment.

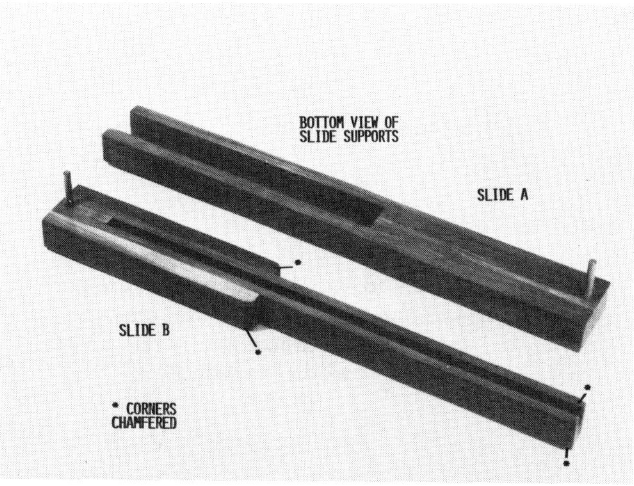

DROP-LEAF SUPPORTS are of walnut; slide B inserts into slide A when slides are fully retracted.

■ THIS COOK-CENTER has a lot going for it if you enjoy year-round entertaining. During the warm months it's sure to draw raves from your neighbors when they spot it on your patio. At season's end, you simply roll it indoors for use in the family room. And, when not in service it's a handsome piece of furniture that will suit any room decor.

The concept started with the electric barbecue cooker manufactured by the Char-B-Que Co., New Shrewsbury, NJ. The cooker can be used outside (indoors in a fireplace) for barbecues and, with its lid closed, for delicate, Chinese smoke cooking. Of die-cast aluminum, the Char-B-Que is offered in four colors—orange, yellow, avocado and black.

The other piece of equipment that played a major part in the cart's design is the coppertone Mini-Fridge from Sears.

The plastic-laminated countertop is an exciting product too. A handsome pattern from Formica Corp., it's called Butcherblock Maple. It looks like the real thing; in all probability, only experienced workshoppers will be able to spot the difference. The drop leaves, on which you cut and prepare vegetables, are the real thing, of course, made up of laminated strips of maple.

At the end of this article, you'll find a list of manufacturers of all major components used—including hardware.

To build your cart, it's a must to have your mini-refrigerator on hand. It will determine the final size of the cart (except for height). The top on the cart shown is at a comfortable, and recommended, cooking height when used with the electric barbecue. If possible, do not alter this dimension.

Start building by laying out the cart parts on two sheets of plywood. Before cutting, take time

SLIDE B TRAVELS on a single 25-in.-long guide. Slide A sandwiches between pair of 12-in. guides.

GUIDES should also be of hardwood. When satisfied with location, secure them with glue and 1-in. screws.

'Butcherblock' top looks like the real thing

Take time to double check measurements and proceed carefully; as a cabinet maker you must be meticulous. In this case, the reward is worth the trouble

to double check those critical dimensions concerning the refrigerator. Assemble the cabinet using waterproof glue and screws and then apply the Gunstock Walnut laminate using contact cement. You can flop the box about so you can trim laminate overhang using your router and a carbide cutter, but you will have to do some hand-filing to square the four corners in each of the two openings at front.

Next, make the cabinet top. After cutting the two pieces, use waterproof glue and 1¼-in. No. 8 screws to join the pieces. The top can now be

Plywood cutting schedule

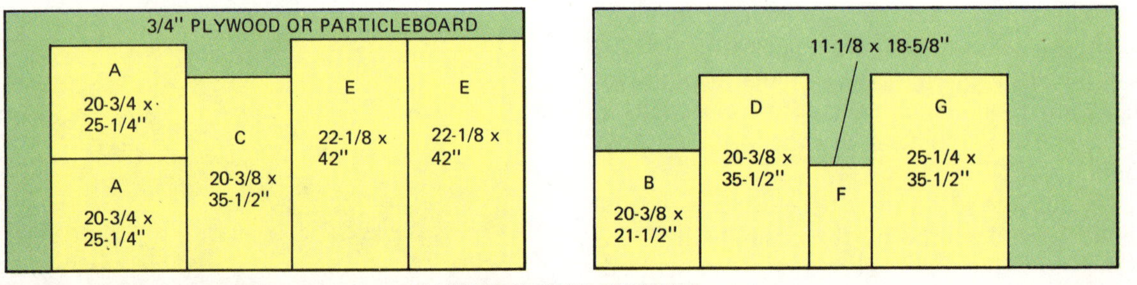

PLYWOOD CUTTING SCHEDULE

How to make the slide supports

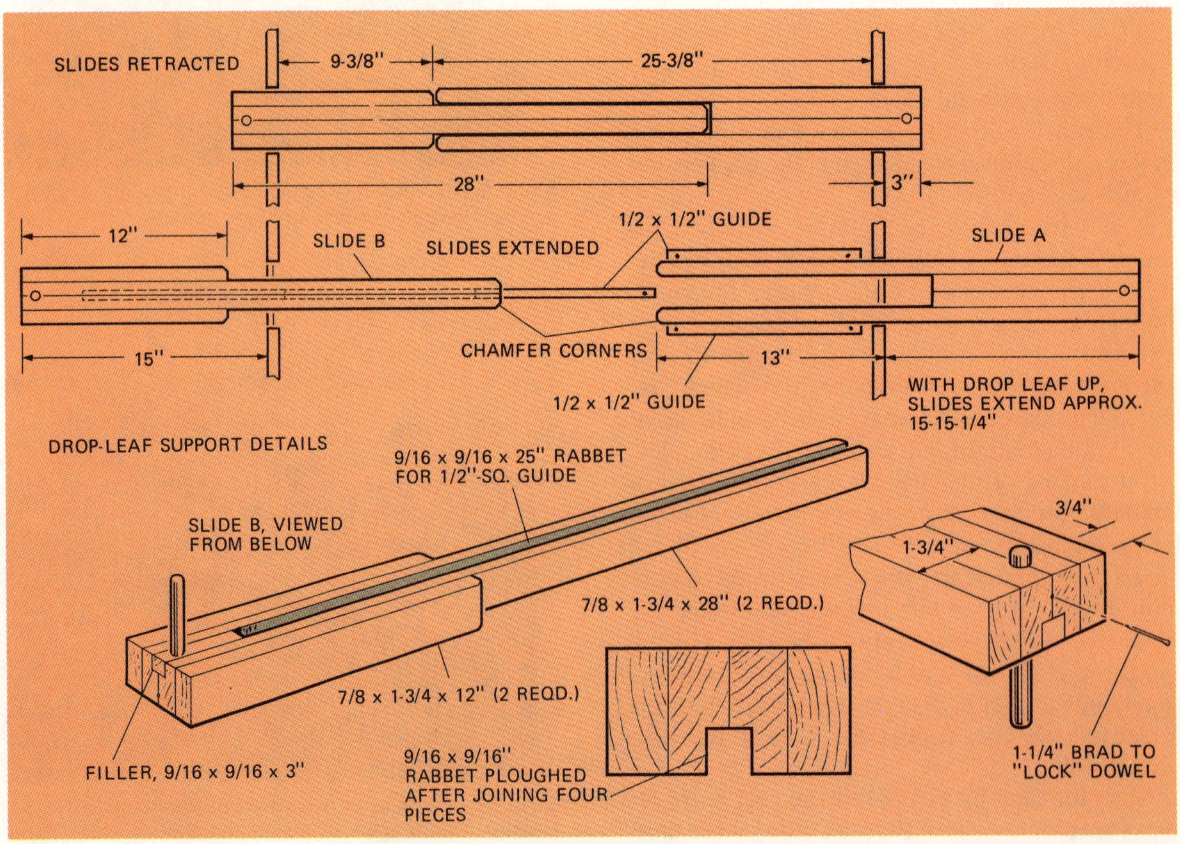

covered with plastic laminate. Do the edges first and finish by applying the top.

Glue-up the maple chopping blocks (or consider having this step done at your local lumberyard mill) and fasten these to the countertop using 2-in. brass-plated continuous hinge. Make absolutely certain that you drill adequate-size pilot holes in the maple chopping blocks for the hinge screws or you are almost sure to pop the heads off a number of screws.

Although the weight of the top itself holds it in place, you are well advised to anchor it using one lagscrew as shown in the drawing below. The four corner blocks prevent lateral movement of the top but at any social gathering there is a chance that a guest will lean on one of the upraised drop leaves. With the cooker going full blast, that could cause a tragedy. The single anchor, we found, absolutely prevents any chance of tilting the top.

When you're satisfied with the installation, remove the lagscrew and top so that you will have less weight to handle while you work on the remaining details. For example, the cart can now

Exploded view of the mobile cook-center

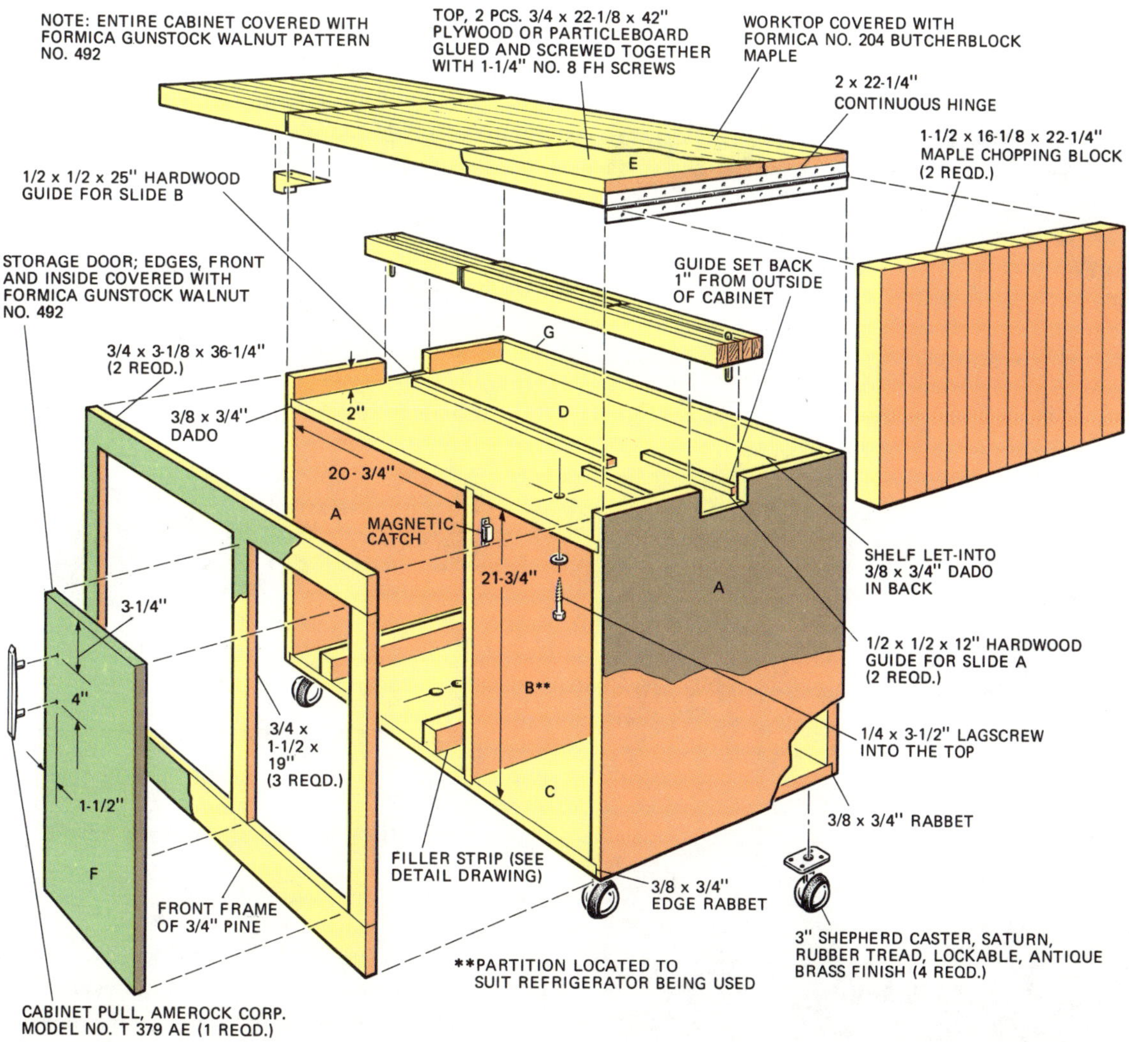

be rested on its back and the casters attached. This makes it easier to move the cart around as you advance to the finishing stages. Right the cabinet and you can go to work installing the flush-mounted storage door (after first fitting and laminating it). To keep this cart's look compatible with its matchmates, Soss hinges were used to mount the door. You could, if desired, pick a pair of flush-mount hinges that will match the door pull, but keep in mind that no such hardware was used on the other two carts (if you plan to build them).

The barbecue tools hang from 2-in. brass L-hooks. Simply lay out your set of tools as you prefer and turn the hooks into predrilled pilot holes. If your cooking-tool collection is substantial, add hooks at the right end of the cabinet.

The slide supports for holding up the drop leaves look trickier to build than they actually are. Take the time to study the details in the drawings and photos. Notice that slide B inserts into slide A when both are pushed into the cabinet. You'll need four lengths of hardwood 28 in. long and four lengths 12 in. long to make the pair. After gluing up the supports, plough the

LOCKABLE CASTERS, by Shepherd Casters, permit cart to roll easily on patio surface. The casters used are mobility-rated at 100 lbs. each.

TO LOCATE TOP on its base, place the top on unit and measure overhang on all four sides. Then, using a pencil draw the cabinet outline on the top. Flop top and locate one block at each corner.

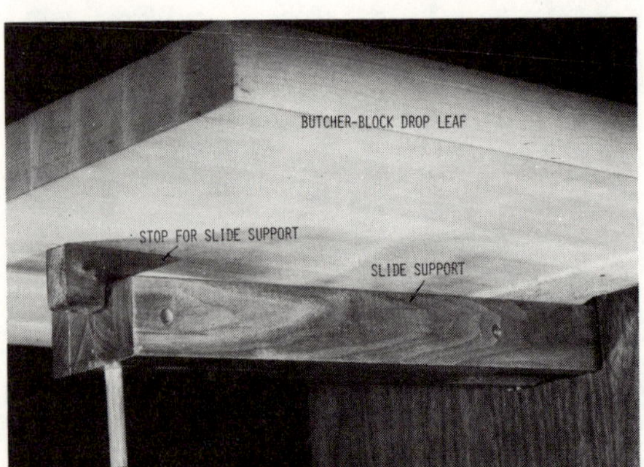

POSITION HARDWOOD STOP so slide-support assures drop leaf is level with cabinet top when extended.

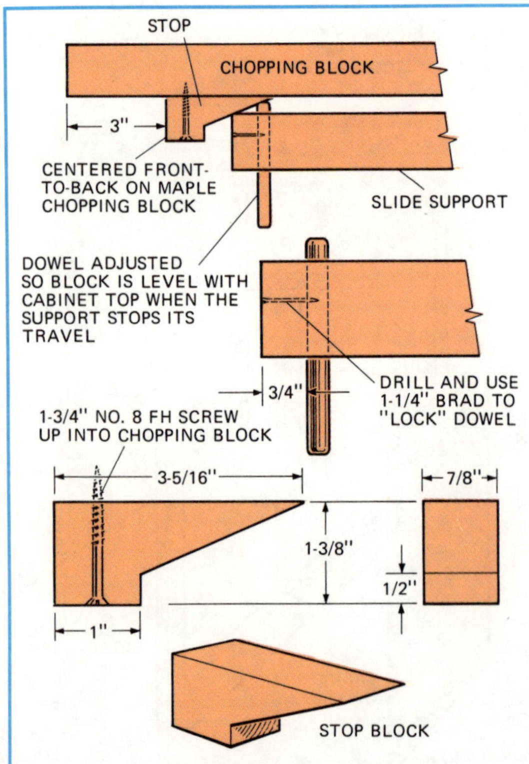

CENTER STOP AND SLIDES on maple chopping blocks. Raise and lower dowel for snug fit. When dowel is located, lock with 1¼-in. brad.

REFRIGERATOR COMPARTMENT must be sized to suit model. Size shims so refrigerator slides in and out easily—with space at top for air circulation.

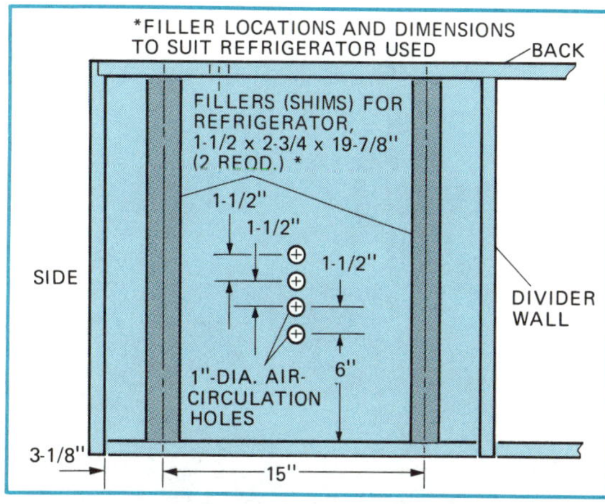

ADEQUATE VENTING is a must. Drill minimum of four holes—more if you select larger-size refrigerator. Then glue and tack shims beneath.

rabbet along the length of slide B which will travel on the ½-in. square guide. You can cut a blind rabbet, but it is easier to run the full length of the slide and then add a small filler strip at the outboard end.

After making your slides, position them in the cabinet to mark the guide location. At this time also check the stop position when slides are retracted—they should stop with 3 in. projecting from the cabinet.

To locate the small triangle-shaped slide support stops, lift the first drop leaf and extend the support exactly 15 in. Note: The slide should butt the stop snugly so that the leaf is level with the top. When you have achieved this position, mark and drill for fastening the stop. Repeat the procedure on the second drop-leaf.

The final step is to install the shims (fillers) on which the refrigerator rests. They should be level with, or slightly higher than, the bottom rail so the refrigerator can be easily removed.

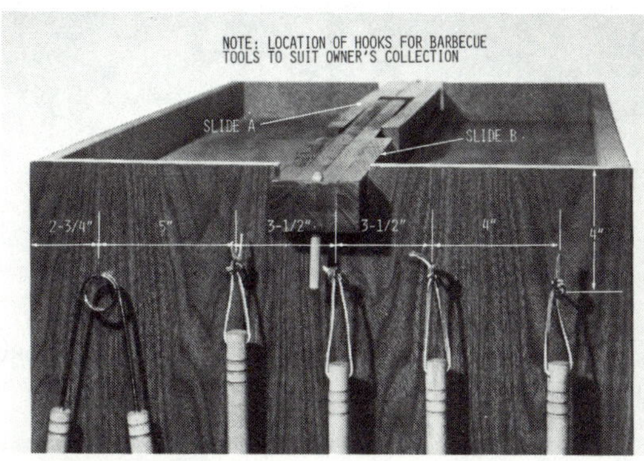

BARBECUE TOOLS are always at the ready on this cart. Hooks are spaced to suit barbecue tools.

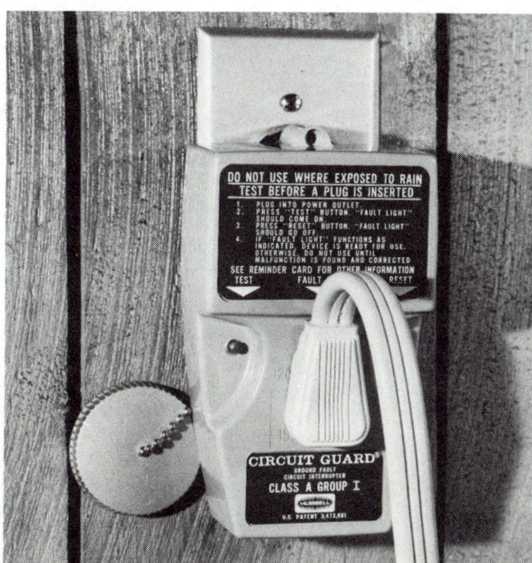

FOR SAFETY, use ground fault interrupter on outdoor outlet. Use No. 12-ga. extension cord to power refrigerator and cooker.

Manufacturers of materials

Plastic laminate, Butcherblock maple No. 204 and Gunstock Walnut No. 492, Formica Corp., 120 East 4th St., Cincinnati, OH 45202

Electric barbecue; Electric Char-B-Que, New Shrewsbury, NJ 07753.

Ground fault interrupter, Model GFP-115, Harvey Hubbell, Bridgeport, CT

Casters; Saturn (SN) 3-in. lockable casters, Shepherd Casters, Inc., St. Joseph, MI 49085.

Refrigerator; Model 644.73872, Sears, Roebuck catalog.

Door pull; Model T 379 (AE). Amerock Corp., Rockford, IL.

2. Roll-around wet bar with running water

WITH TOP OPEN, bar provides a two-level work and serving counter for mixing drinks, with sink at right end on lower level. Slide-out drawer stores ice cooler, matches similar wings on the hi-fi cart.

■ YOU DON'T USUALLY EXPECT to turn on a faucet in a small home bar and really get running water—but you do with this one. Not only does the novel unit feature a built-in sink and water supply, but, like the mobile cooking center shown on the preceding pages, it's also designed for versatile, go-anywhere use—out on a deck or patio for summer entertaining or indoors in a play or family room for year-round enjoyment any time. Like the cooking center, it rolls on heavy-duty, ball-type Shepherd casters and is finished in the same exterior materials to have a similar appearance. The sink board is covered with Butcherblock Maple laminate—a Formica countertopping that so closely duplicates the look of a real wood chopping board you have to touch it to tell the difference. The top, sides and doors are faced with Gunstock Walnut—another excellent Formica pattern with deep, rich, wood-grained walnut tones.

The rolling bar is designed around a trim little 12-in.-square Kohler sink with a handsome chrome single-post, pantry-type Kohler faucet. The sink comes in several striking colors—bright red, deep blue, brown and orange. We chose the red, which adds a gay, colorful, festive touch to the maple bartop and walnut exterior. The pantry-type faucet is ideal for bar use because its high-mount spigot is easy to reach under for filling drinks and rinsing glasses. The water

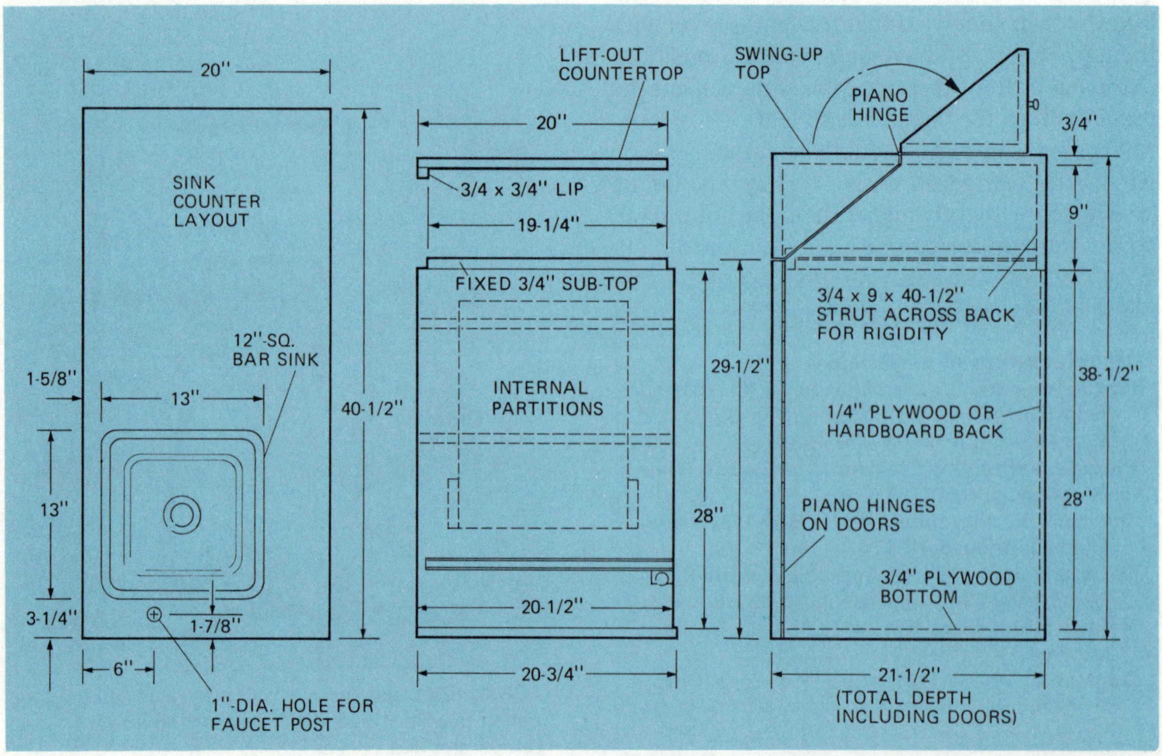

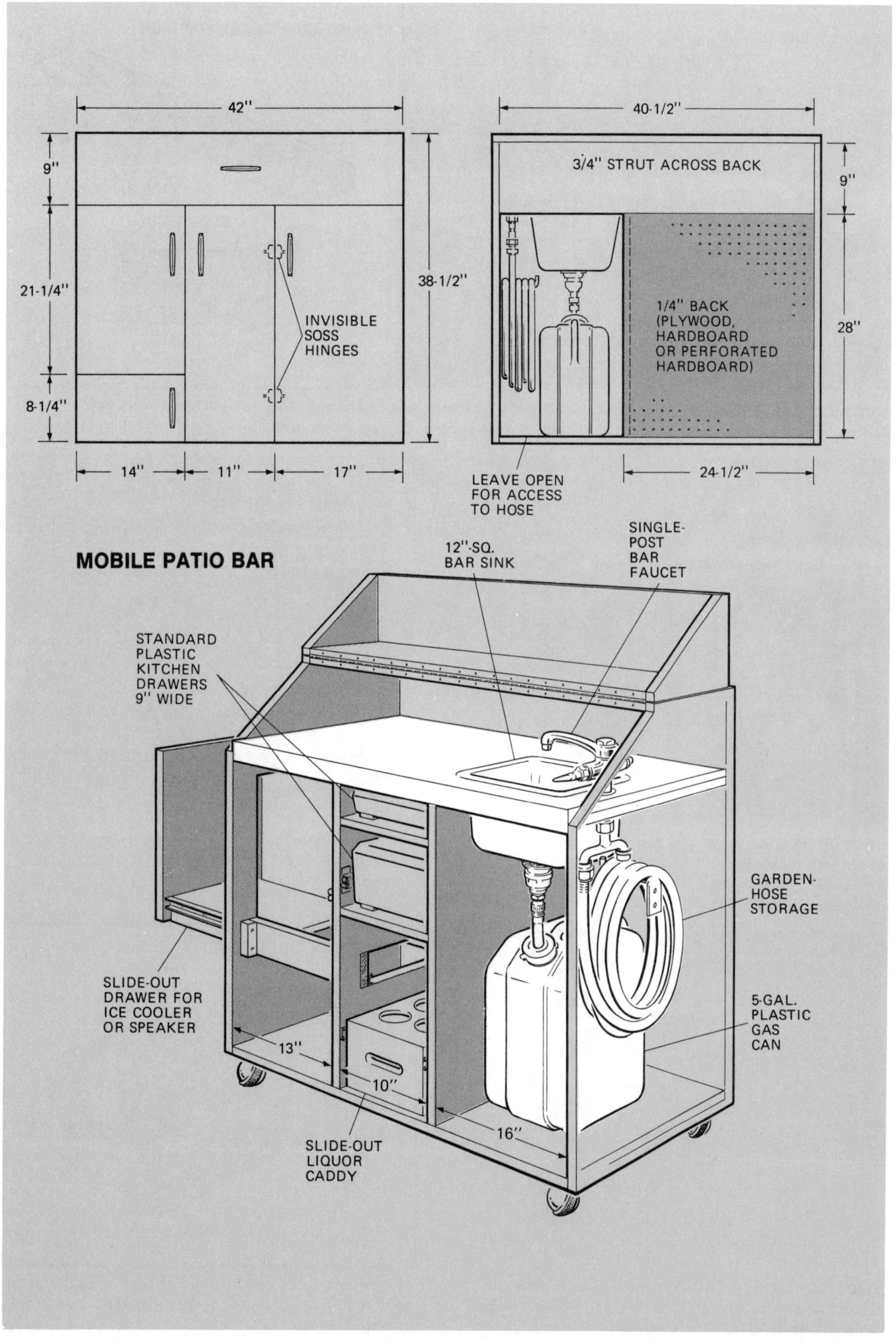

MOBILE PATIO BAR

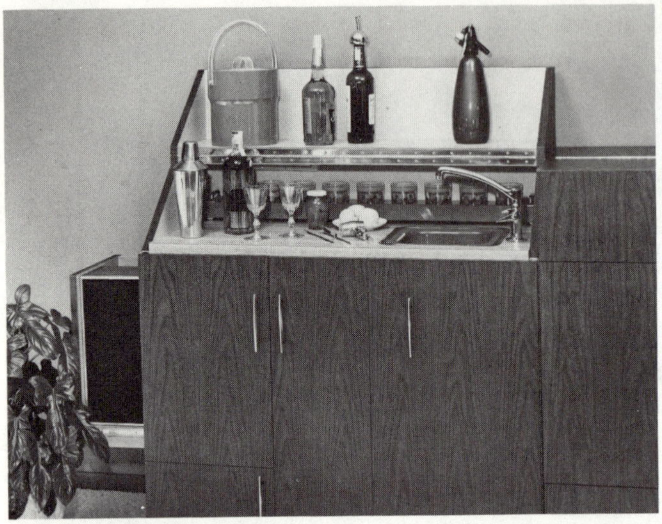

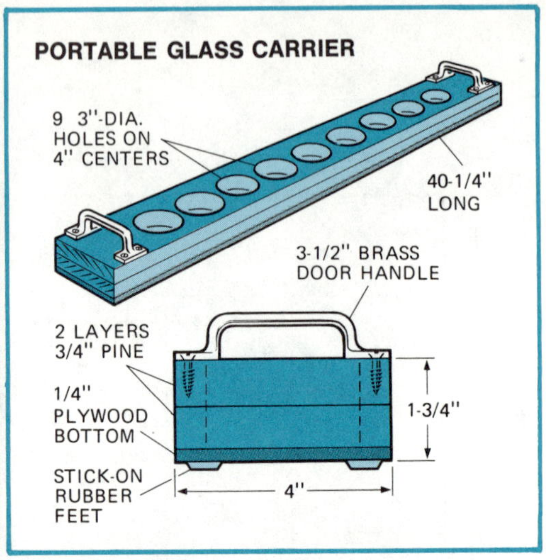

PORTABLE GLASS CARRIER stores at rear of counter on lower level, but can be lifted out and placed on upper shelf for easier access when bar is in use. It holds nine short glasses in holes in rack.

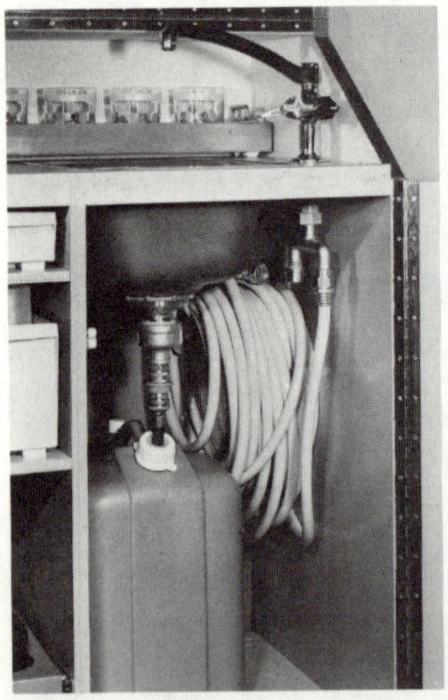

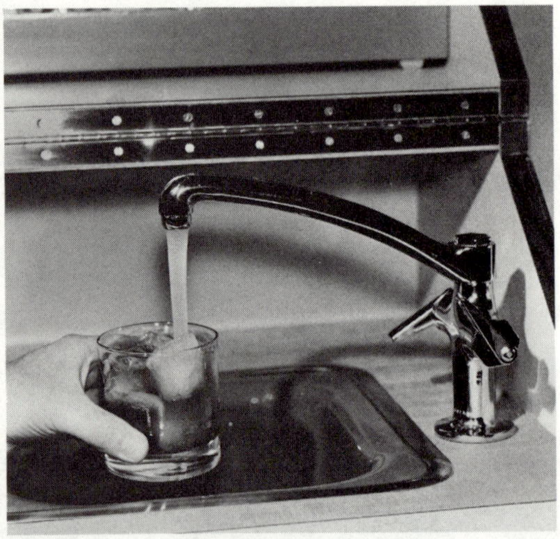

SINK DRAINS into 5-gal. gas can (left, above) used as temporary "holding tank." Water is fed from hose stored on hanger alongside tank. The single-post pantry faucet (right) has highmount spigot, making it easy to slip a glass under it. Plastic drawers (center) hold glasses, supplies.

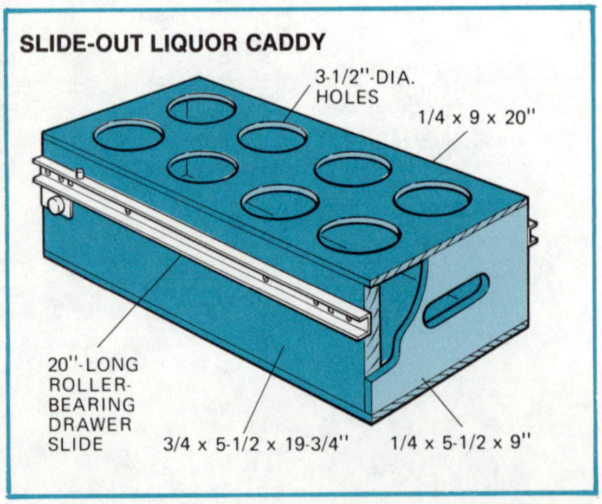

SLIDE-OUT LIQUOR CADDY is located at bottom of the center section in cart, rolls on standard 20-in-long metal drawer guides. It is a simple box of ¼-in. plywood with ¾-in. sides. Eight 3½-in.-diameter holes in the top hold most types of liquor bottles and keep them from tipping when cart is moved.

OPTIONAL ACCESSORY that adds usefulness to bar is NuTone's built-in countertop kitchen-appliance center. Motor unit recesses into counter (right), takes snap-in drink blender (left) and ice crusher (center).

hookup is simple—merely a garden hose connected to the faucet's cold-water inlet by means of a hose adapter fitting, as shown in the photo at left. To be sure the hose stays clean, buy a new one and keep it for bar use only—never use one that's been lying around the yard collecting dirt.

Indoors, the hose can be connected to a laundry tub, washing-machine filler pipe or similar water source, or you can make a semipermanent hookup with plastic pipe or copper tubing. Since hot water is rarely needed in a bar, the faucet's hot-water inlet is capped off and not used.

The sink drains into a five-gallon plastic gas can that serves as a "holding tank" like those used in motor homes and campers. The can easily holds the small amount of water used in the course of an evening's party and eliminates the need for complicated waste plumbing. Since nothing really dirty goes into the tank, sanitation isn't a problem. Just remember to empty its contents after each use and rinse it out to keep it clean. The can stores in a compartment under the counter and is quickly detached from the sink drain for emptying. Using a slip-type, quick-disconnect hose coupling speeds the job.

Besides the built-in sink, the mobile bar cart offers several other novel features. A hinged top swings up to form an extra serving shelf above the sink counter and closes to conceal the bar when it's not in use. There's a portable glass rack, a slide-out bin to hold an ice cooler at one end and a handy liquor caddy that stores whiskey bottles in neat, partitioned compartments to keep them from spilling when the cart is moved about.

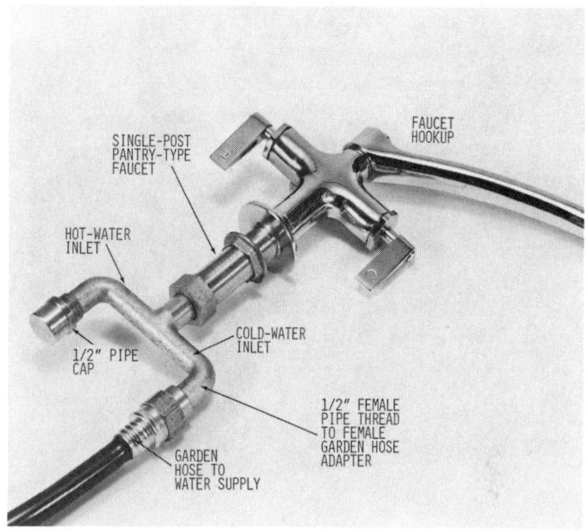

SIMPLE FAUCET HOOKUP to garden hose is shown above, using pipe-to-hose adapter. Hot-water inlet is capped off.

SINK DRAIN requires 1½-to-½-in. pipe reducing adapter, plus garden hose coupling, to feed sink waste into tank.

3. Mobile hi-fi for music outdoors or in

A suitable companion for the bar is this complete stereo system on casters. It not only contains full-size hi-fi speakers and other components but also plenty of storage space for records, tapes and supplies

CLOSED, the mobile hi-fi becomes a stylish credenza, a "plus" in any living room.

SPEAKER WINGS extend for good stereo separation and hinged top flips open to form another shelf.

As a companion to the bar, the identically styled mobile music center shown on the following pages makes an attractive and useful match mate. Like the bar, it rolls on 3-in. Shepherd casters for use indoors or out, has a similar hinged top to hide its contents when not in use and is finished with the same Butcherblock Maple laminate for the counter and Gunstock Walnut for the exterior. In addition, the inside of the top on both the bar and hi-fi carts is finished with Formica's Harvest Gold laminate or can be painted if you prefer. To tell how these handsome look-alike carts appear in color, see pages 1866 and 1867. Here they're shown in an outdoor

OUTSIDE END PIECES

(SAME FOR BOTH CARTS)

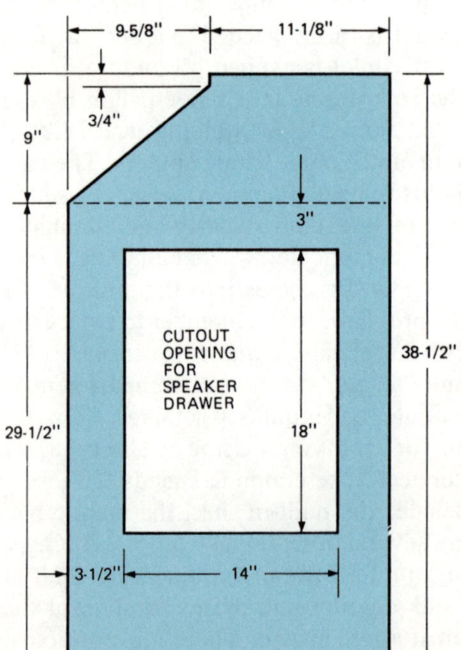

CONSTRUCTION of speaker wings is revealed here. Wings slide on drawer guides held by side rails.

WOODEN SIDE RAILS which support the 14-in. drawer guides extend through partition for good clearance.

ROLL-AROUND HI-FI CART

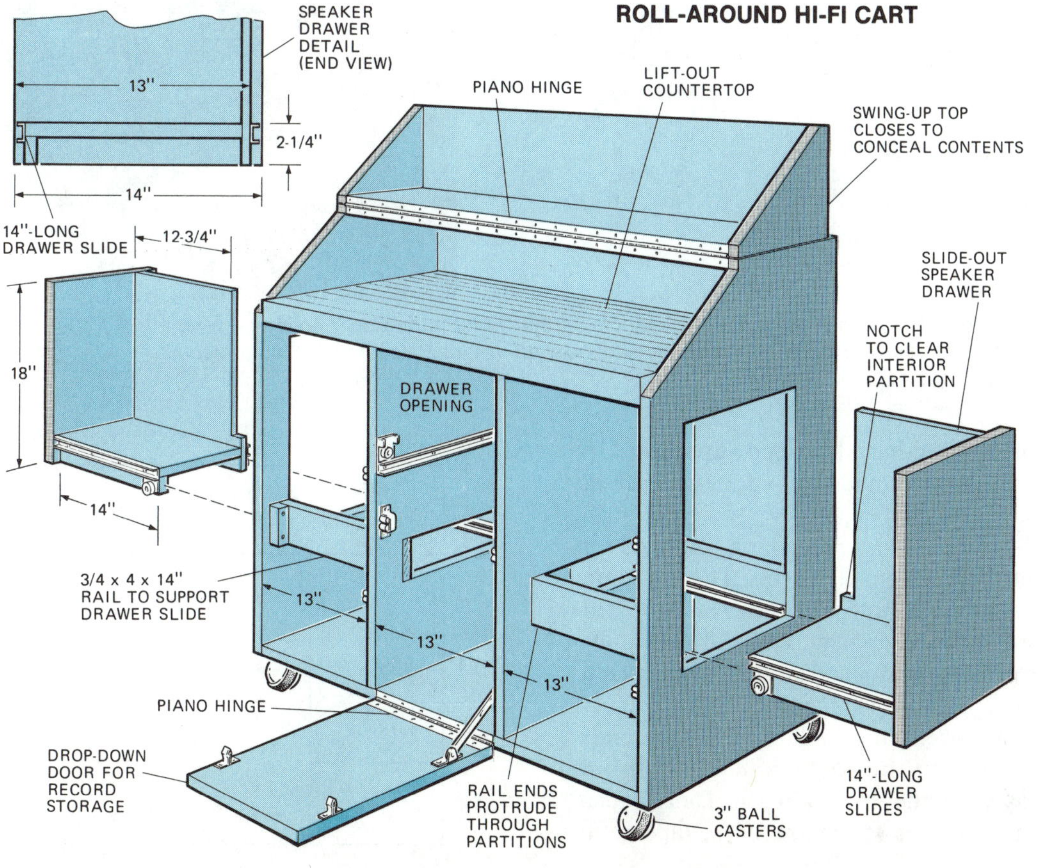

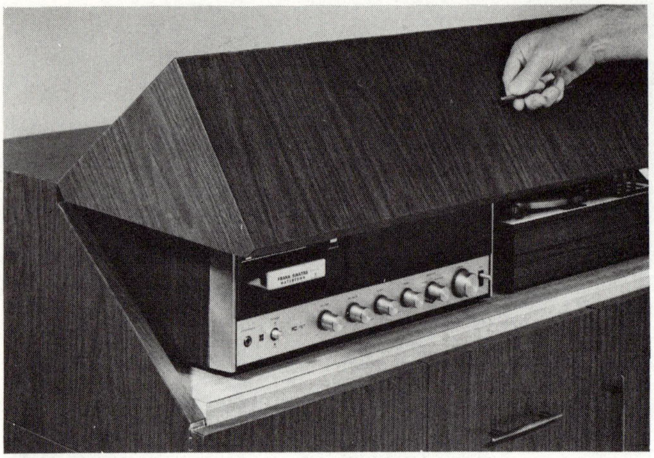

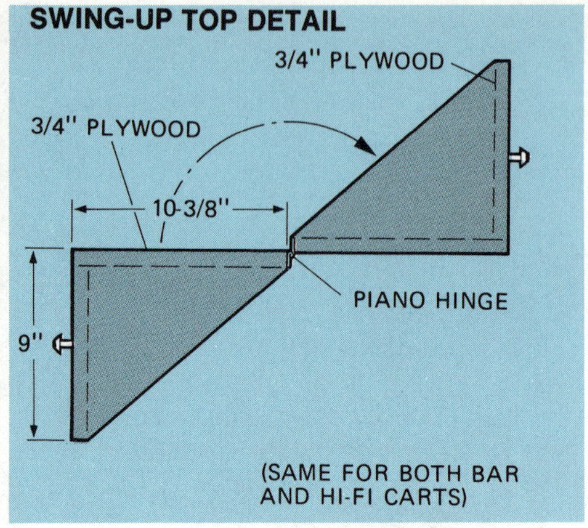

HINGED TOP swings down to conceal contents when bar or hi-fi cart is not in use. Hinged section is deliberately made ¾ in. shallower than rear half so that handle won't hit wall when top is swung back.

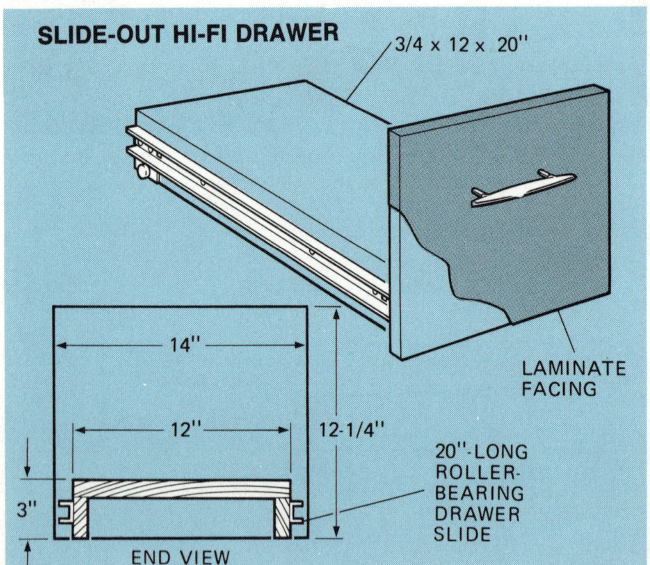

SLIDE-OUT DRAWER in music cart holds hi-fi equipment that won't fit on upper counter—here, a Panasonic cassette deck. It rolls on standard metal drawer guides, can also house slide projector.

setting on Ozite's colorful, striped Sunnyside Up outdoor carpeting—an ideal covering for a deck or patio.

The music cart stows everything you need for a complete hi-fi system on wheels. There's room on the counter for both a receiver and record player or similar equipment, and a drawer pulls out from underneath to hold additional gear such as a cassette deck, tape recorder or slide projector. Twin speaker wings pull out from the ends for good stereo separation, then slide back in out of the way when they're not in use. There's also plenty of space for storing records, tapes and

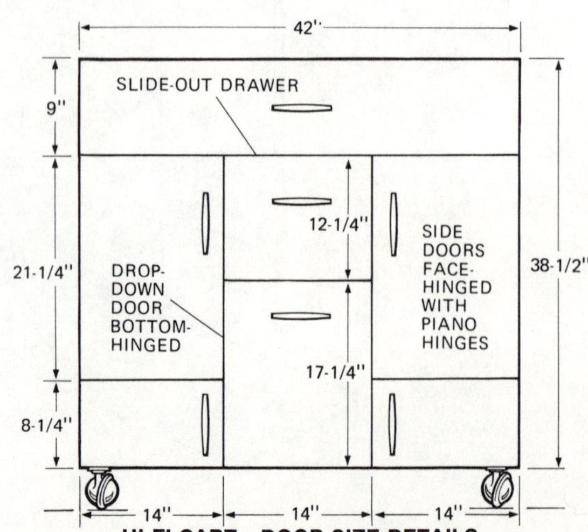

HI-FI CART—DOOR SIZE DETAILS

DRAWERS under speakers store tapes, other hi-fi and supplies. Door backs hang headphones.

RECORD-STORAGE COMPARTMENT has drop-down door that doubles as convenient shelf.

LIFT-OUT COUNTERTOP is removable for easy cleaning. Note deep lip.

continued

other supplies in drawers and compartments at the base of the cart.

To simplify construction, ready-made plastic drawers are used in several places in both the bar and music carts. These are the type made by Rubbermaid for kitchen use and are readily available in hardware and variety stores. They come in stock 9 and 12-in. widths for several dollars apiece. The carts' dimensions have been carefully worked out to accommodate these standard sizes. There's provision for two 12-in. drawers at the bottom of the hi-fi unit and one in the bar cart under the ice cooler. The bar also takes two 9-in. sizes in its center compartment for bar utensils, cocktail glasses and other supplies.

lift-out counter board

The bar and hi-fi carts are identical in construction except for the arrangement of their internal compartments. Each is 42 in. long, 21½ in. deep and 42 in. high. The basic parts are all of ¾-in. plywood with lighter ¼-in. material for the backs, either plywood or hardboard. Note that the countertop in each is actually double-thick. There's a fixed sub-top to give the cart rigidity. On top of this is a separate lift-out counter board that can be removed for easy cleaning or for replacing should the board become marred or you wish to change to a new color scheme. This lift-out top has a ¾-in.-square strip tacked across its front edge to form a 1½-in. deep lip. The lip is self-edged in the same Butcherblock Maple laminate as the top surface, giving the counter the thick, rich appearance of a real chopping block. For tips on applying the laminate, see the section on building the mobile cooking center.

The dimensions shown here are for the wood parts alone and do not take in account the extra thickness of the plastic laminate. This is done for the convenience of those who may prefer to give the carts a natural-wood or painted finish, omitting the laminate. If you decide to apply the laminate facings, slight adjustments must be made in a few of the dimensions to allow for their 1/16-in. thickness. With one exception, the doors and swing-up tops are all face-attached with full-length piano hinges, eliminating fussy fitting and mortising. The exception is on the center door in the bar where there's no way of hinging it directly to the cart without its interfering with the door to the holding tank under the sink. To simplify matters, this door is hinged to the edge of the sink door next to it, using invisible Soss hinges. Thus, the middle door can be opened separately or both doors can be opened together for access to the tank.

There are only two tricky steps in construction—fitting the slope-sided swing-up tops and installing the slide-out speaker and ice-cooler drawers. Start by laying out the end pieces first since these determine the carts' overall shape—the rest of the parts will fall into place naturally from there. If you're building both carts, cut all four end pieces at one time—they're identical. The slide-out drawers for the speakers and ice cooler are also identical and offer a special advantage: If you want to place the two matching carts end-to-end to form one long credenza, you can use the ice-cooler drawer in the bar cart to hold the speaker normally stored in the left-hand end of the hi-fi cart. This will allow both speakers to be extended even when the carts are butted together. It will also improve stereo separation by putting the speakers farther apart. Handles on the drawers are intentionally omitted so the carts will fit flush together without any hardware to get in the way. The drawers are easily opened by reaching in and pushing them out from inside.

Standard K-V roller-bearing drawer guides are used on all slide-out parts. The speaker and ice-cooler drawers take stock 14-in. lengths, while the liquor caddy and tape-recorder drawer need longer 20-in. sizes. These metal tracks require a ½-in. clearance on each side so make the drawers an inch narrower than the openings into which they fit. The ready-made Rubbermaid drawers come with their own plastic slides and are easily mounted with four screws in each.

plumbing facts

The 12-in. sink used in the bar cart is Kohler's Addison Model K-6550. The pantry-type faucet is the Simplex Model K-7890. These are available at plumbing-supply dealers. If you have difficulty locating one in your area, write the Kohler Co., Kohler, WI 53044, for information on local sources. If you should select a faucet other than the one shown here, be sure it stands no higher than 7 in. above the top of the counter. This is maximum height to allow adequate clearance for the top to swing down over the faucet without hitting it. Note that the faucet is mounted off-center to the sink, close to the front edge of the counter. This makes it more readily accessible and gets it out from under the overhanging shelf above. All handles on both carts are straight modern pulls in antique brass finish and match the one on the mobile cook-center. They're Amerock Model No. T-379.

Build models like a pro

Here's a bagful of tips that will help you build plastic models to museum standards

By PHIL JENSEN

■ FOR MORE THAN two decades, plastic kits have been quietly revolutionizing the hobby of model building. Time was when the hobbyist who wanted to recreate in miniature any object from the world around him, had to be a highly skilled craftsman and possess an extensive collection of hand and power tools. Now, however, almost anyone can walk into a store, purchase a kit, and in a few hours turn it into an acceptable model of anything from an antique car to the latest Detroit hot rod, from a Roman bireme to the nuclear-powered aircraft carrier USS *Enterprise*, from the Wright Brothers' frail biplane to the Apollo 11 spacecraft or a supersonic transport.

Early kits were quite crude and often difficult to assemble, but today's kits are made of top-quality materials with parts carefully engineered for ease of assembly. With a little extra care during assembly, a plastic model becomes a masterpiece.

SEE ALSO

Airplane models . . . Cannon models . . . Hobby centers . . . Jeweler's saws . . . Ship models . . . Shops, modelmaking . . . Tools, hand

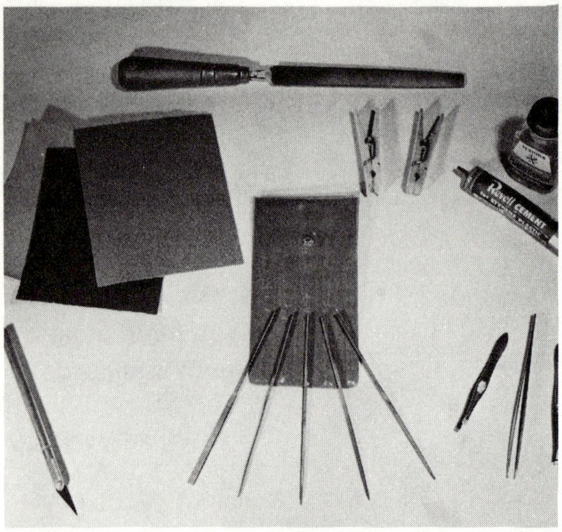

TOOLS NEEDED include knife, jeweler's files, tweezers, sandpaper, emery cloth, clothespins and cement.

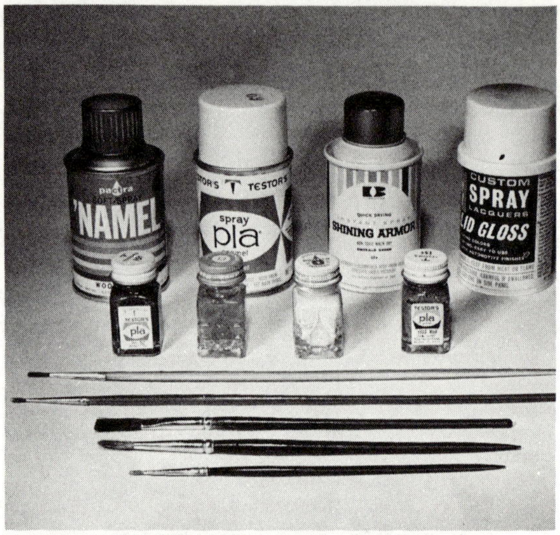

NAME-BRAND ENAMELS are the best bet when choosing a finish. Suitable brushes for details are shown.

continued from previous page

To illustrate the steps necessary for a perfect job, we've chosen Monogram's "Phantom Huey Chopper," a highly detailed, $^1/_{24}$th-scale replica of the Army Bell UH-1B gas-turbine-powered helicopter.

what you'll need

• *Tools and materials.* Have on hand an X-Acto knife, set of jeweler's files, 8-in. fine-cut mill file and several tweezers. You'll also need medium and fine sandpaper or emery cloth for smoothing rough spots, spring-type clothespins and rubber bands for "clamping" and, if the model includes decals, small scissors. Be sure to buy the cement made for styrene plastics. It comes as a liquid, either in a small bottle with applicator brush in the cap or in a tube. The latter seems to be thicker, thus allows better control, and the resulting joint seems stronger. It's also wise to have a small amount of automobile rubbing compound. If you get cement on a finished surface or clear plastic part, the damage can be rubbed out.

understand each step

• *Preassembly instructions.* Most instructions recommend that you study all steps before starting. However, it's more important that you un-

WATCH FOR PARTS, such as seat belts, that should be painted although not so mentioned in the instructions.

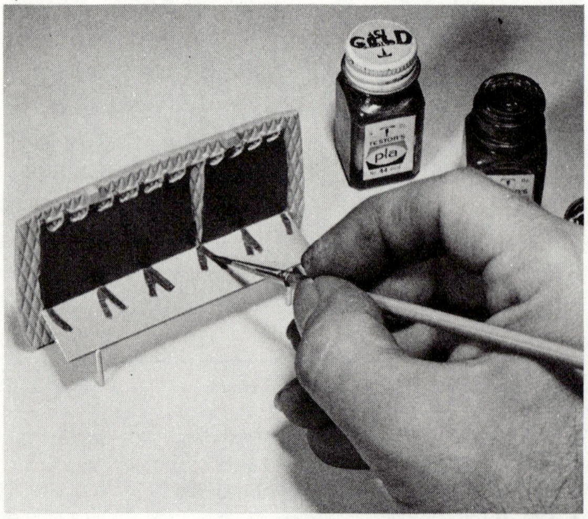

SCRAPE "CHROME" from all surfaces to be joined. Both halves of the detailed jet engine are scraped here.

derstand *each* step before proceeding. Then you can locate and identify the needed pieces. In top-quality kits, parts are usually identified by numbers molded into the parts or adjoining mold-runner and corresponding to those shown in the instructions.

As you proceed, cut each part loose from the runner and examine it for imperfections. Look for flash, ridges at the mold parting-lines and sinkholes in the surface over the heavy sections. Carefully trim flash and ridges with your knife, then sand, file and polish the surface until smooth. Sinkholes are more difficult. Usually the surrounding surface can be filed until the hole disappears. Again, follow up with sanding and polishing. Plastic putty, available in hobby shops, can be used to fill sinks, but the part must then be primed and painted.

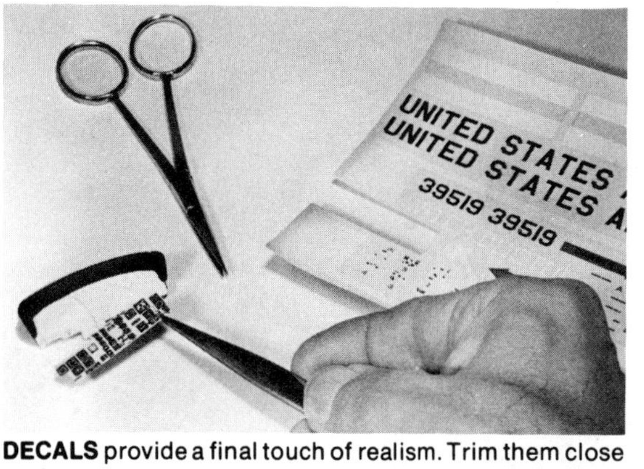

DECALS provide a final touch of realism. Trim them close to the actual pattern so unsightly edges don't remain. A handkerchief is ideal for smoothing them. If a decal sticks before it's in place, lift it off with tweezers, dip it in water and reposition. When the decal is dry, rub it lightly to give it a sheen.

spray-paint before assembly

• *Paint as you go*. Spray-paint all large parts before assembly. If this isn't possible (as with auto hoods, trunk lids and doors), tape the parts together on the inside so they all turn out the same shade. For two-tone paint jobs, always paint the lighter tone first. When it's *thoroughly* dry, cover the area to remain that color with masking tape. Press tape edges tightly against the surface to prevent the second color from bleeding onto the first.

Detail painting can be done before or after the part is in place. For example, if you paint a small part in another color than that of the large part to which it will be cemented, you can attach and brushpaint it in place.

• *"Chrome" plating*. Actually an extremely thin layer of aluminum (deposited in a vacuum) plating is easily damaged by careless handling. Thin as it is, this metallic layer interferes with proper cementing and must be scraped or filed away. Be careful to remove just the unwanted chrome; once it's removed you cannot replace it.

In some cases you may decide the manufacturer has gone chrome-happy and plated parts shouldn't have this shiny finish. Paint may be applied directly over chrome but, according to Monogram, it's better to remove all plating from parts by soaking in flux (zinc chloride). Next day, wash them in clear water and allow to dry. This treatment does not harm the plastic but provides a superior surface for model enamels.

• *Assembly*. The important points are:

1. Check each part for position and proper fit before applying cement. Locating pegs may be oversize, surfaces may not meet exactly or a missed piece of flash may prevent flush mounting. Use your knife and a small file to rectify these conditions.

2. Apply only a minimum of cement, especially on clear plastic parts. For the strongest bond, apply a thin coat of cement to parts to be joined, allow to dry a few minutes and then press them together. Hold the parts until the joint sets, or use rubber bands or clothespins as clamps. Should any cement squeeze out, *do not* try to wipe it away. Let it harden thoroughly and then scrape it away with your knife. Repair any damaged surface with sanding and polishing.

don't force parts

3. Never try to force parts together. Even the best, high-impact styrene is easily broken. But if you do happen to break a part, don't despair. Cracks in large parts can be repaired by cementing; smaller parts such as axles or ship masts, should be reinforced. Drill both ends of the break to receive a short piece of common pin, apply cement and press them together. Allow plenty of time to harden completely.

• *Finishing touches*. Unless parts will get in the way, apply decals after the model is painted and assembled. Trim as shown and follow instructions for applying. Use a smooth cloth to smooth and rub out air bubbles to the edges.

Touch-up painting is a last step. Small imperfections in chrome can be repaired with aluminum paint, but don't overdo it.

The important tip is to *take your time*. If you find yourself tiring, just put the model away and go back to it after a couple of days.

By FRED L. WOLFF

ENGINE of the F-15 Eagle (above left) bolts to the firewall, whereas engines of the Vigilente III (left) and F-105 Thunderchief (above) are fastened to the side of the fuselage.

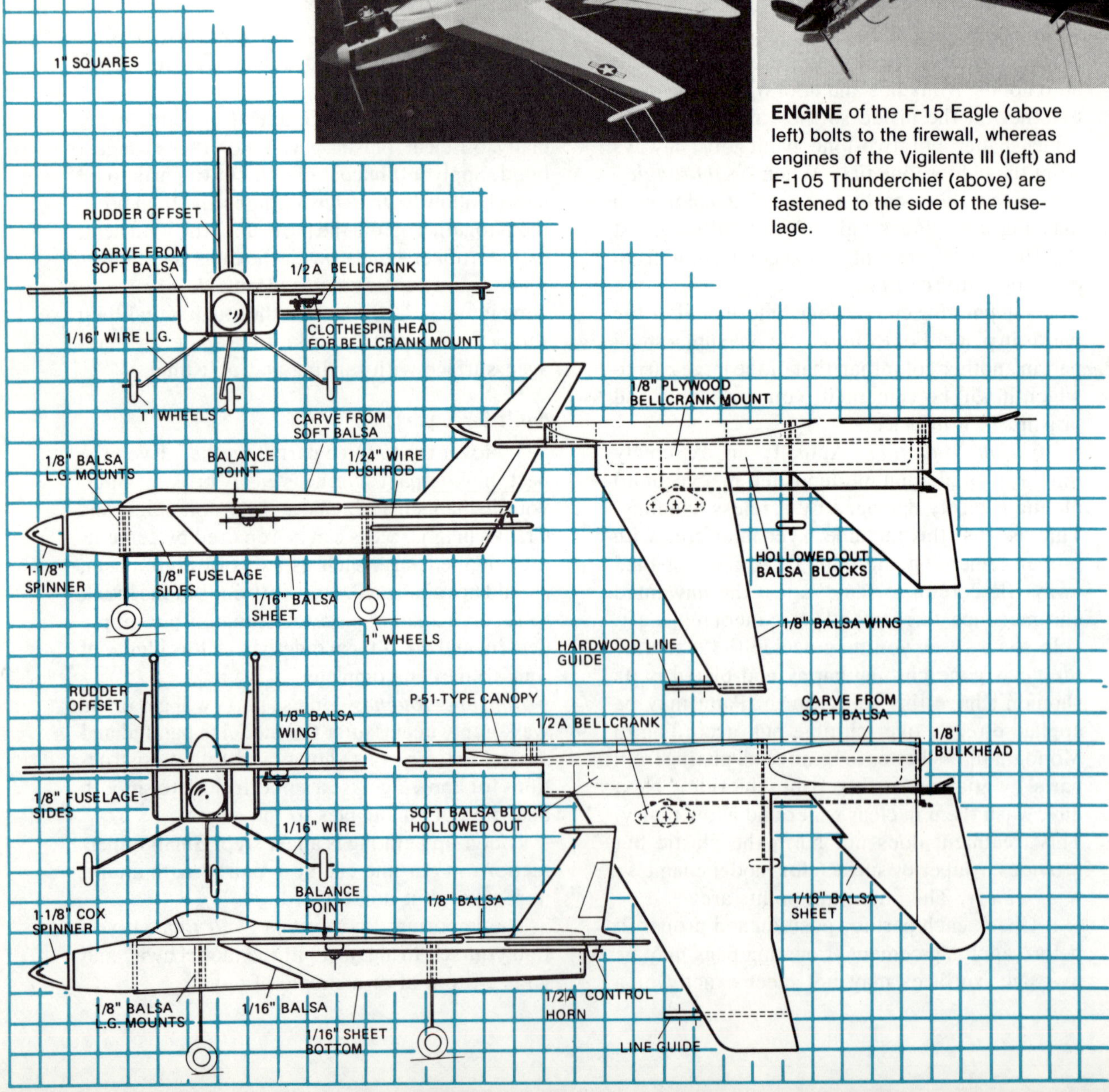

Three scratch-built control-line fighters

■ IF YOU HAVE a perfectly good model engine salvaged from the crash of a ready-to-fly plastic job, you can put it to work again powering one of these three easy-to-build control-line models made of balsa. Components such as bellcranks, elevator horns, wheels, tanks, lines and the like, are inexpensive and available at any hobby shop.

Vigilente III

Building the Vigilente III is relatively simple. After studying the plans, shape and sand the fuselage sides from ⅛-in. balsa. Cut the plywood firewall and the balsa rear bulkhead and cement them to the fuselage sides with epoxy. Bend the landing gear from 1/16-in. wire, apply epoxy and sandwich the gear between the landing-gear mounts. Clamp in a vise until dry and epoxy to the fuselage. Next, shape, sand and hollow out the fuselage side blocks (1 x 1½ x 12 in.) and cement in place.

Cut the bellcrank platform from ⅛-in. plywood, epoxy the hardwood bellcrank to it (the top of a clothespin can be used for a mount) and attach the bellcrank with a screw.

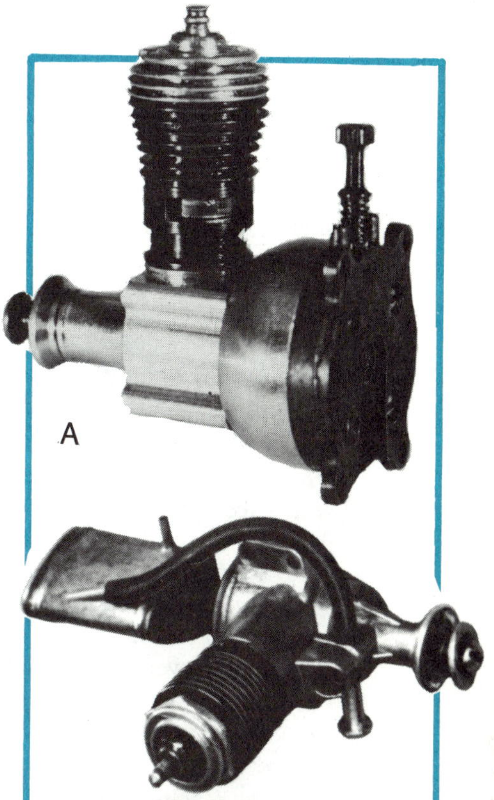

ENGINES

Most small engines used to power ready-to-fly models can be easily adapted to homebuilt designs without modification. In some cases, flywheels must be removed and a new propeller added. Engines that have built-in fuel tanks (A) can be mounted directly to the firewall. Others require separate fuel tanks connected with small tubing to the needle-valve assembly (B). Here, the fuel tank is mounted behind the engine so the fuel outlet is level with engine's needle valve and fuel has a direct path to the engine. Most current engines utilize miniature "glo plugs" for ignition which require a 1½-v. battery to start.

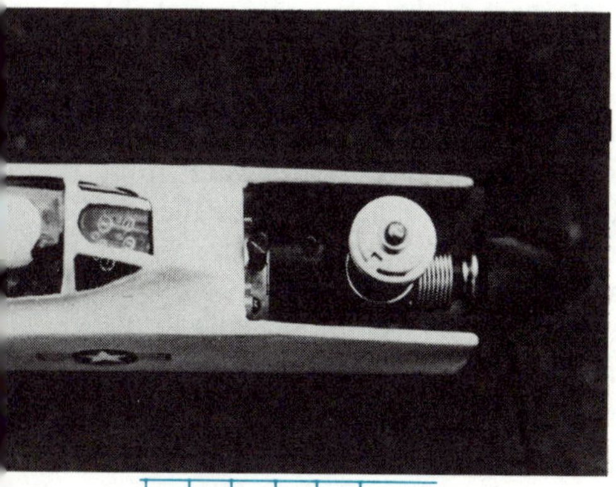

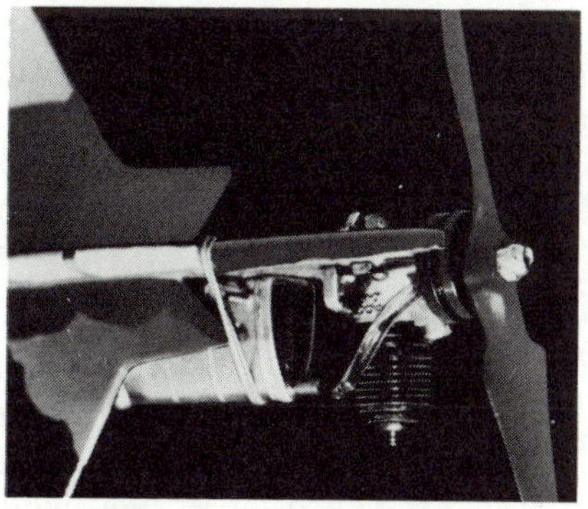

ENGINE with built-in fuel system (left) is mounted to firewall. Engine with separate fuel tank, rubber-banded to fuselage, bolts to side of fuselage.

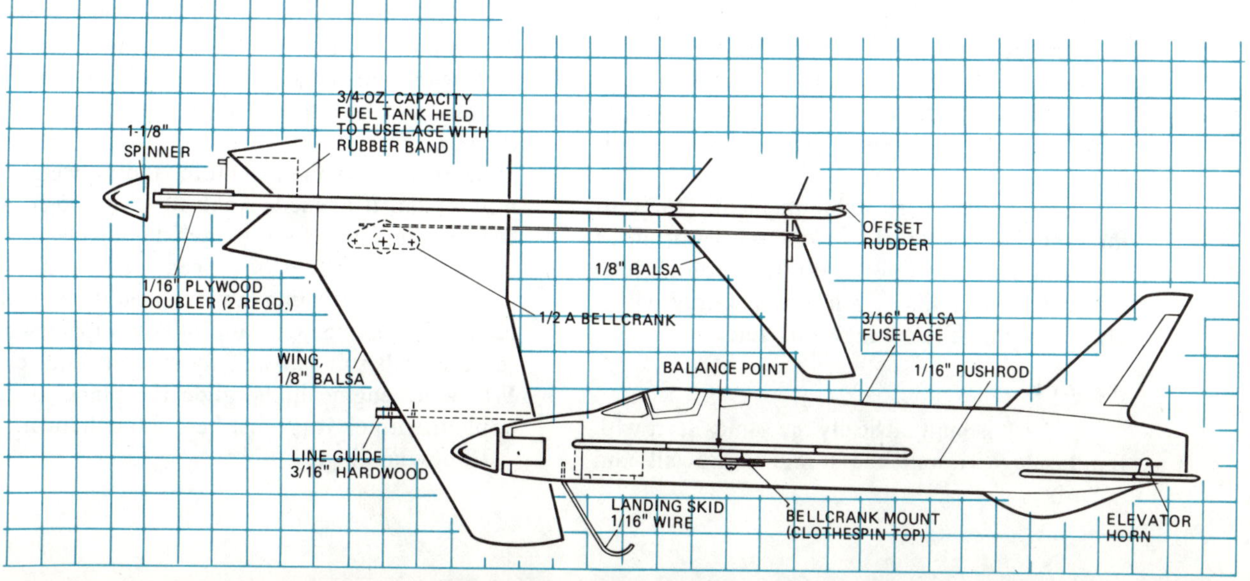

Cement the wing in place, add the fuselage top sheeting and then the horizontal stabilizers. The elevators are connected with a ⅛-in. dowel and attached to the stabilizers with cloth hinges. Before hinging, epoxy the control horn to the left elevator. Attach the wire pushrod to the bell-crank and horn, cement the vertical stabilizer in place, offsetting the rudder as shown, and epoxy the hardwood line guide.

glue canopy to fuselage

After shaping and gluing together the cockpit canopy from four pieces of ⅛-in. balsa, glue it to the top of the fuselage. All that remains is to add the wheels which are held in place by collars and washers, and the engine which is attached to the firewall with four small screws.

Before cementing the wing and the horizontal and vertical stabilizers in place, cover them with Silkspun Coverite. It saves tedious filling and sanding and enables you to apply a good finish without the usual problems. Brush on several coats of clear dope, covering both sides, and when dry, sand each coat with No. 400 wet/dry sandpaper used dry. Now cement the wing in place, then the tail sections after first painting.

Apply three coats of clear dope to the rest of the plane and sand each with No. 220 sandpaper. Follow with four coats of sanding sealer, let dry for several days and sand again.

painting the model

Paint the upper half of the fuselage sides light gray, the lower half and the underside of the wing white. The cockpit windows are silver, the jet intakes black and the intake rims red. Add Navy decals. The panel lines are made with a pen. Protect the decals and panel lines from fuel damage with clear dope, spraying or brushing very lightly. Allow to dry for several days.

Tie a length of thread to a pin and press it into the fuselage at the balance point indicated. Raise the craft by the thread and add weight (wood scrap or light metal) to the nose or tail until the airplane hangs level. Never fly a plane that's tail-heavy.

Vigilente III is very stable in flight. On landing, anticipate when the engine will run out of fuel and take her down near the ground. The craft won't drop like a brick, but neither will it glide very far. It has a high sink rate.

the F-15

The F-15 is built basically the same. Start with the fuselage, install the formers, firewall and landing gear. The fuselage sides are made of 1/16-in.-thick sheet balsa. The canopy is from a Scientific or similar Mustang kit, and is blended into the fuselage with plastic balsa or a filler of your preference. Finally add the remaining essentials—engine, bell-crank, wire and control horn. Wing and tail surfaces are installed in the same way as the Vigilente III.

the F-105

The F-105 is simpler to build than the other two because it has a "profile" fuselage that requires no bulkheads, coverings and the like. The wing is cut from ⅛-in. balsa and brushed with several coats of clear dope. Apply it to both sides at a time to avoid warping. When dry, sand with No. 400 wet/dry sandpaper.

The fuselage is cut from 3/16-in. balsa and is notched where the wing goes. Cut the engine doublers from 1/16-in. plywood and epoxy them to the nose as shown. Cut the fuselage and doublers to fit your engine. The vertical stabilizer is cut from 3/16-in. balsa and can be either glued to the fuselage or be a part of the same piece. Cut the rudder and glue it into the offset shown. The ventral fin is cut from ⅛ or 3/16-in. balsa and glued to the bottom of the fuselage.

Cut the horizontal stabilizer and elevator from ⅛ or 3/16-in. balsa. Sand to shape and glue the stabilizer to the fuselage. Attach the elevator to the stabilizer with cloth hinges. Add the ⅛-in.-plywood horn to the elevator. Sand the edges of the fuselage, vertical stabilizer and ventral fin.

epoxy wing to fuselage

Install the wing to the fuselage with epoxy. Epoxy the bellcrank mount and the hardwood line guide, then the balsa tank-position guide.

Since the wing is already treated with clear dope, brush several coats on the fuselage and the rest of the model. Sand and camouflage the plane and install the engine. Lash on the ¾-oz. fuel tank with rubber bands. An optional wire landing skid can be added. Install the bellcrank and the wire.

Balance the plane as before, adding weight to nose or tail if needed. Hook up 25 to 35-ft. dacron flying lines. Before each flight, check the elevator for freedom of movement. On take-off have your helper run a few steps and then gently launch the plane. On landing, anticipate when the fuel will run out and fly straight and level. When the engine quits, glide the plane in and apply the up elevator just before touchdown.

Happy landings!

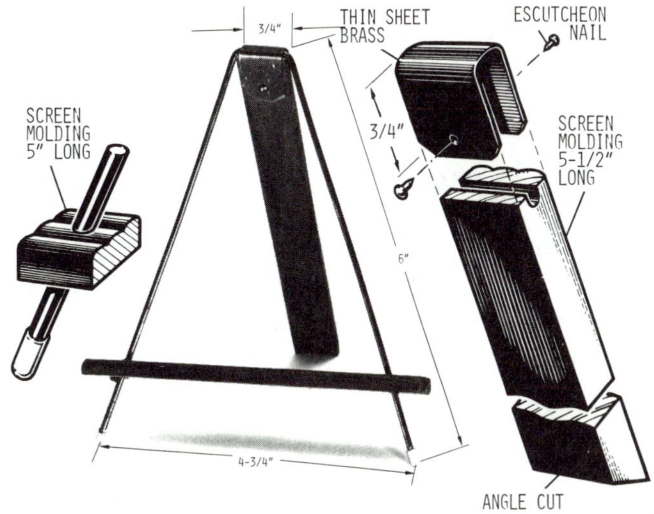

MINIATURE EASELS will attractively display objects such as nameplates and postcard paintings. These easels can easily be mass-produced using screen molding, coathanger wire and sheet brass. The easel's support leg is hinged with a U-shaped clip so that the leg can be adjusted to the desired angle. Holes for the wire should be drilled to fit tightly. When not in use, the easel can be folded flat.—*Henry Stainken, Staten Island, NY.*

A FELT-TIP marking pen makes a good substitute for regular layout dye when you need to mark and inscribe metal. You can scribe it when it dries and it will wipe off easily with a lacquer thinner.—*Doug Blodgett, St. Charles, MO.*

A STRONG SUPPORT rod for unwieldy plants is a real necessity, especially when soil in the pot won't hold a stake. For my tall philodendron, I welded three metal rods (one 24-in., the others 12-in.) to an 8-in.-dia. steel plate as shown above, removed the plant from the pot, put the welded plate in the bottom and repotted the plant. I stuck lengths of bamboo fishing pole over pointed ends of the rods and changed to longer lengths as the plant grew.—*G. H. Willard, Seattle.*

Easy-build modular furniture

Starting with one basic frame, you can create five different pieces. They all have efficient, built-in lighting to suit many tasks

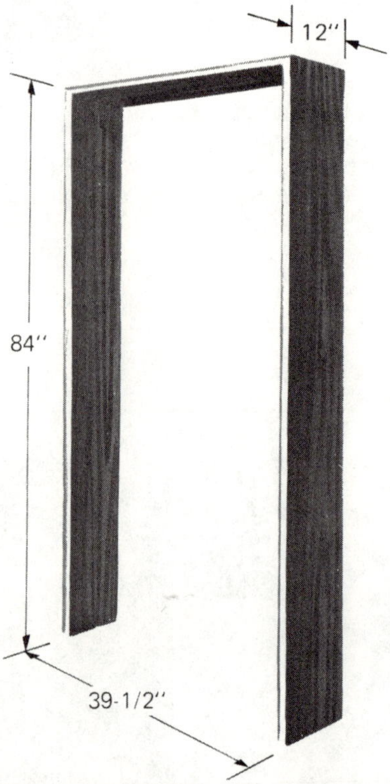

BASIC FRAMEWORK FOR ALL CONCEPTS

ROOM DIVIDER is simplest of five handsome furniture pieces. It's accented by reflector lamps at the top.

THE CHALLENGE: Create a versatile module that can be used in almost any room for any purpose and lighted to suit the particular function the piece is designed for. Designer Bill Ingham at General Electric fielded the challenge and came up with a series of good-looking furniture pieces including the handsome room divider shown.

The basic form with its standardized dimensions can be quickly adapted to serve any number of family needs. The five most common uses are you wish to build. The idea is to get the most use from a minimal amount of space—essentially a simple enclosure measuring a foot in depth, 39½ inches in width and 84 inches in height.

The material to use on this project is ¾-in. A-D plywood. And stick to the very basic construction techniques. Simply use butt joints, glue and screws. Finishing the various pieces is a matter of personal preference. They can be painted, stained if a cabinet-grade plywood is used, or covered with plastic laminate. Or the units can be finished using a combination of two or more finishes.

SEE ALSO

Ceilings . . . Doors . . . Finishes, wood . . . Frames, picture . . . Joinery . . . Remodeling . . . Sanding . . . Sewing centers . . . Staining, wood

A modern hutch

THE ROOM DIVIDER can be used as a breakfront by simply parking it along a wall. Because the shelves are of glass and the unit has three 50-watt reflector lamps, it can serve handsomely to highlight decorative objects or favored family collections. The storage space below is a bonus sure to be welcomed in most households. The beauty of the modular concept of construction is that the pieces all have the look of custom built-ins, yet should you ever move you can take the furniture with you. Wires from the lights exit through small holes in the top and are held fast to the back of the piece with insulated staples.

For a neat job, simply measure the exact length of the extension cord you will need and cut it to suit. Then attach the extension cord to the baseboard, running it along the wall using insulated staples.

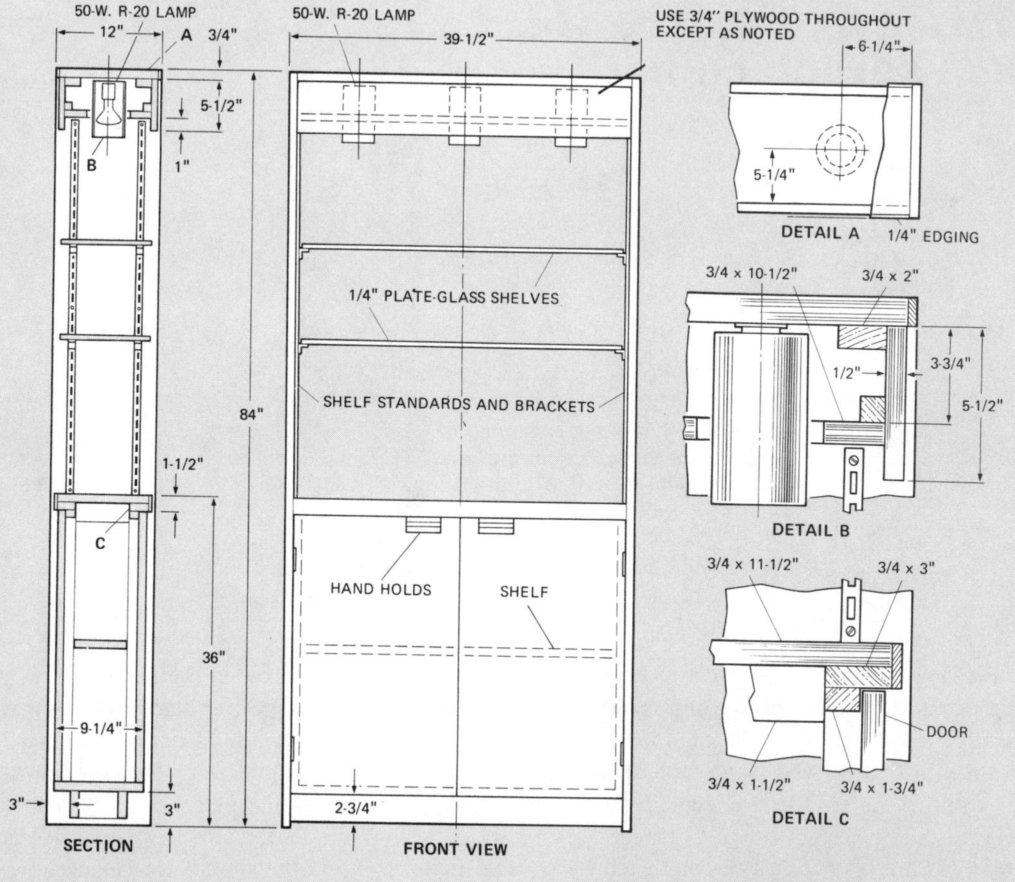

Compact sewing center

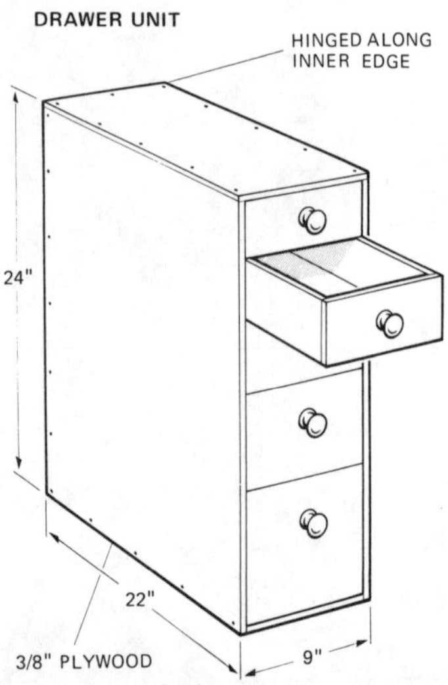

OPENED sewing center reveals a full-length mirror on the left door and a storage unit on the right. Four-drawer pedestal in the drawing at left is built using simple, basic construction techniques.

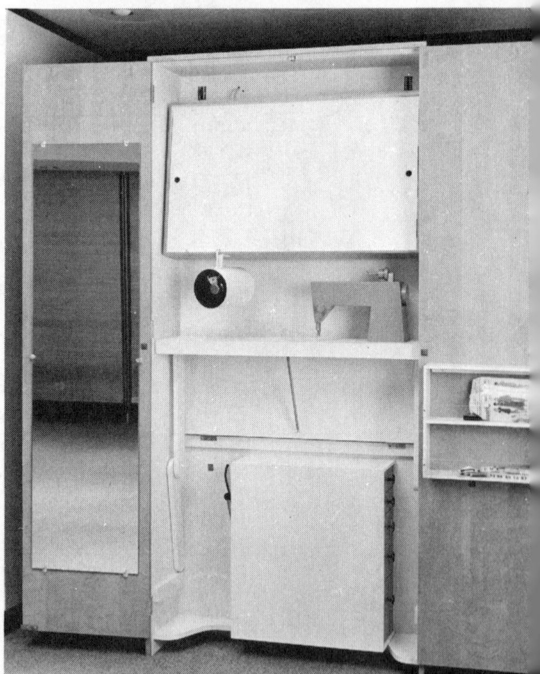

WHAT APPEARS to be a handsome wardrobe here actually becomes an efficient sewing center when opened for use. The design is intended to solve the problem for those who want such a facility and have no place to put it except in the bedroom.

When the doors are opened, a full-length mirror is revealed on the left door, and at right is storage for all the accessories a busy seamstress likes to keep close at hand. There is also additional storage available in the pull-out drawers.

The sewing-machine counter pulls down to create a full 24-in. depth. The panel then swings up on a spring device, allowing for an extra-deep lighting fixture to fit into place. Four 30-watt Deluxe Warm-White fluorescent lamps provide general lighting, while the spotlamp—angled toward the machine's needle—provides the pinpoint light necessary to see thread against fabric without causing squinting and eyestrain.

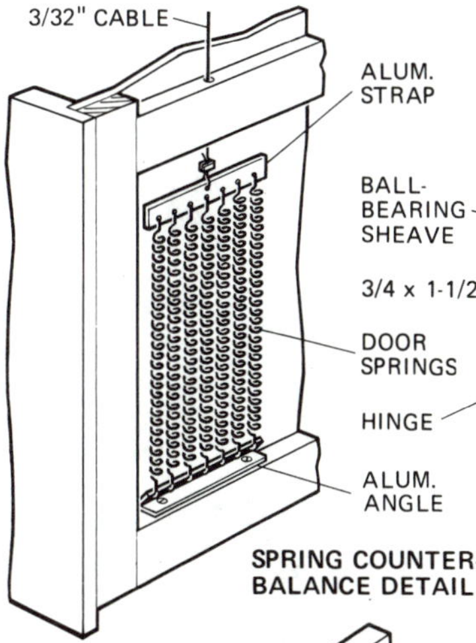

SPRING COUNTER-BALANCE DETAIL

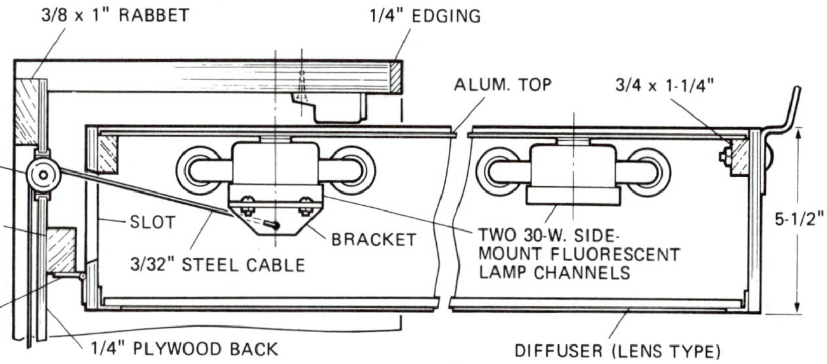

LAMP-BOX DETAIL

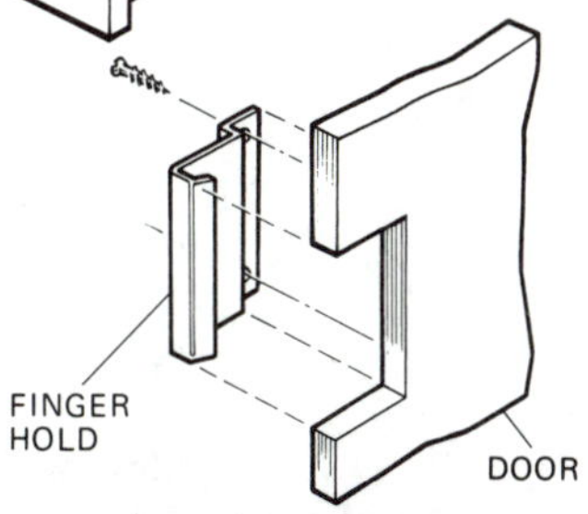

FLUSH DOOR HANDLE

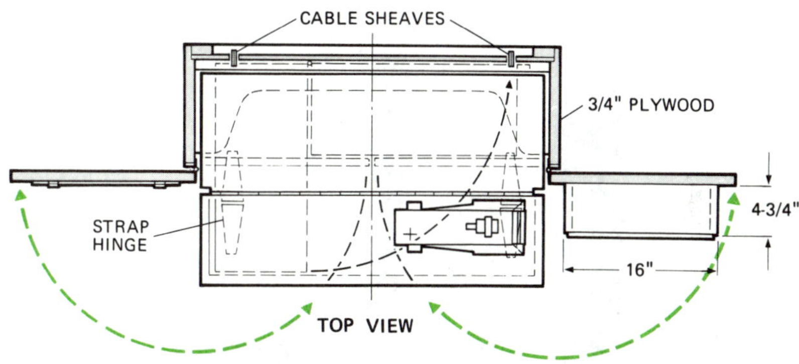

TOP VIEW

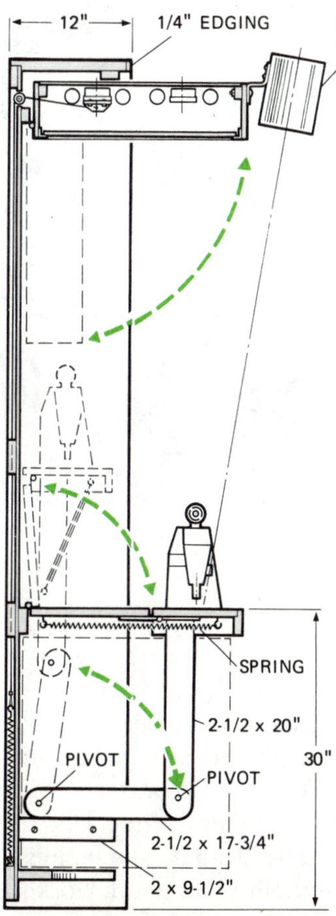

END-VIEW SECTION

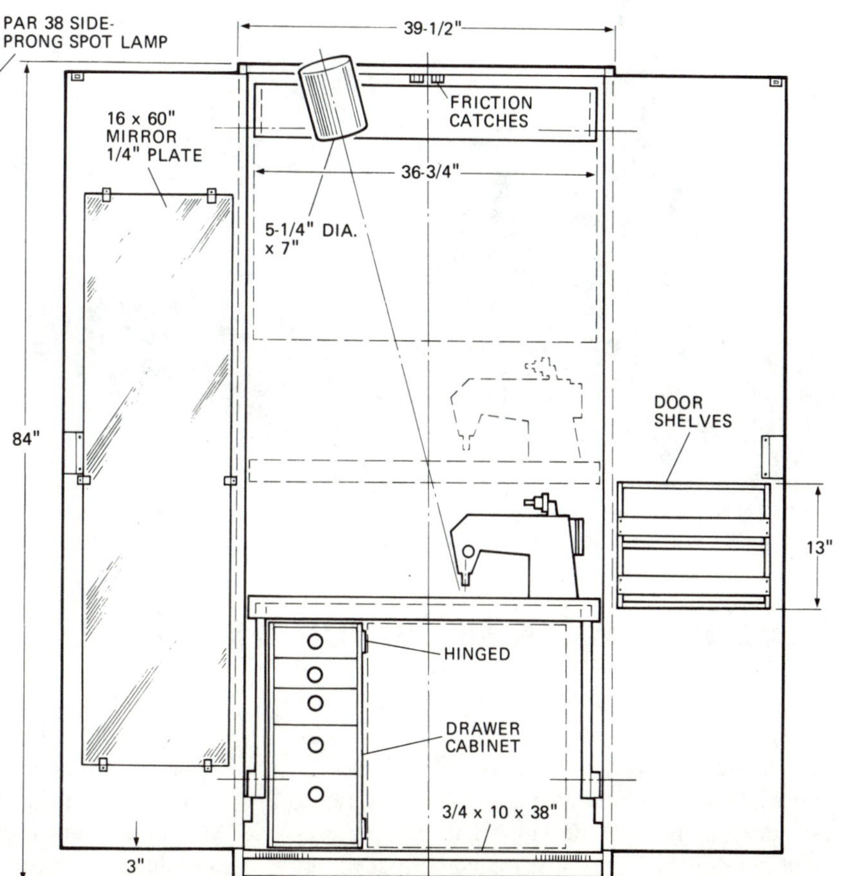

FRONT VIEW

BY OPENING the lower cabinet doors to expose filing space and lowering the upper door, you get a 24-in. desktop. The lighting unit pulls out to light up the shelves and desk surface.

Versatile work or hobby bench

AT FIRST GLANCE (see right photo on facing page) the closed desk appears to be a shelf-storage area. However, when you open the lower pair of doors a counter flips down and becomes a 2-ft.-deep convenient desktop. The lighting element pulls out so light is distributed both down on the desk work area and up toward the shelves where reference books and knicknacks can be stored. Note the convenient file storage bins that appear on the sides of the lower doors.

For work surfaces such as the desktop (and the sewing center on page 1892), a plastic laminate should be used for durability, a smooth working surface, and to keep maintenance at a minimum.

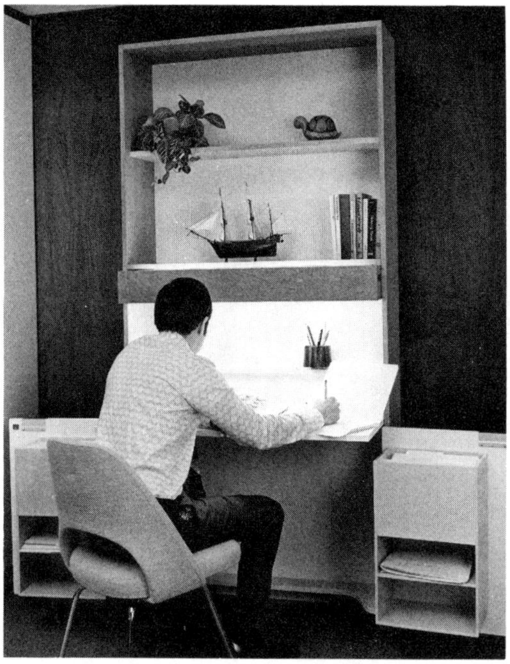

WOULD YOU believe it's a desk? When closed (right photo), unit seems to be something it's not — a breakfront. The simple structure provides necessary room for the family record-keeping.

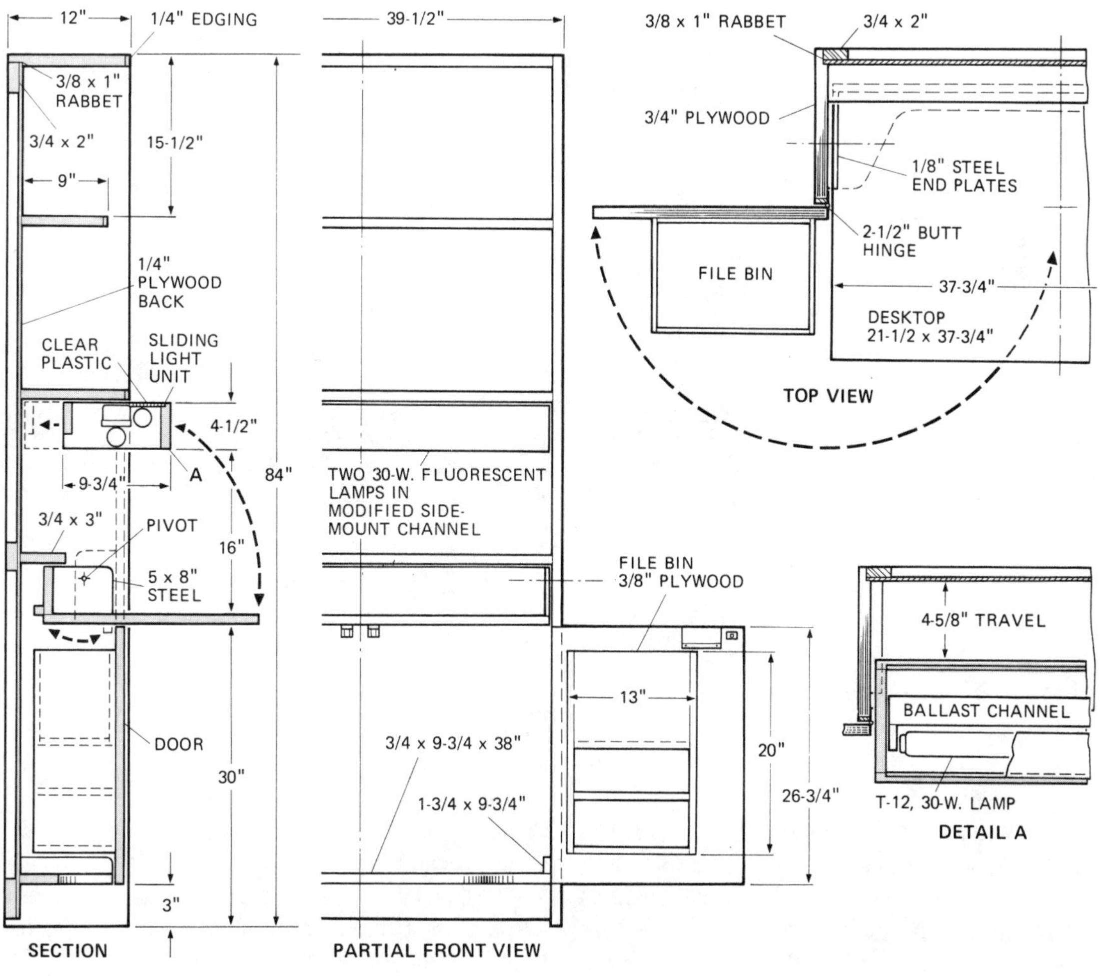

PERSONAL GROOMING center for the lady of the house is a scant 1 ft. deep and 39 in. wide. Height can be varied to suit the room's decor.

Build a vanity

THE VANITY CENTER is planned for personal grooming and can be used either sitting down or standing. Since the top surface (shelf) will not be exposed to rough treatment which might scratch or mar it, it is of ¼-in.-thick clear sheet acrylic plastic (such as Plexiglas or Lucite) so it is possible to utilize the full-length mirror. The lighting is a combination of decorative incandescent globe-shaped bulbs (14 25-watt No. G 18½ lamps) on both sides of the mirror and a pair of 30-watt deluxe fluorescents in the hood overhead.

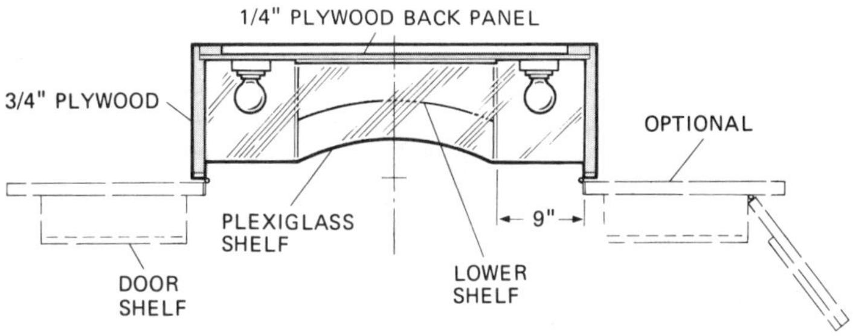

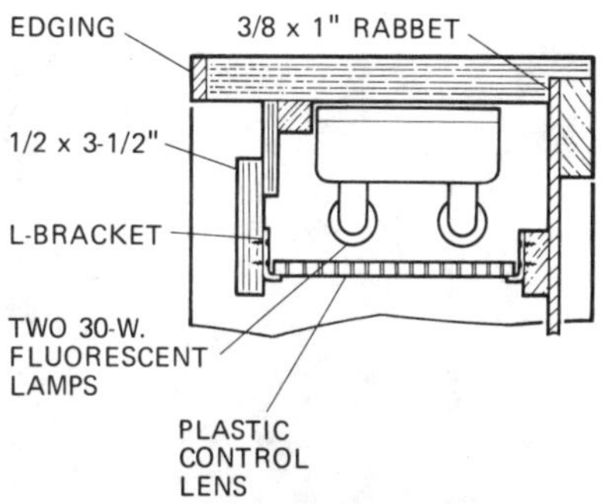

TOP VIEW

LIGHT WHERE you need it—at a makeup table: Two Deluxe Warm-White fluorescents overhead and 14 incandescent bulbs give all you could ask for.

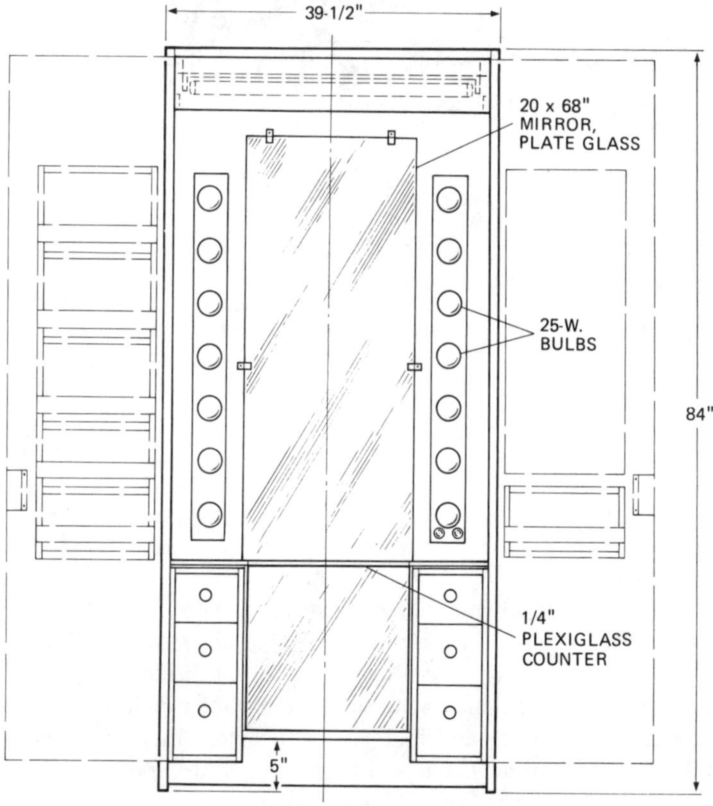

FRONT VIEW

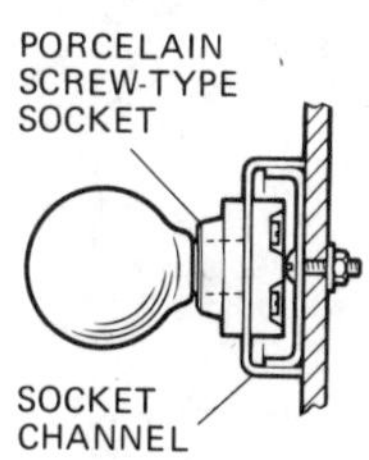

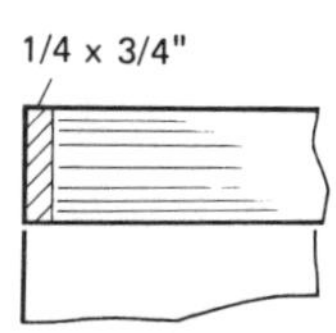

DETAIL A

DETAIL B

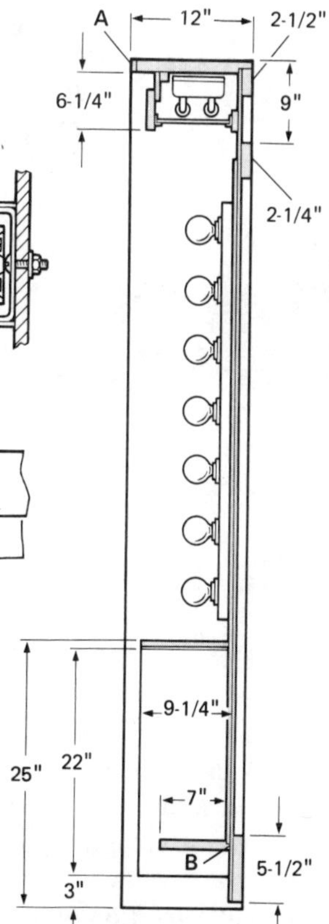

WHEN USED AS a bar-counter, the modular unit provides convenient storage under fluorescent lights.

Service bar

THE SAME MODULE with slight variations becomes a handy service bar with ample room for storing potables and ice cubes.

Wall systems such as these units are popular in the furniture market now, and by starting with these concepts, recognizing that sizes and designs are not fixed, you can design your own wall system at a fraction of what the commercial equivalents cost. For example, consider combining several modular elements. Two wall dividers used with a desk unit and the bar above will give about 13 ft. of wall with plenty of space. Turn your imagination loose, rearrange the wall however you want and find the arrangement that's most convenient for your current activities. You may even want to consider an L-shaped island or peninsula.

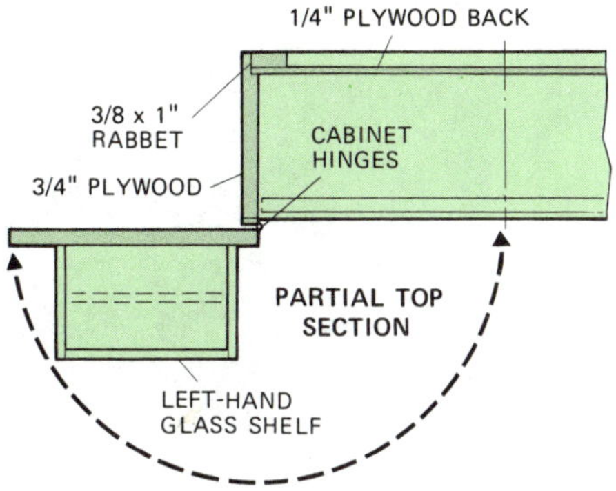
1/4" PLYWOOD BACK
3/8 x 1"
RABBET
3/4" PLYWOOD
CABINET
HINGES
PARTIAL TOP
SECTION
LEFT-HAND
GLASS SHELF

CLUB SODA
7-UP
7UP

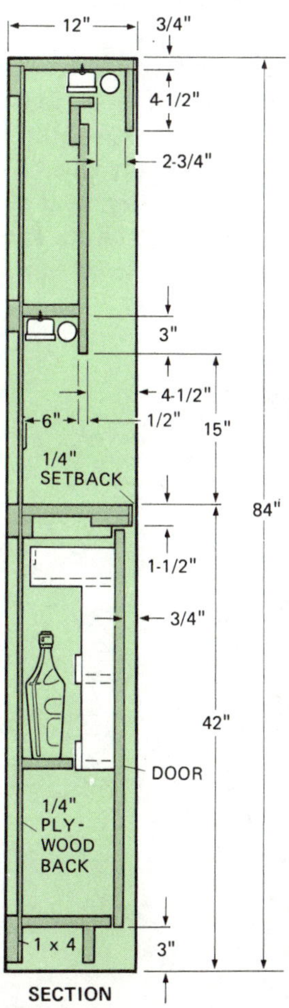
12"
3/4"
4-1/2"
2-3/4"
3"
4-1/2"
6"
1/2"
15"
1/4"
SETBACK
84"
1-1/2"
3/4"
42"
DOOR
1/4"
PLY-
WOOD
BACK
1 x 4
3"
SECTION

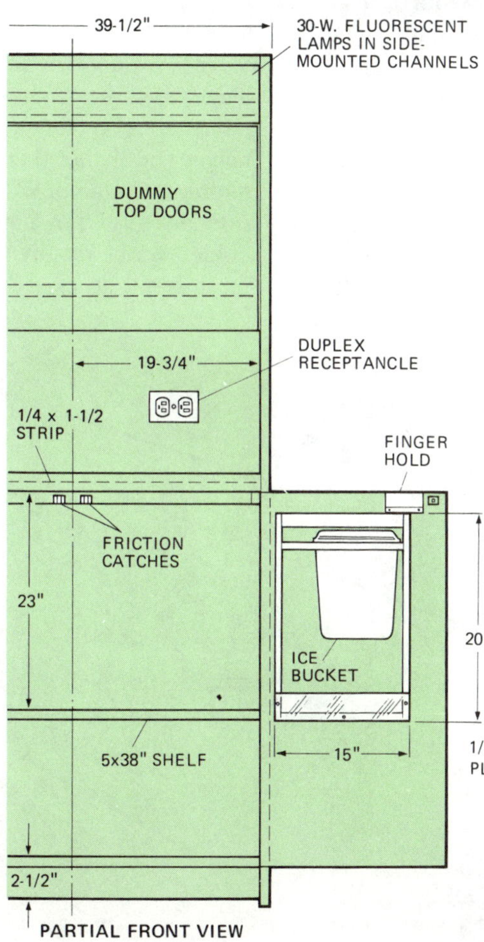
39-1/2"
30-W. FLUORESCENT
LAMPS IN SIDE-
MOUNTED CHANNELS
DUMMY
TOP DOORS
DUPLEX
RECEPTANCLE
19-3/4"
1/4 x 1-1/2
STRIP
FINGER
HOLD
FRICTION
CATCHES
23"
ICE
BUCKET
5x38" SHELF
15"
2-1/2"
PARTIAL FRONT VIEW

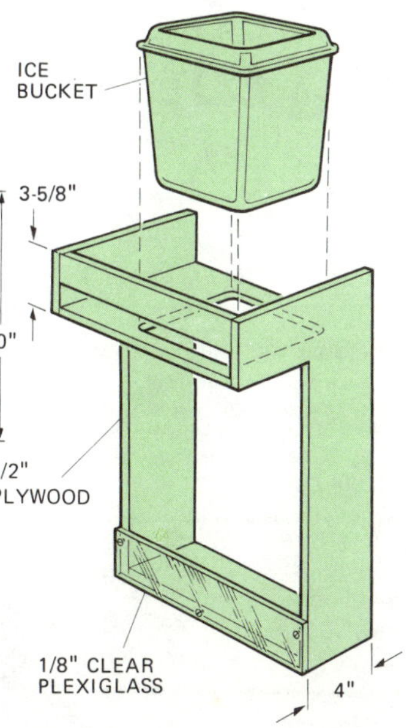
ICE
BUCKET
3-5/8"
20"
1/2"
PLYWOOD
1/8" CLEAR
PLEXIGLASS
4"

HOLDER KEEPS cutters sharp. It can be stowed in a drawer. Use a dado head (right) on a radial-arm saw or a table saw to plow the grooves and dadoes. Tilt saw's head 15° to create the slightly angled dadoes.

Storage for molding cutters

By C.E. BANISTER

■ LOOSE CUTTERS, banging around in a drawer with other tools, are easily dulled and damaged. This cutter holder solves these problems.

Start by cutting a 1 1/16-in.-thick board to the dimensions given in the materials list. Set a dado head 5/8-in. wide and at a 15° angle to cut 3/4-in.-deep dadoes. Rotate workpiece and reset saw to 90° and the dado head for cutting the 1/4-in. grooves, 3/4 in. deep. Use marks at the edges of the base (A) to locate the cuts.

Now cut divider strips (C) slightly higher and longer than the grooves into which they are to be inserted. Also cut the sidepieces (B) slightly longer and higher than required. Apply glue, assemble and clamp. When the glue is dry, sand all surfaces flush for a good-looking project. The holder can be readily varnished, if desired, but a finish is not necessary.

MATERIALS LIST

Key	No.	Size and description
A	1	1 1/16x5 1/4x9" hardwood
B	2	1/4x1 1/8x9 1/16" hardwood
C	3	1/4x13/16x9 1/16" hardwood

Misc.: White glue, polyurethane.

SEE ALSO

Jointers . . . Moldings . . .
Radial-arm saws . . . Routers . . .
Saws, radial-arm . . . Table saws

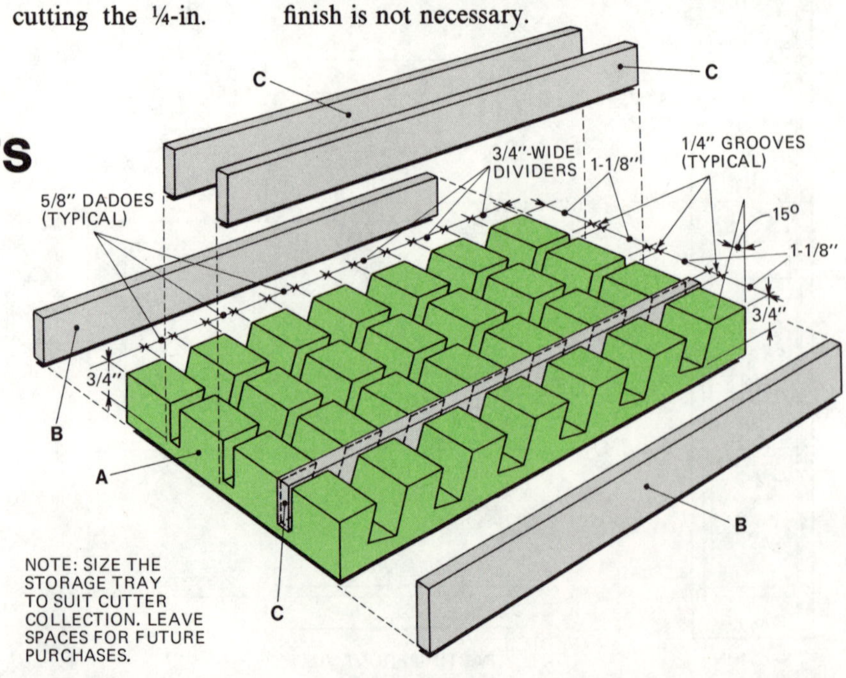

Moldings—the finishing touch

By W. CLYDE LAMMEY

Any woodwork without moldings has a certain unfinished look. It leaves you with a sense of incompleteness. Here are the molding shapes most readily available

NO MATTER WHERE located, moldings are a basic of design, an element to be utilized in a wide range of applications. Without moldings almost any structure, anything with dimension, is little more than a box shape with stark overhangs and uninteresting square corners.

But a molding is a shape that catches the eye It adds something both elemental and decorative, the finishing detail, leaves you with the feeling that the job is complete.

Traditional architecture utilizes a range of applied moldings both inside and outside the structure; inside as a finishing detail in a room, such as picture molding; a coved mold in the corner where wall meets ceiling; as a baseboard with quarter-round and as door and window trim with stops having one molded edge. Outside you see moldings in various forms under cornices, around sash frames and around and over door frames.

Common applied moldings are combinations of curves, reverse curves and plane surfaces generally worked on the face, corners and edges of both hard and softwood lumber. As a rule these shapes come in the form of strips varying in width and thickness and are sold by the lineal foot.

Common among the applied moldings are the simple cove and quarter-round shapes which are cut on small square or rectangular strips. The former shape is ordinarily used as trim under an overhanging member such as a mantel, shelf or similar application. The latter you'll see forming the trim where a baseboard meets flooring. Of course, there are variants in the application and shape of these forms which are commonly known as bed moldings.

Crown and cove moldings are similar in that both shapes are usually cut on one face of stock varying in width from 2 or 3 in. to 5 in. or more in the standard sizes.

As these moldings are usually intended to span a right-angle corner, as in a room where wall meets ceiling, the back corners are cut at a 45-deg. angle and the adjacent corners are trimmed at 90 deg. to the 45-deg. corners, the flats serving as "stops" for the curves cut on the face.

Cove moldings are commonly cut with a single concavity on the face, often the full width of the stock, but these also are cut in combinations of concavity and reverse curve, the former shape usually the wider of the two. A narrow plane surface, or flat, is usually cut between the shapes to serve as a stop at the ends of the curves.

Common crown moldings consist of variations of reverse-curve and cove cuts in combination on the same face of the stock. They come in standard widths from about 1½ in. up. Like the cove moldings, crown moldings in the larger sizes are designed to span a corner.

Half-round moldings, of which there are various sizes, generally are applied as nosings, that is, are nailed or otherwise fastened to square edges to serve either a practical or decorative purpose. On old work you will sometimes see half rounds attached to the outer edges of stair treads. Much the same is true of the combination half-round-and-cove mold which you will often find serving as a nosing on later-type stair treads. These usually have a half-round-and-cove shape cut on the same face of the strip. Such moldings generally come as strips ranging in widths from fractions of an inch to about 2 in. or more.

Stops commonly range in thickness from ⅜ to ½ in. and in widths up to 2 in. or more. These usually come with a reverse-curve molding on one corner but there also are variants of the shapes available. Some are supplied with only one corner slightly rounded to a uniform radius. Stops are used mainly in door and window

SEE ALSO

Ceilings . . . Doors . . . Finishes, wood . . . Frames, picture . . . Joinery . . . Molding cutters . . . Sanding . . . Shapers . . . Shop techniques . . . Staining, wood

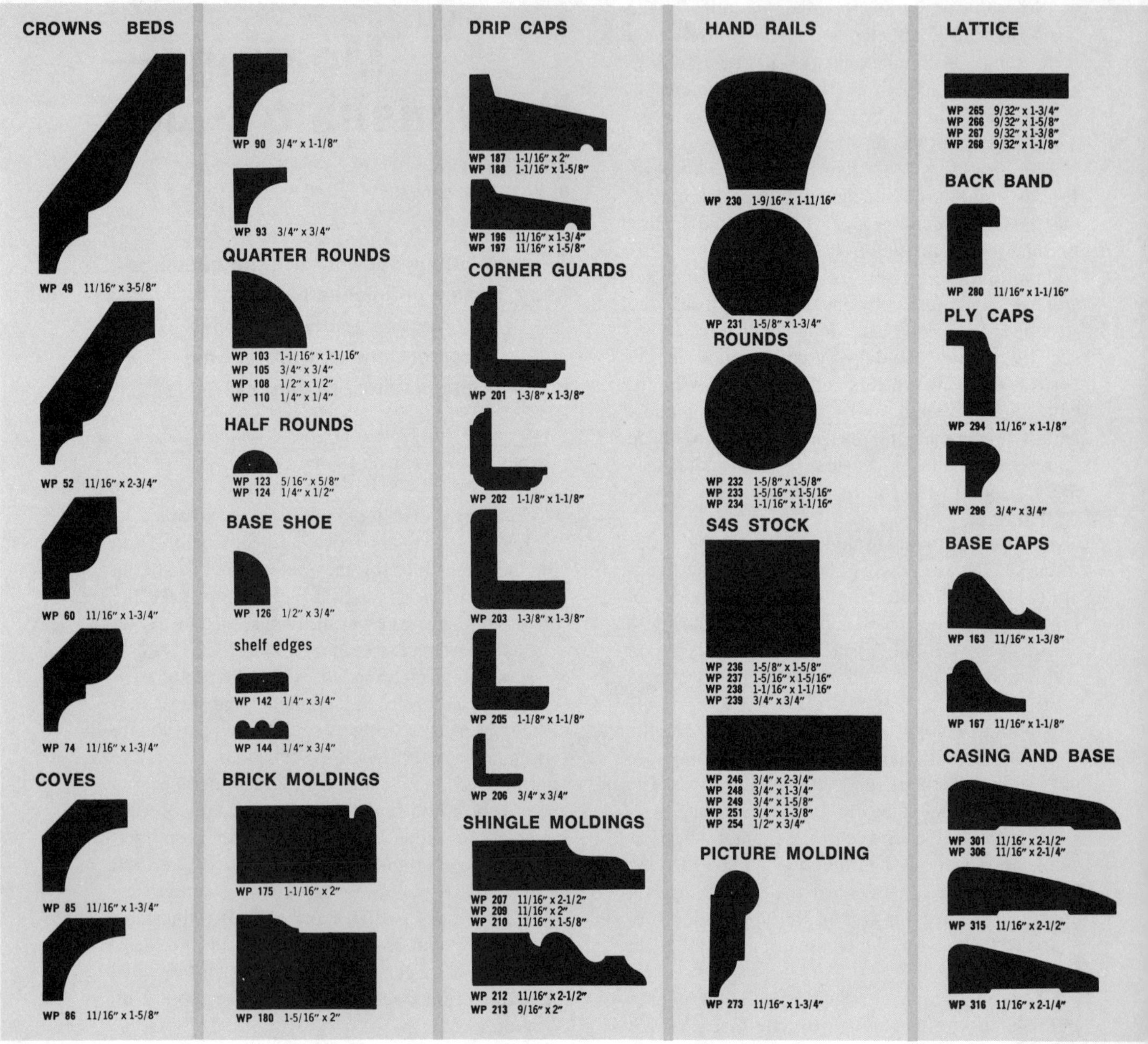

Western Wood Moulding Producer

framing and are ordinarily attached with small finishing nails having the heads set below the surface and the holes puttied flush. On the finest work the stops are attached with ovalhead screws, the heads being countersunk flush or turned down on plated washers.

Other shapes which classify as moldings are full rounds, screen moldings, chair rails, window stools and corner beads to name a few of the many shapes. Some of these are not so commonly used in present-day construction but most are still available as replacements. Full rounds in larger sizes are often utilized as stair rails. A variant (although it does not classify as molding) is the well-known dowel, which is regularly supplied 36 in. long.

If you've ever made screen frames you've used one of the several forms of screen moldings and you'll see many of the other forms illustrated in nearly all old work and occasionally in newer structures.

All the illustrations, which are end views of the shapes, show only one size. But, of course, many of the moldings come in several widths and thicknesses to adapt them to various types of work.

When installing moldings around outside corners the ends are mitered and it's the usual prac-

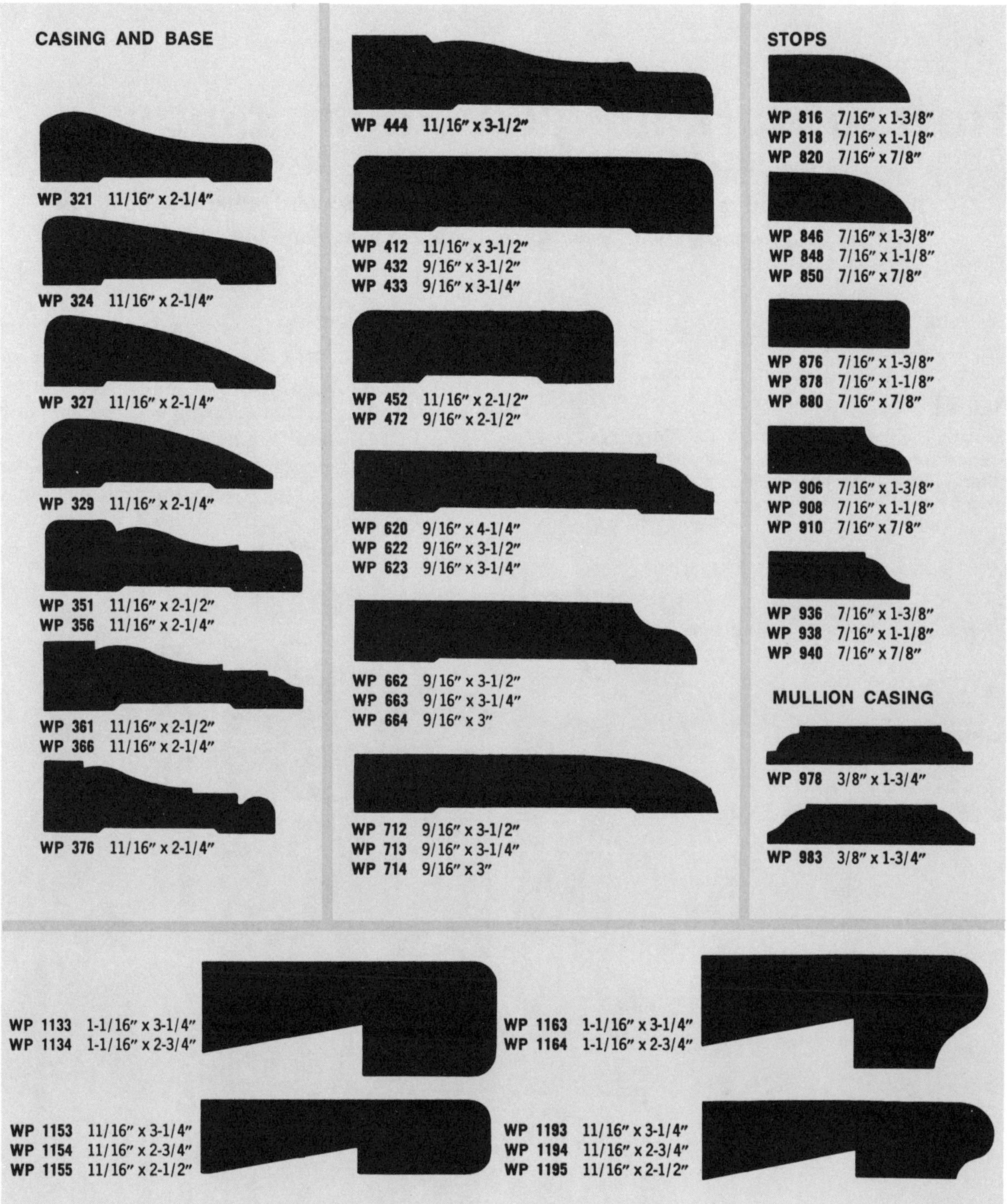

tice to cut the two members just lightly over at the mitered ends. This assures a tight fit (if the miter is properly cut, of course) and should there be slight shrinkage of the wood, or movement of the framing due to shrinkage, the mitered joint will remain a tight fit.

Moldings that meet in an inside corner should always be coped, that is, one member is cut and nailed in place the full length, the end in the corner being cut square off. Then the end of the meeting mold is cut to a shape that will fit tightly against the first member, using a scroll, or coping saw, and making the cut at a very slight angle. Moldings that fit between walls should not be forced; rather they should be cut slightly under.

How to work magic with moldings

Inexpensive and readily available at your local lumberyard, standard moldings let you work wonders with your walls. Here are ideas and instructions

By HARRY WICKS

SEE ALSO

Basement remodeling . . . Doors . . . Entryways . . . Frames, picture . . . Joinery . . . Miter boards . . . Miter joints . . . Molding cutters . . . Nails

THE NEXT TIME you plan to redecorate a room, pause a bit before deciding that a coat of paint or wallpaper is all you need to get a fresh look. With some planning, you will be pleasantly surprised at how dramatic a change can be achieved by simply adding wood moldings to the walls. Placing moldings on a flat wall surface is

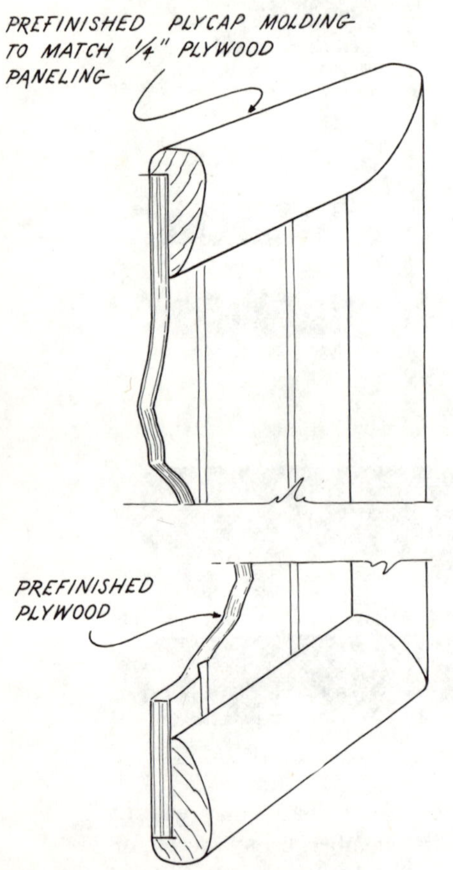

FRAMED plywood panels have a look of luxury, yet cost less than a fully paneled wall. The plywood is glued to the wall, then surrounded with lengths of prefinished moldings.

PANELED WAINSCOTING helps to reduce the feeling of height and emptiness along a stair wall. Section drawings of the moldings used in room on this page are shown on the following pages.

WALLPAPER OR FABRIC can be used in conjunction with moldings to create a new room mood. Here, wallpaper is pasted on inexpensive C-D plywood that is then trimmed with selected moldings. Each framed panel is then suspended against the wall from two hooks.

YOU CAN DRESS UP an inexpensive flush door with wood moldings. Two versions—hung in the same opening show how the moldings can change the look.

ATTACH THE MOLDINGS to an exterior door using waterproof glue and finishing nails. All 24 of the corner joints shown here were carefully mitered.

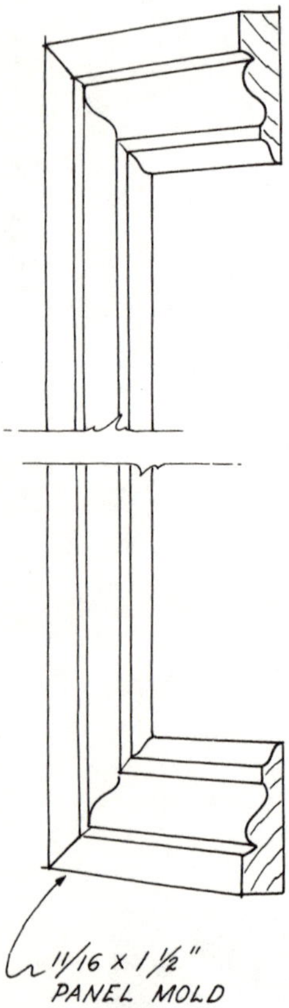

MOLDING DETAILS can be effectively used to set the period of design. To duplicate the room shown above, panels must be sized proportionately to suit the size of the wall.

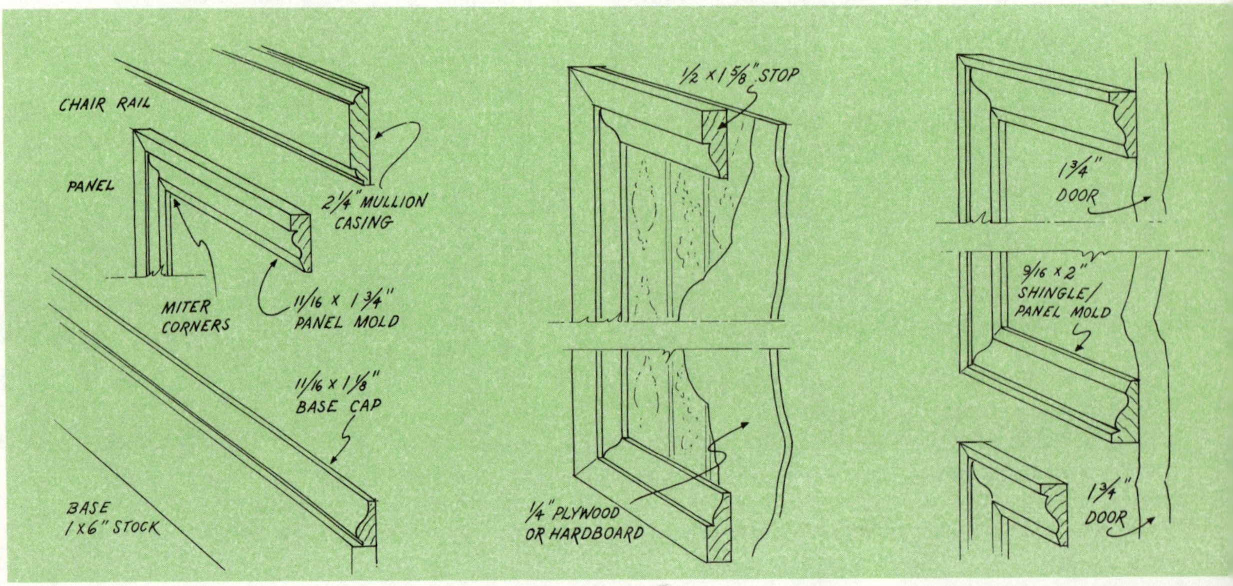

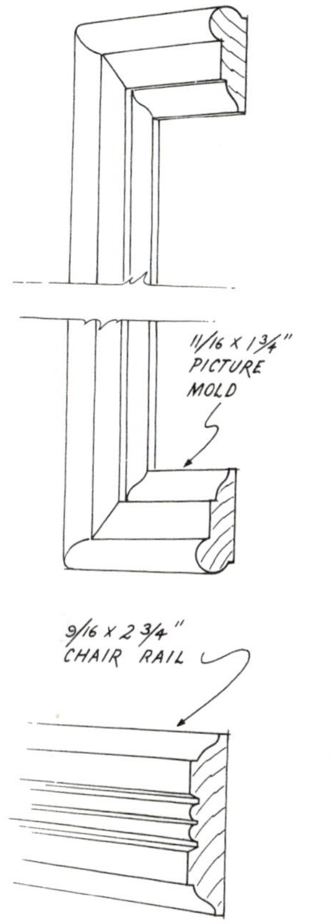

FRESH, CRISP LOOK is achieved by painting moldings to contrast with the walls. The chair rail not only looks good, but acts to protect the walls from chair bumps.

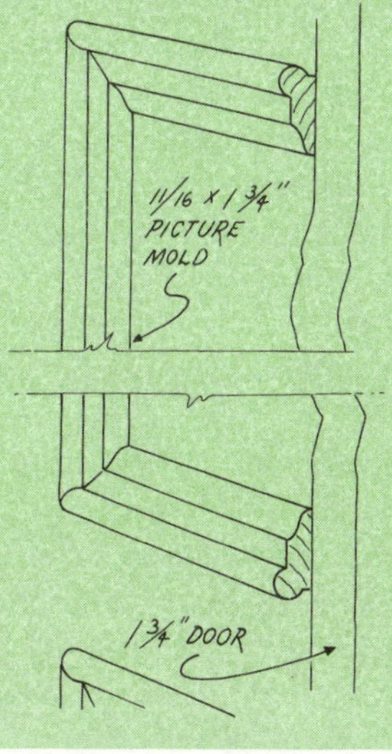

an inexpensive way to create a luxurious look.

Wood moldings are available in a large variety of styles and sizes at most lumberyards. The rooms shown are good examples of what you can accomplish through thoughtful use of moldings. And when you have the know-how for working with this shaped stock, you'll be able to duplicate these examples more easily than you might suspect. The key to successful use of molding lies in careful planning.

Your first step should be a trip to your local lumberyard to learn which moldings it keeps in stock. Armed with this information, take the time to draw a scale floor plan and wall elevations of the room. To lay out a room such as the one above, the elevation drawing should indicate the

How to miter and cope moldings

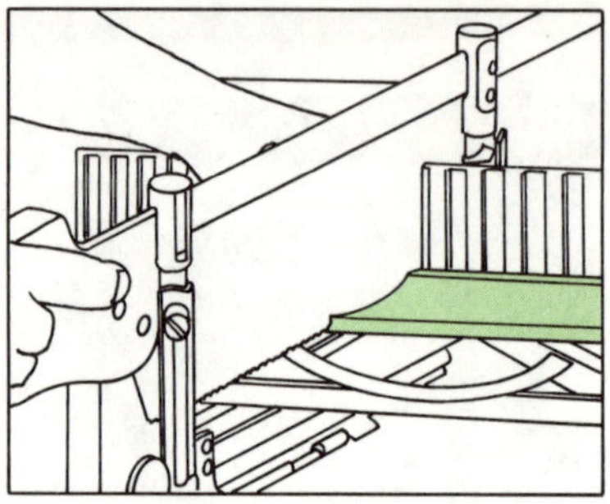

SET MITER box saw at 45° for miter cuts. Always hold molding securely while doing the cutting.

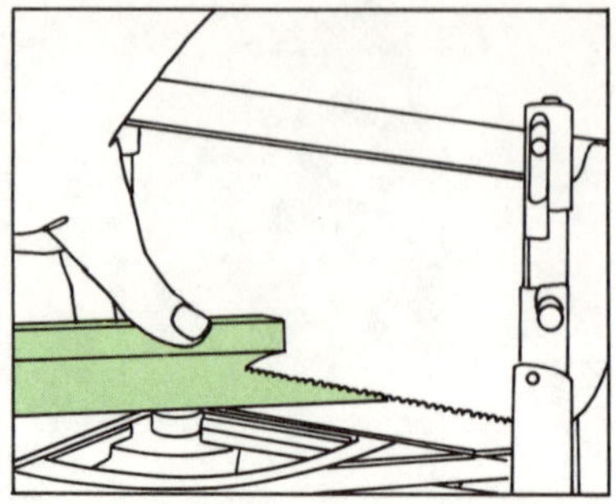

TO COPE a joint, first make the miter cut to the exact length desired as shown in diagram.

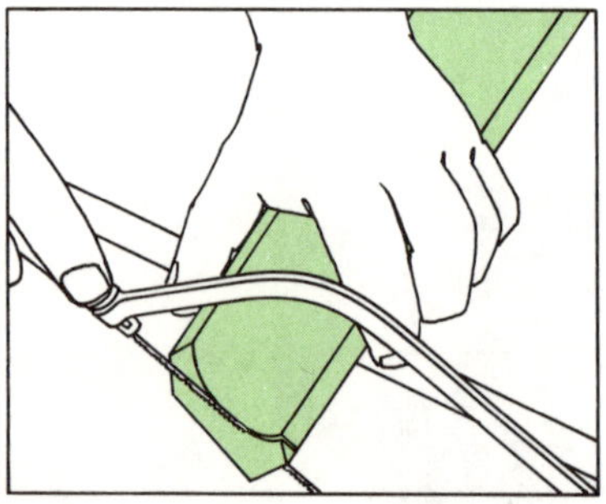

NEXT, with coping saw held at 45° angle, follow miter line (profile) to cut out wedge-shaped piece.

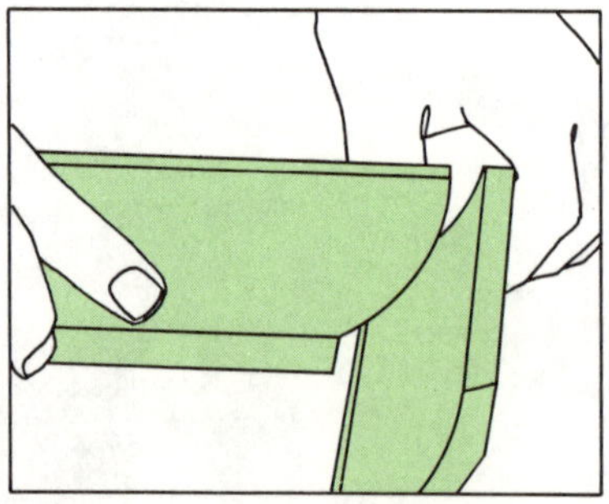

TEST-FIT the coped molding against piece of molding it will abut. In sequence shown, it's cove mold.

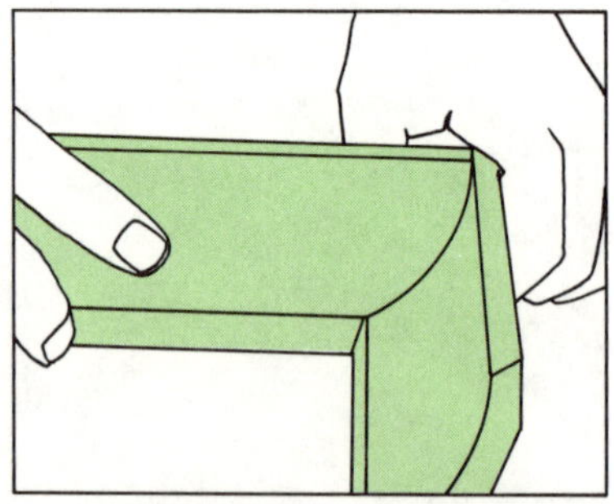

YOU CAN use a block plane and sandpaper to ensure a tight-fitting joint. Glue and nail to fasten.

chair rail at desired height (36 to 42 in.). Work out panel design and sizes so the wall will be symmetrical with panels balanced in height and width, and the spaces between panels equal.

The examples shown in photos and section drawings on these pages can be duplicated or can serve as a springboard for your own creative designs. For more information, write to Western Wood Moulding and Millwork Producers, Dept. PM, Box 25278, Portland, Ore. 97225. Or check out the free literature rack at your local lumberyard.

molding know-how

Make no mistake about it, your molding job will look only as good as the craftsmanship you put into it. How joints fit and nails are placed reveal just how much effort was applied. The first rule is never to guess at miter cuts—always use a miterbox. Also, get in the habit of using sharp saws only. A dull saw—no matter how great your patience and effort—is almost certain to produce unsightly, amateurish-looking joints. Always place the piece of molding in the miterbox as it is to be installed on the wall. (It is important to remember this rule or you will waste a lot of molding by making miter cuts in the wrong plane.)

Because they tend to open, inside joints should always be coped as shown. Here, after cutting miter at desired point, use a coping saw held at a 45° angle, *a must on all convex moldings,* to create a back-cut. Follow the miter-cut profile to cut out this wedge and you'll have a perfect joint. A coped joint—like all molding joints—should be installed with glue as well as nails.

How to do blind nailing

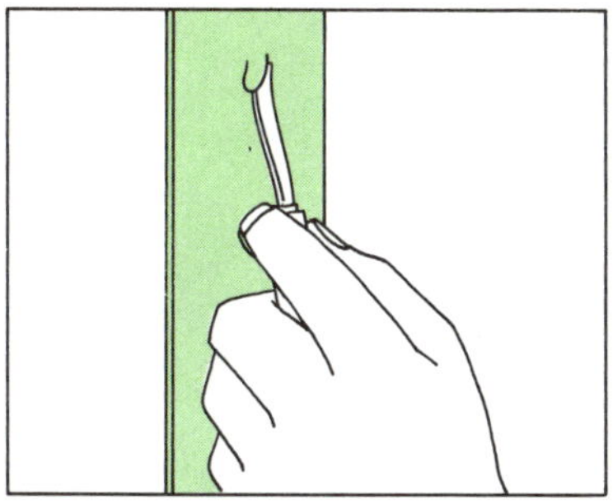

CAREFULLY gouge up a small sliver of wood that's wide enough to conceal the finishing-nail head.

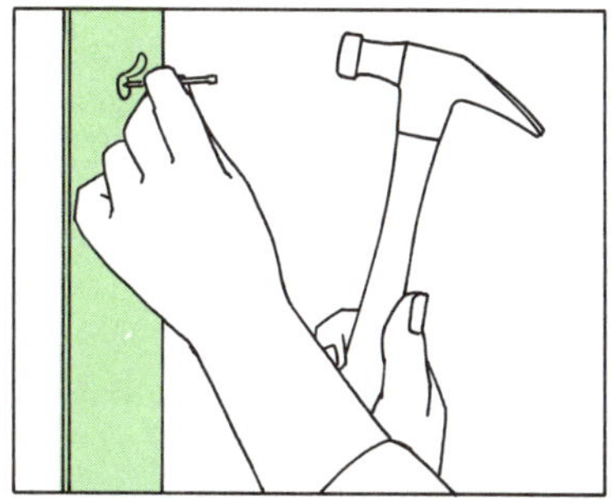

SWING the sliver carefully out of the way and drive the nail. Then set the nailhead well.

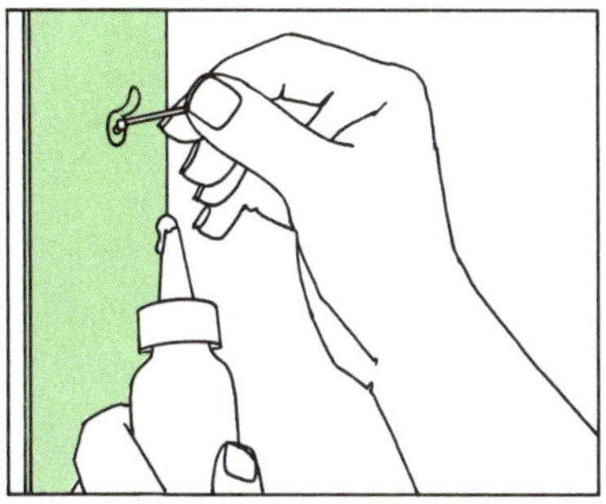

APPLY white glue to the sliver and push it into place. Immediately wipe off any glue ooze-out.

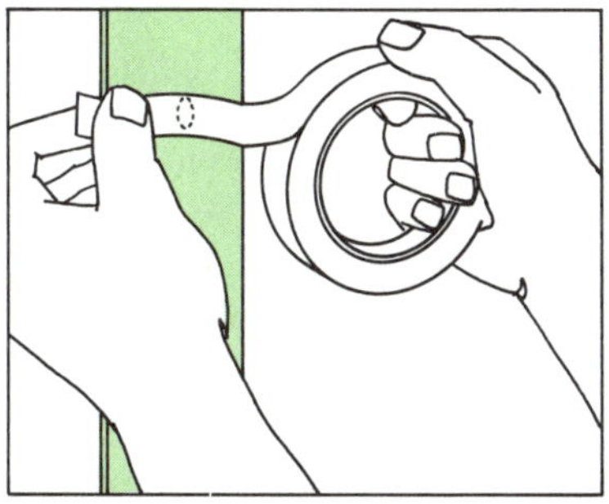

PRESS on a piece of masking tape to hold the sliver in place until the glue is completely dry.

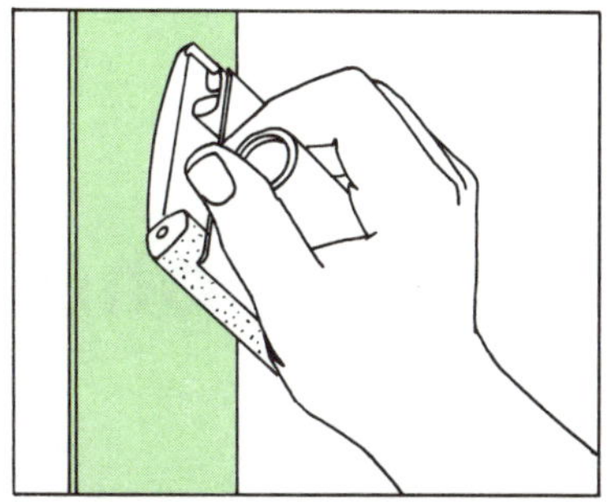

AFTER glue dries, remove masking tape and touch up the blind spot with a fine-grit sandpaper.

Where moldings meet at right angles

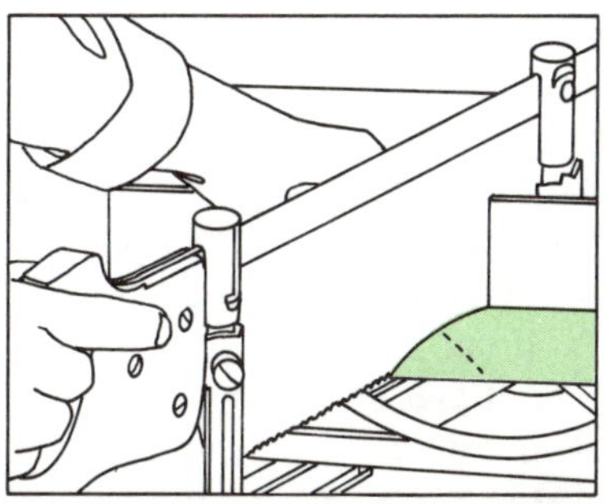

TWO 45° CUTS are made to create point with length equal to exactly half-width of the molding.

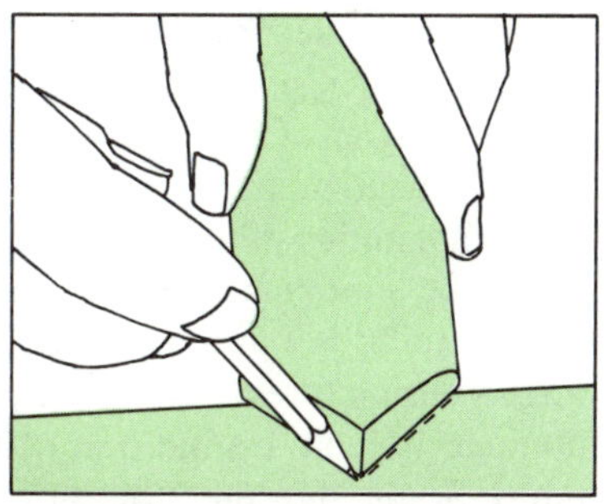

USE THIS piece as the layout pattern for cuts to be made on the piece it will join.

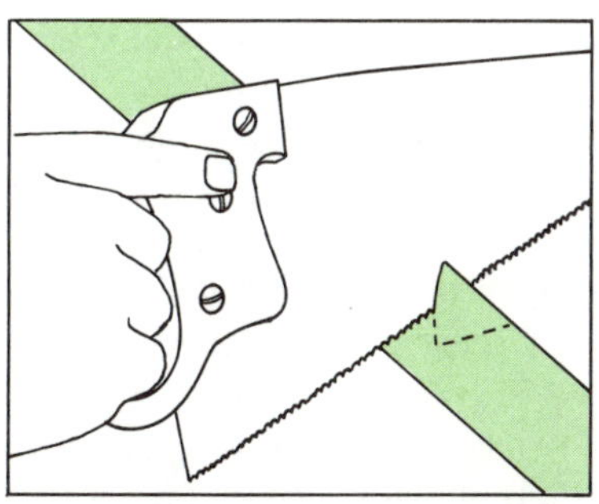

FOLLOWING the lines, use a fine tooth, crosscut saw to make the cutout on the mating molding.

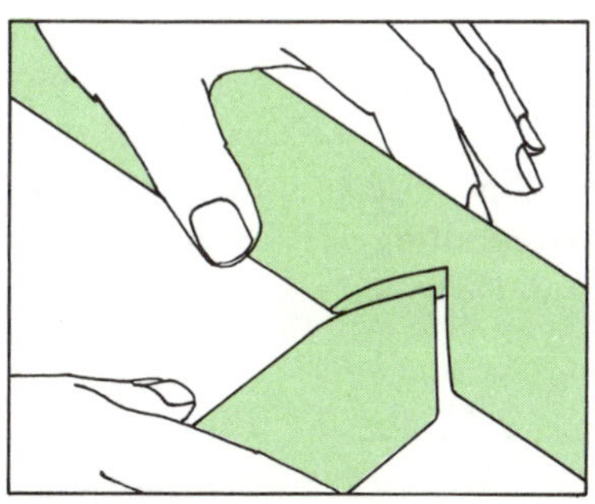

CHECK joint for fit. If you made the cuts carefully, joint should be practically invisible.

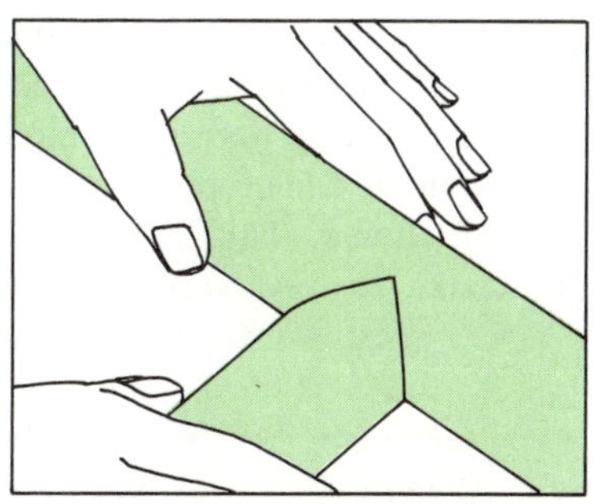

WHEN satisfied with the joint, use glue and toenail several brads through one mold into other.

Mounting a whole collection of prints on a background panel is a handsome way to display photos that usually get stored away in the bottom of a bureau drawer

OUTDOOR PHOTOGRAPHER E.P. Haddon is shown here displaying some of his many montages of animals. Note the arrangement around a dominant photo.

Make a photo montage

By E. P. HADDON

SMALL PICTURES often don't look like much by themselves so there's a tendency to file them away. But put a whole collection of pictures together and you suddenly have an interesting, story-telling display that can make an attractive wall decoration. Montages are an ideal way of capturing events that require a variety of photos instead of just one big picture—scenes from a vacation trip, animals at the zoo, the humerous antics of a baby learning to walk.

Making a montage requires just enough artistic skill to be fun and a challenge. You can arrange your pictures in many ways. Sometimes a montage is built around one central, dominant photo. Sometimes the repetition of a single subject shown in different poses or wearing different facial expressions can be effective. Generally, the most interesting arrangements are a combination of both vertical and horizontal views. Group your subjects so they're looking in toward the center rather than off the edges.

A montage can be any size, but 16x20 inches is a good choice. This is a standard mounting-board size, readily available at photo and artists' shops. Use a white pebble board and leave a border of 1 to 1½ inches around the edges.

The prints are held to the board with dry-mounting tissue, also available at photo and artists' shops. This is an adhesive sheet that's slipped between the print and the board and then melted with an electric clothes iron to bond the two firmly together. First, tack the tissue temporarily to the back of each print with the tip of the iron. This way, print and tissue are trimmed together to the final shape. You then cover the prints with a protective sheet of typing paper and iron over the top to bond the pictures to the mounting board. Never use rubber cement to mount photos as it will bleed through and discolor the surface.

In fitting your pictures together, make the lines between them deliberately irregular to create a natural, random look. To get neat seams between prints, cut the edge on one first, then use this as a template and trace its outline onto the edge of the adjacent picture. Do not, however, butt the edges tightly together. Leave a small gap—about ⅛th of an inch—between them. This outlines the prints in white and adds a dramatic effect.

Don't attempt to mount all of the prints at once or they may shift out of place. Mount one or two at a time, working from the borders toward the center. The photos on the opposite page show the various steps necessary in putting together the montage and mounting the photos.

SEE ALSO

**Bird photography . . . Close-up photos . . .
Frames, picture . . . Mountings, photo . . .
Outdoor photography . . . Panorama photos . . .
Photography . . . Prints, photo**

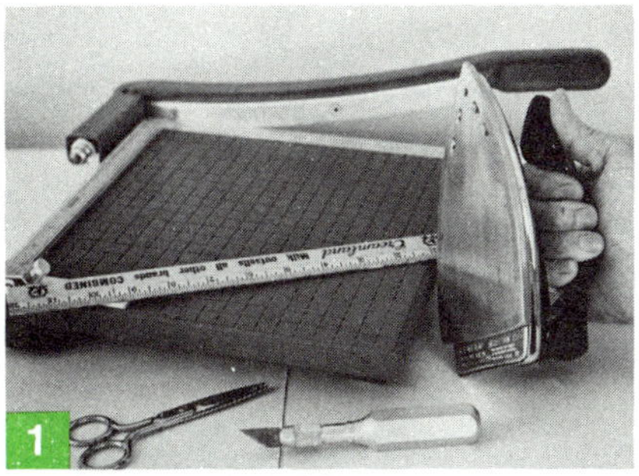

1. ONLY TOOLS needed are scissors, a ruler and an electric iron. Paper cutter speeds trimming, and a sharp mat knife is useful for intricate shapes. 2. Lay out your pictures to get an idea of how many you'll need and which looks best. Mix verticals and horizontals. 3. Tack dry-mounting tissue to back of each print with tip of iron. Cover tissue and run medium iron down the center for about an inch.

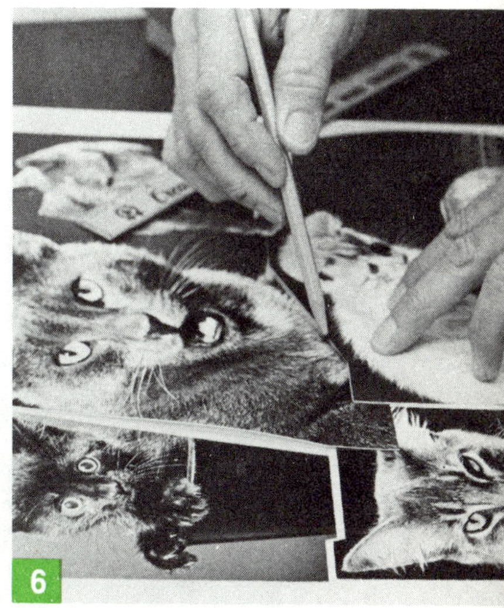

4. ROUGH-TRIM each print to remove the borders and excess background. Cut close to image without slicing into it. Cut right through dry-mounting tissue. 5. Make trial arrangement of rough-trimmed prints to find the most pleasing order. Group should have one or two dominant pictures. 6. Overlapping edges are trimmed off to create interesting patterns. Trace cut edge of one picture onto edge of adjacent.

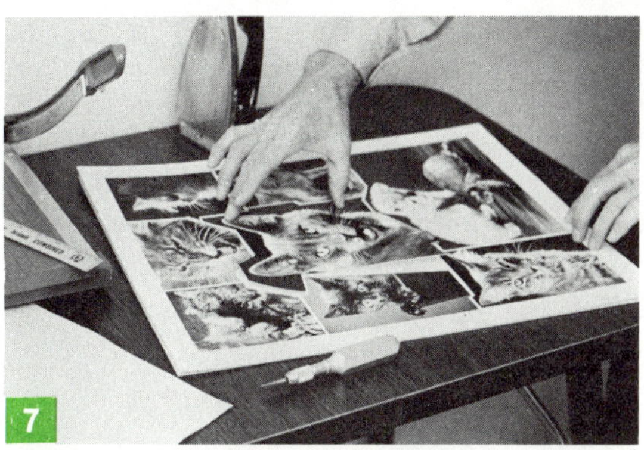

CAREFULLY FIT the pieces in place, leaving narrow gaps between them. Cover the prints with paper and iron over the top to bond the pictures firmly to the mounting board. Do one or two prints at a time.

FINISHED MONTAGE shows the random shapes and white outlining that give the grouping a free-form appearance. Note how the careful cutting around the cat's head in the center photo breaks up the square lines of the other pictures and establishes a strong focal point of interest for the entire montage.

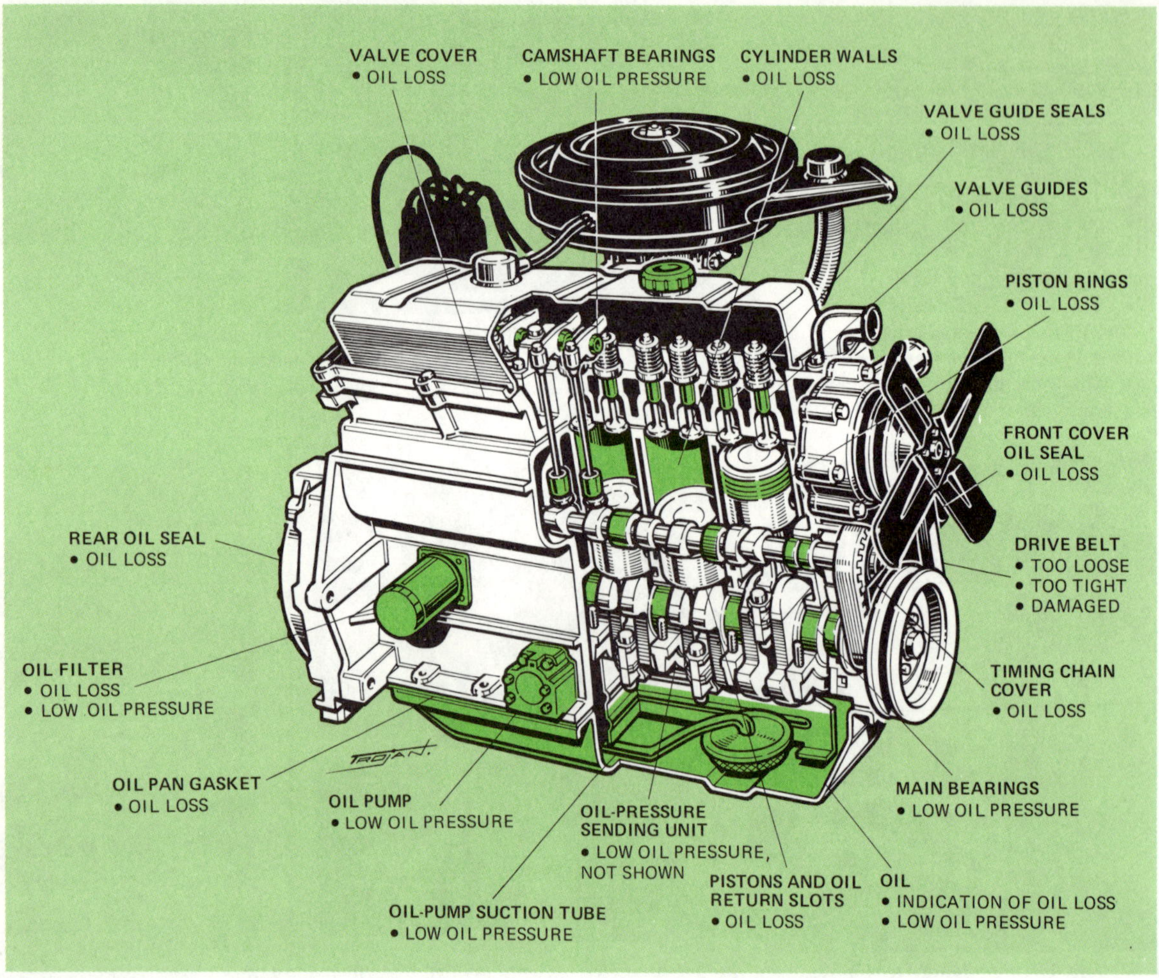

How to diagnose oil consumption

Does it seem that your engine is burning too much oil? How much is too much, and what can be done about it? Here's what you need to know to keep your engine's lubrication system in top shape

MANY CAR OWNERS are unsure what constitutes excessive oil consumption and what they can do about it. If your new car's engine uses oil in excess of the manufacturer's minimum, you have a warranty claim. If it doesn't, you don't have a claim.

SEE ALSO
Engines, auto . . . Lubrication, auto . . . Misfiring, auto . . . Noises, auto engine . . . Tune-up, auto . . . Winterizing, autos

As the years have passed, the manufacturer's "minimum" has shrunk. A while ago, using a quart of oil every 1500 miles was considered normal. Today, some manufacturers state that a new engine which uses a quart of oil every 700 miles is performing normally.

However, a certain number of new engines

(and engines that have been overhauled) are oil consumers because of errors in production. An engine may get into the field with a defective front or rear oil seal, piston rings that have been improperly installed, or a defective oilpan gasket. After verifying the loss of a significant amount of oil because of a defective product, no reputable manufacturer or shop will refuse to take steps that will rectify the situation.

There is another reason for a new engine to demonstrate abnormal oil consumption. It has to do with the way some people "baby" a new car.

The cylinder walls in a new engine are smooth, and about 1000 miles of driving are needed before piston rings seat sufficiently to effectively prevent oil from seeping past.

However, if driving is too "cautious" during this period, piston rings may never seat. "Babying" the engine could cause glaze to build up between cylinder walls and rings, preventing effective sealing. If this happens, dismantling the engine, honing cylinder walls and replacing piston rings will be the only solution to solving the oil consumption problem.

When breaking in a new car, you should follow the instructions laid down in the owner's manual.

If your driving is confined to the city, drive your new car on the expressway at least 10 miles at the speed limit. Doing otherwise will make the engine a candidate for oil loss.

Older engines, obviously, can become oil consumers because of wear. Any one of a number of defects will result in loss, including worn valve guides, damaged valve guide seals, worn piston rings, scored cylinder walls, worn piston-ring grooves, worn pistons and clogged oil-return slots that prevent oil from returning to the oil pan.

TYPICAL ENGINE lubrication system. Cause of low oil pressure can be anywhere along the line.

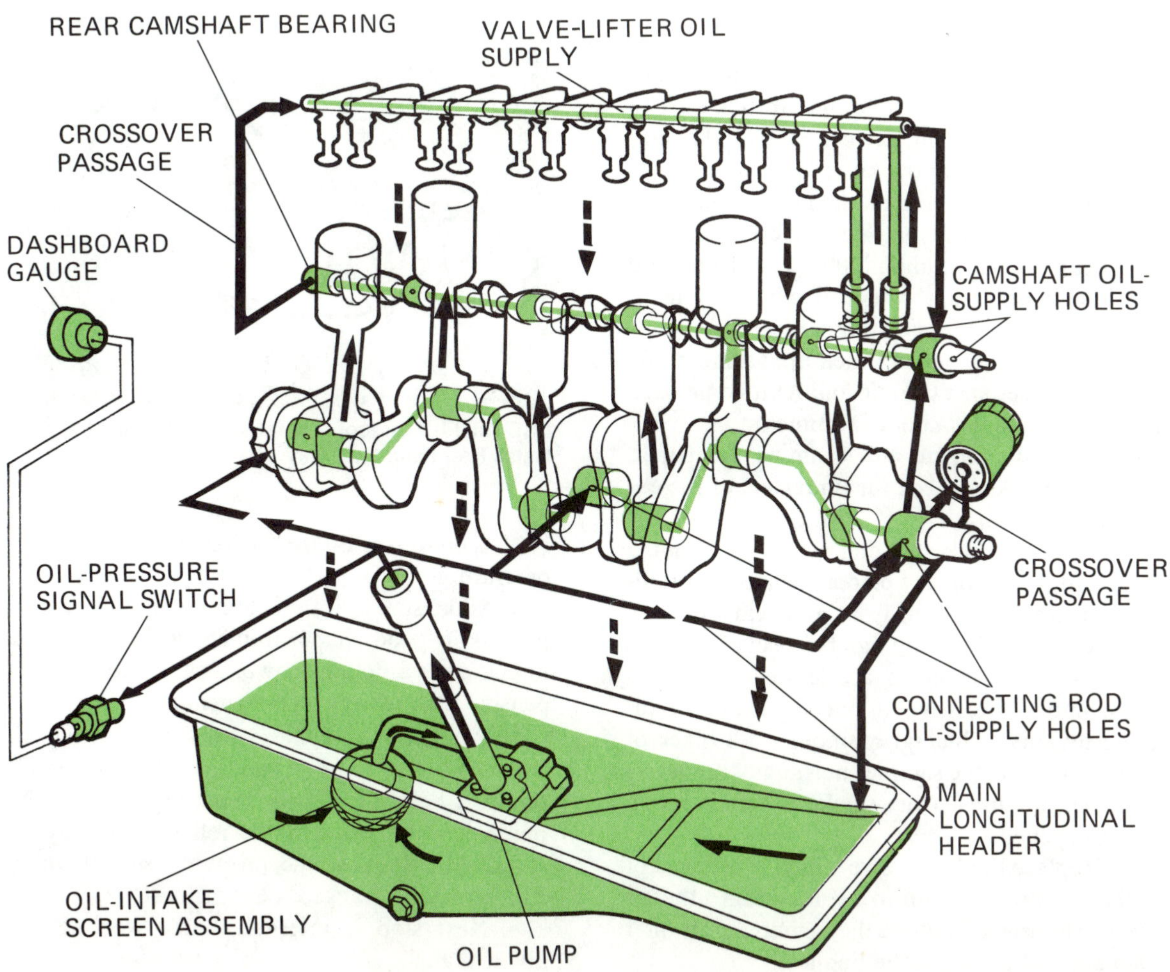

However, things other than an internal engine problem cause oil loss in both new and old engines, and it pays for you to make careful checks before deciding to tear the engine apart.

troubleshooting the problem

Here is how to proceed:

1. Start with the oil itself. Are you using oil designated by the car's manufacturer? Is the amount of oil in the engine to capacity? Does the car possess the right dipstick?

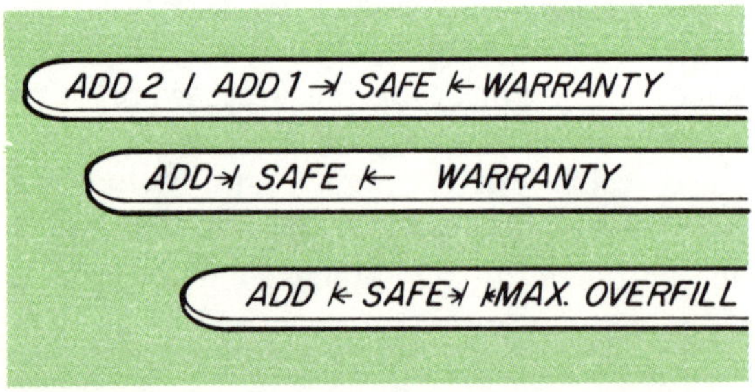

MANUFACTURERS make many different dipsticks; make sure you have the right one.

The dipstick is often overlooked in troubleshooting new cars. Occasionally, the wrong dipstick is put into an engine. To be sure this has not happened in your case, hold the dipstick next to one from the same model car, and make sure marks and length are the same.

2. Spread clean paper on the floor beneath the engine and transmission. Keep the engine at a speed equal to 20–25 mph (1000–1200 rpm), and continue running it for several minutes after it has reached normal operating temperature.

After the engine has warmed up, momentarily race it at wide-open throttle and let it come back to fast idle. Do this about five times.

Shut off the engine and examine the paper. Look for oil. Also check the underside of the engine for fresh oil.

If a leak is uncovered, find where it is coming from and fix it. Primary places include the oil filter connection, oil pan, front and rear oil seals, valve covers and the timing-chain cover.

3. As the car is being accelerated, check exhaust smoke. Excessive oil burning is often indicated by gray or blue-gray smoke—not black or white. Black smoke signifies burning of an overly rich fuel mixture—white smoke is condensation being expelled.

4. Replace the PCV valve which, if clogged or defective, can cause oil to be drawn into the air cleaner housing. Examine the carburetor air filter element. Oil on this is the tipoff.

5. Check sparkplug tips for oil, which indicates oil loss.

check low oil pressure

Oil pressure that is consistently low or pressure that takes a long time to reach acceptable limits after an engine is started are problems that shouldn't be sloughed off. But neither should you panic over them.

Low oil pressure, especially when accompanied by a loss of oil, could mean that main or camshaft bearings are in poor shape. The engine may need overhaul. However, low oil pressure also has several other causes, which are less troublesome to eliminate. These are the ones to tackle first.

Important: Do not run the engine if low oil pressure is indicated. You could force the engine to freeze if a low oil pressure condition does in fact exist.

To get at the cause of low oil pressure, proceed as follows:

1. Check the engine oil level. Is it low?

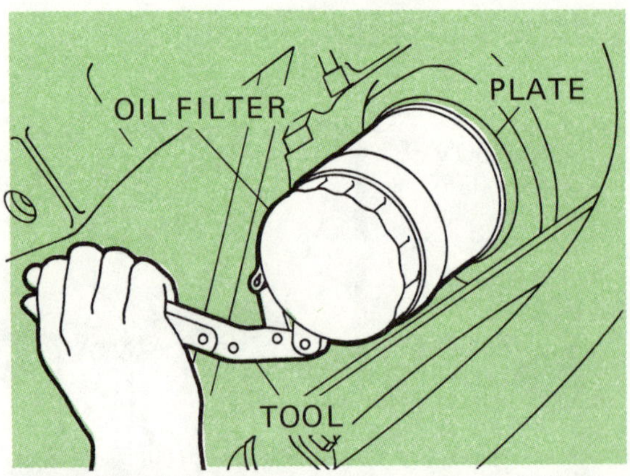

USE OIL-FILTER tool only for loosening a tight filter. Install filter hand tight only.

2. Is oil thin or diluted? Change the oil—check pressure.

3. Make sure that the oil pressure sending unit itself is in good shape. Replacing the unit on a hunch costs a dollar or two. That's a lot less expensive than tearing the engine apart.

4. Replace the oil filter. Maybe it is clogged.

5. You have to go inside now. Start at the oil pump. Check the pump pressure. Parts of the pump may be worn or the relief valve may be stuck. Also look at the oil-pump suction tube, which may be cracked, bent or loose.

6. Next stop is internal engine work. Sorry about that.

THE CARRIER holds a 315-lb. trail bike—too heavy for bumper-mounted types. It slides into mounts or is bolted to the underframe and leaves the bumper unmarred.

A trail-bike carrier for your car

By DWAYNE L. HARLAN

Why leave your bike at home when you go on an outing? This handy detachable carrier lets you take your bike where the fun is

■ IF YOU HAVE A TRAIL BIKE that weighs more than 300 pounds, you can't use bumper-mounted brackets to carry it.

This sturdy, removable carrier will safely handle any bike your car's suspension can, and should cost less than $20 for materials. If you don't do the welding yourself, measure and cut the parts in advance and take them to a local welding shop. It shouldn't cost more than an additional $10. (Check for gas leaks before welding.)

Dimensions will vary, of course, to suit your car and bike. You'll also find the carrier strong enough to incorporate a trailer hitch (where permitted by law).

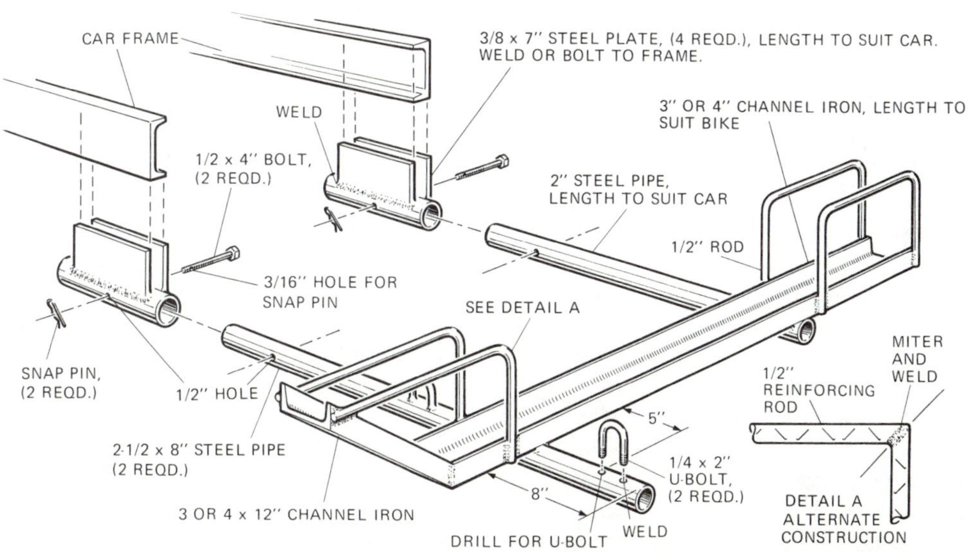

SEE ALSO

Bicycles . . . Minibikes . . . Tune-up, bicycle

The secrets of safe cycling

By WILLIAM HAMPTON

■ WHAT DO YOU DO when that summer thunderstorm hits—stop, or keep going? With a little common sense, you can keep right on going and arrive safely at your destination. That is, if you know a few basics about slick-surface cycling.

One of the basics of successful motorcycle riding is to feel relaxed with it. You must imagine that two-wheeler as a natural extension of your mind and body. Because the bike is so responsive to your slightest movements, you must be careful not to *overcontrol* it on a slippery surface.

SEE ALSO
Bicycles . . . Minibikes . . . Tune-up, bicycle

But before you can feel relaxed with that two-wheeler, you must first have the right frame of mind. You must believe that you're capable of riding safely on slick surfaces.

If you have a strong fear of spilling, your negative attitude will affect your riding. Remember: Don't fear wet roads; respect them.

what to wear

A good helmet and rainsuit are necessary, along with effective eye protection. For maximum eye and facial protection, a face shield is ideal. It not only protects the eyes, but it also saves your face from the stinging impact of raindrops.

WATCH ROAD SURFACES

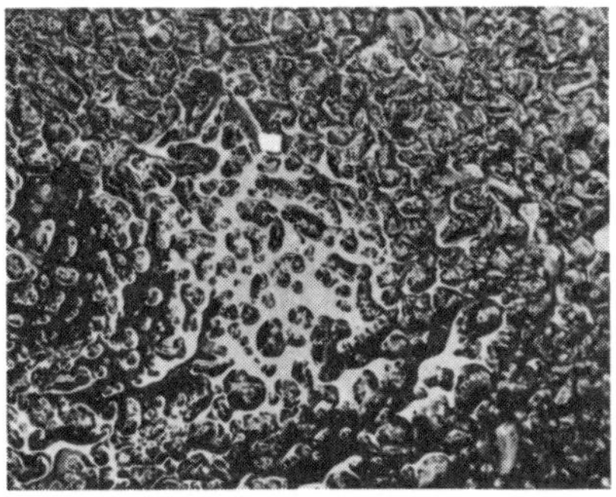

KEEP YOUR EYE on the road surface: At left is an asphalt surface; it's slippery, but tires get some bite on the high spots. Center is a classic hazard of wet leaves on a turn. On the right is a combination of slippery surfaces: leaves on shiny, smooth crosswalk markings, and loose pieces of broken pavement that increase the danger.

WATCH ROAD HAZARDS

ROAD HAZARDS are many and varied, but three of the most dangerous are shown above. Railroad tracks shown at left should be crossed at right angles; watch for washouts alongside the tracks. Gratings (center) come in all shapes and sizes and are slippery when wet. Also watch out for expansion joints (right) such as on bridges.

CHECK TIRE PRESSURE

TIRE air pressure is critical. It is better to be underinflated than overinflated, but the best situation is to check the p.s.i. at every gas fill-up and see that it is as specified.

CHECK CHAIN TENSION

PROPER CHAIN tension is important for insuring that power delivery to the rear tire's contact patch is smooth and positive. There should always be ¾-inch play midway between the sprockets. See the text.

SELECT RIGHT TIRES

RIGHT TIRES are a must for staying up on two wheels. Cross-blocked tread (above, right) provides good power delivery to road while allowing dispersal of water. Ribbed tire (right) is ideal front tire. It minimizes sideslip.

KNOW ABOUT HYDROPLANING

WHEN YOUR TIRES lift off the pavement and ride on a thin layer of water, you're hydroplaning. The speed at which this occurs depends on many variables (see text). Since control is lost when this happens, be prepared for the phenomenon especially if there's enough water on the road for raindrops to dimple.

Snug-fitting, large-lens goggles offer good eye protection, but they don't provide the facial coverage of a face shield. Whether you use goggles or a shield, get the Hydron-treated plastic as it absorbs moisture and minimizes "fogging-up."

Waterproof gloves are necessary, if you want to keep your hands from slipping off the grips and controls.

Top off your wet-weather gear with a pair of nonslip-soled, lightweight boots.

prepping your bike

Besides getting yourself prepped for slick-surface cycling, you've got to make sure your bike is ready, too.

■ **Tire condition is extremely important, so let's start with tires.**

If you do much road riding, you should have suitable tread designs. The two basic road-tread designs are the ribbed and the universal. The ribbed design is good for up front because its circumferential-rib construction resists sideslipping when the bike is banked. This tire design wears well and provides good steering. Its lack of cross-block tread, however, makes it unsuitable for the rear, as it'll spin rather easily under power.

The universal design, on the other hand, can be used on both front and rear. This tire features a closely spaced tread-block pattern, which makes it effective for delivering the engine's power to the ground.

A variation of the universal design is the trials-universal tread pattern. Its tread blocks are more widely spaced than those on the universal; therefore, it doesn't provide as good a "bite" on a slippery surface as does the universal.

The sports knobby has even less rubber to contact the road than the trials-universal design. If you must ride on a wet surface with the knobby type, use extreme caution. This tire is meant for dirt riding *only.*

■ **The rear chain must be lubricated and tensioned properly to insure smooth delivery of power to the rear tire's contact patch.**

A dry chain will bind and jerk around the sprockets. If it's too loose, it'll surge or whip as it travels between the sprockets. A primary-drive chain (if your bike has one) is even less tolerant of lack of lubrication and improper adjustment when it comes to delivering the engine's power smoothly.

■ **Check the sprockets, too.** If their teeth are pointed, hook-shaped, or—worse yet—worn to nubs, replace them. Worn sprockets will make a worn chain alternately tighten and loosen at certain points of its travel.

Don't run a worn chain with new sprockets; by the same token, don't put a new chain on worn sprockets.

■ **Don't overlook the throttle, clutch, and brake cables either.** They need adequate lubrication so that they won't bind anywhere. Make sure the throttle-cable housing doesn't bend sharply anywhere and restrict the movement of the cable inside.

Also check for throttle-cable binding as you move the handlebar from side to side.

■ **Check the brakes to see that they don't grab or drag.** They should take hold without requiring heavy applications of pressure. It's important, too, that the clutch engage and disengage smoothly. Furthermore, you'll need to keep that engine tuned. When you twist that throttle, you want the engine to respond at that instant—not a moment later when the rear tire is on some slippery substance.

surface conditions

Although there are only two basic kinds of paved road—asphalt and concrete—there are infinite variations of them regarding surface conditions.

For that reason, you must be on your toes constantly, scanning the road ahead for anything that can make the tires lose adhesion with the road. An otherwise tractional surface can be made slippery by the presence of oil deposits, sand, leaves or other debris. And, especially at night, you may not notice these substances lying on the road.

Now if you've had little or no experience on wet roads, you might want to conduct an "eyeball" inspection of different surfaces some time. That is, squat down and really look a wet surface over. Feel it with your hand. Look for any substance that could enhance the slipperiness of the road surface.

New asphalt generally has a coarser surface texture than concrete. So, even with residual water lying on the road, the tires can still get some adhesion. There are exceptions, however, as some asphalt sections may be worn smooth. Also, beware of worn asphalt roads that have smooth, tarred areas. They can be very slippery when wet.

Furthermore, in hot weather, those tarred spots will be soft and unstable, adding to their slipperiness. They may even have sand sprinkled on them.

The camber of a road must be considered, too. If it has little or no camber, deposits of water will be trapped on the surface.

Regardless of the type of road you ride on, never ride in the middle area of the lane, especially on uphill approaches.

Why?

The center area of a lane is the final resting place for oil drippings from other vehicles. You'll find heavier deposits of oil on those long uphill lanes frequented by truck traffic. Watch out for concentrations of oil drippings at traffic lights and stop signs, too.

Whenever possible, ride to either side of the lane's center. Riding to one side of the lane has another advantage when it's raining: By staying in the "tire wipe" areas of the vehicle in front of your bike, you can take advantage of the squeegee effect of that vehicle's tires.

If there's any time that you should be particularly cautious of a wet road, it's during the first few minutes of rainfall that follows a long dry spell.

Those first drops of rain mix with all sorts of oil, dirt, tire-wear particles and other debris to form a slimy mixture that coats the surface. You can't really see it, because it's not very thick. But it's extremely slippery. And until it's had a chance to be washed away, you should "tip-toe" over the road, or even pull off to the side for a few moments.

road hazards

What makes slick-surface motorcycling so challenging is the variety of surfaces you encounter. You've read about the need to be on the lookout for oil deposits, leaves, sand and other debris that can enhance the slipperiness of an already slick surface. But what about bridge-floor gratings and expansion joints, manhole covers, crosswalk markings and railroad crossings?

Take railroad crossings: Ever since the first motorcycle sputtered down the road, they have been responsible for cyclists parting company with their bikes. Even when they're dry, rails can be slippery; but when they become wet, they can send a two-wheeler slithering in an instant.

Just remember to approach them at a right angle. Go easy on the gas and stay off the clutch and brakes when traveling over them. Do your braking and down-shifting before you get to them.

And watch it around gas stations. Cars that have just had their tanks filled may slosh gas onto the road as they exit from a station. Gasoline is slipperier than water and it is also virtually unnoticeable on a wet surface.

hydroplaning

Skidding is a constant threat on wet surfaces, if you don't know what you're doing. But there's another phenomenon that can create moments of panic: hydroplaning. It occurs when a layer of water actually wedges itself between the road and one of the tires, most often the front tire.

Whether hydroplaning occurs or not depends mostly on the speed of the motorcycle and on the amount of water on the road. With modern motorcycles, it's not hard to cruise at speeds higher than 50 mph on wet surfaces.

Because hydroplaning can occur at speeds as low as 35 mph, providing there's enough water on the surface, your bike can turn into a motorized surfboard. Here's a rule of thumb for figuring if there's enough water present to induce hydroplaning. If there's enough water lying on the road for raindrops to make a dimpling effect, there's enough water for hydroplaning. *Watch it!*

riding technique

Other factors that enter into hydroplaning are the width and tread design of the tires. A worn, wide tire will plane at a lower speed than a narrow tire with a deep-tread design. In addition, the lighter the combined weight of bike and rider, the lower the speed at which hydroplaning will occur.

When it comes to stopping your bike on a wet surface, you must develop a touch of finesse with the brakes. Learn how to decelerate by using the brakes and engine compression together. You can apply the rear brake an instant before the front brake to help stabilize the machine.

If you apply *only* the rear brake, you run the risk of locking it up. It takes more pressure to slow the machine with just one brake. With both brakes, you're distributing braking pressures between them, in smaller amounts. And by downshifting, you employ the services of a third brake: engine compression.

Taking advantage of the retarding effect of engine compression lets you apply less pressure to the brakes than you normally would without downshifting. What's more, a four-stroker will provide more retarding effect than a two-stroker. Take that fact into consideration when you switch from one type of engine to the other.

Once you master slick-surface motorcycling, you'll never have to worry about getting caught in the rain miles from home and having to pull over until the rain stops and the roads dry.

Loose rungs make wobbly chairs

The rungs on my wooden kitchen chairs are loose, but only pull out part way from the hole in the leg. Is there some way to tighten them without taking the chair apart . . . perhaps a glue that can be forced into the joints around the end of the rungs?—Lee Bower, Sacramento, Calif.

It may be possible to tighten the rungs by pulling them out as far as possible and applying a product called "Chair-Loc" or white glue around the rungs. Push the rung in and out of the hole to force the glue into the joint. Then push the rung as far as it will go and hold it in place with a tourniquet or clamp. Allow the glue to set. You might also force glue into the hole with a needle-nosed glue injector that can be purchased from Craftsman Wood Service Co., 2727 S. Mary St., Chicago,Ill. 60608.

Wallpapering plasterboard

I want to wallpaper over unfinished plasterboard walls, but I'm told that I will not be able to remove the paper later the usual way by wetting and scraping. How can I prepare the wall to permit easy removal of the paper?—Ed Gibson, Montreal.

Assuming the joints of the plasterboard walls have been nailed, taped and spackled in conformity with generally approved practices, the walls might be coated with a latex or semigloss paint. I would give the taped joints a prime coat of paint (or shellac) and allow this to dry thoroughly before applying the final coat. As a rule, one coat of either type of paint will be sufficient, if applied unthinned with a roller. Be sure the paint is completely dry before you hang the paper.

Condensate on aluminum frames

During cold weather moisture gathers in drops on the frames of my aluminum window sashes. In time—if I don't wipe the frames regularly—a black mold forms. What can I do to prevent this? I don't mind the moisture, but I can do without the mold.—Jim Neitzel, Shelley, Idaho

Yours is a common problem and there seems to be no completely effective remedy that I know of. I do know that coating the metal frames with ordinary glycerin tends to reduce the formation of condensate, often to the point where it is no longer especially troublesome. Of course, one hesitates to suggest this step due to the greasy accumulation as a result of this remedy. Though as a last resort it is helpful. Storm sashes also will help, but to be effective they must be fitted tightly.

Musty basement

We have installed a modern heating and cooling system in our older home. Some part of the musty odor in the basement is being picked up by the fan, located in the basement. I have tried the obvious, checking and sealing all my plenums, but the odor persists. I might add that the basement is a partial one. About half the crawl space is open. I know that venting is important to reduce the odor, but if we do this in the winter, our pipes will freeze. Any suggestions?—Bill Lewis, Noble, Okla.

Musty odors are sometimes the result of invisible moisture. Chances are good that there is excess moisture in your basement, whether half the ground area is basement and the other half crawl space, or whether the basement/crawl space is only partly in the ground as with an English basement.

To track down the musty odor first look at the outside of your home to see if any of the adjacent ground slopes toward the foundation. If so, cut a swale (ditch) in the ground to divert the surface water away from your house as shown in the house illustration. Earth fill at the foundation must be higher than, and slope away from, the adjacent ground.

Also, check your downspouts to make certain that they discharge onto splashblocks and wash away from the house. If your crawl space has an earthen floor, it is your most likely culprit. Cover your crawl space with a 4-mil polyethylene vapor barrier. Lap the joints at least 6 in. and seal them with roofing cement. Extend the plastic at least 1 ft. up the foundation walls and fasten the plastic to the walls with roof mastic.

Hammering noises in pipes

I recently replaced my iron-pipe plumbing with copper pipe. Now I get a water hammer, especially at the kitchen sink. Both hot and cold lines have air chambers about 20 in. long inside the wall next to the shutoff valves under the sink. If water is drained at the valves, there's no noise for a day or so; then the hammer develops again. What's the solution?—Fred W. Krebs, Seattle, Wash.

If draining eliminates the trouble temporarily, it indicates the air chambers may have filled gradually with water through leakage or be of insufficient size. Ordinarily, air chambers are located near the meter and are of the same size or of larger diameter. A chamber so located and increased to a length of 30 in. cured my own similar problem.

Check the new lines for looseness at supports and a tendency to vibrate when water is drawn, which can also cause plumbing noises.

METRIC CONVERSION

Conversion factors can be carried so far they become impractical. In cases below where an entry is exact it is followed by an asterisk (*). Where considerable rounding off has taken place, the entry is followed by a + or a - sign.

CUSTOMARY TO METRIC

Linear Measure

inches	millimeters
1/16	1.5875*
1/8	3.2
3/16	4.8
1/4	6.35*
5/16	7.9
3/8	9.5
7/16	11.1
1/2	12.7*
9/16	14.3
5/8	15.9
11/16	17.5
3/4	19.05*
13/16	20.6
7/8	22.2
15/16	23.8
1	25.4*

inches	centimeters
1	2.54*
2	5.1
3	7.6
4	10.2
5	12.7*
6	15.2
7	17.8
8	20.3
9	22.9
10	25.4*
11	27.9
12	30.5

feet	centimeters	meters
1	30.48*	.3048*
2	61	.61
3	91	.91
4	122	1.22
5	152	1.52
6	183	1.83
7	213	2.13
8	244	2.44
9	274	2.74
10	305	3.05
50	1524*	15.24*
100	3048*	30.48*

1 yard =
.9144* meters
1 rod =
5.0292* meters
1 mile =
1.6 kilometers
1 nautical mile =
1.852* kilometers

Fluid Measure

(Milliliters [ml] and cubic centimeters [cc or cu cm] are equivalent, but it is customary to use milliliters for liquids.)

1 cu in = 16.39 ml
1 fl oz = 29.6 ml
1 cup = 237 ml
1 pint = 473 ml
1 quart = 946 ml
= .946 liters
1 gallon = 3785 ml
= 3.785 liters
Formula (exact):
fluid ounces × 29.573 529 562 5* = milliliters

Weights

ounces	grams
1	28.3
2	56.7
3	85
4	113
5	142
6	170
7	198
8	227
9	255
10	283
11	312
12	340
13	369
14	397
15	425
16	454

Formula (exact):
ounces × 28.349 523 125* = grams

pounds	kilograms
1	.45
2	.9
3	1.4
4	1.8
5	2.3
6	2.7
7	3.2
8	3.6
9	4.1
10	4.5

1 short ton (2000 lbs) = 907 kilograms (kg)
Formula (exact):
pounds × .453 592 37* = kilograms

Volume

1 cu in = 16.39 cubic centimeters (cc)
1 cu ft = 28 316.7 cc
1 bushel = 35 239.1 cc
1 peck = 8 809.8 cc

Area

1 sq in = 6.45 sq cm
1 sq ft = 929 sq cm
= .093 sq meters
1 sq yd = .84 sq meters
1 acre = 4 046.9 sq meters
= .404 7 hectares
1 sq mile = 2 589 988 sq meters
= 259 hectares
= 2.589 9 sq kilometers

Kitchen Measure

1 teaspoon = 4.93 milliliters (ml)
1 Tablespoon = 14.79 milliliters (ml)

Miscellaneous

1 British thermal unit (Btu) (mean) = 1 055.9 joules
1 calorie (mean) = 4.19 joules
1 horsepower = 745.7 watts
= .75 kilowatts
caliber (diameter of a firearm's bore in hundredths of an inch) = .254 millimeters (mm)
1 atmosphere pressure = 101 325* pascals (newtons per sq meter)
1 pound per square inch (psi) = 6 895 pascals
1 pound per square foot = 47.9 pascals
1 knot = 1.85 kilometers per hour
25 miles per hour = 40.2 kilometers per hour
50 miles per hour = 80.5 kilometers per hour
75 miles per hour = 120.7 kilometers per hour